Gaia in Acti

Gaia in Action

Science of the Living Earth

Edited by Peter Bunyard

Floris Books

First published in 1996 by Floris Books

British Library CIP Data available

ISBN 0-86315-202-3

Printed in Great Britain
by Cromwell Press, Wilts.

Contents

Introduction

La vida se ha extendido por todas partes, dando vueltas cada vez más amplias. Por eso su camino tiene la forma del caracol.

(Kogui — Sierra Nevada de Santa Marta, Colombia)

The Gaia thesis remains controversial. Its basic tenet, that life on Earth is part of an interlocking, interconnected system that binds the atmosphere to the continents and oceans in a quasi-physiological process, may never be categorically proved. Yet however elusive the final goal of proof, Gaia remains a tantalizingly persuasive idea that nevertheless can be readily modelled. Like Darwinism the Gaia thesis is a theory of evolution. But in contrast to Darwinism, which maintains that evolution is primarily a struggle of living forms to adapt to a fickle environment, Gaia holds that life forms have co-evolved with their environment in such a way that environmental conditions are held steady in the face of a continual flux of energy and matter. Gaia is a theory of stability and is therefore paramount, as Lovelock has emphasized, to viewing the planet as a remarkably robust geophysiological system.

On what grounds can we claim the planetary system to be robust? First, we now know that life in the form of bacteria has been on the planet for at least 3.8 billion years and probably even longer. Moreover, life, having come into being, appears never to have lost its hold, despite apocalyptic events such as the impact of massive asteroids. Second, the basic chemistry of life and the underlying metabolism has remained remarkably constant. Some forms too have retained their constancy and their biochemical function, for instance, the plastids and mitochondria of eukaryotic cells. As Lynn Margulis discusses in Chapter 12, such vital organelles probably had their origin aeons ago as free-living bacteria, only later to become incorporated into nucleated cells. Symbiogenesis — the generation of new forms through the integration into one organism of separate life forms — was undoubtedly a major spur to evolution as it opened up the possibility that organisms from distinct evolutionary pathways would be able to share metabolic strategies and so avoid the need to repeat a complex evolutionary history.

A physiological system requires cyclic renewal of matter and energy in finely-tuned quantities and qualities. It is surely relevant in this regard that the eighteenth century scientist James Hutton should have looked to William Harvey's discovery of the circulation of blood as a model for the cyclic nature of living processes on Earth. How apt too, that following Alfred Wegener's idea of 'continental drift,' we should now have discovered the geological mechanisms by which matter is cycled across the Earth's surface, with floor-spreading and volcanism being balanced by crustal subduction. Venus too has volcanism, but apparently no continents or continental drift, its crustal matter bubbling chaotically, compared to the distinct circulation cells that comprise plate tectonics on Earth. Is it too far-fetched to look to life on Earth as having made all the difference, somehow transforming a chaotic system into one that has a measure of order? We may never have a direct answer to such questions, yet the association between life and the changing surface of the Earth is there to see in the 'bygone biospheres' of Vladimir Vernadsky.

Paradoxically, it makes more sense to view the processing of minerals on the Earth as part of a self-regulating system, rather than as a concatenation of haphazard events that fortuitously generate the right conditions for life on Earth. And why should this planet alone of its flanking planets have retained water? Lovelock first raised this question some twenty years ago and considered whether such retention was connected to photosynthesis and the generation of free oxygen. Thus, whereas free hydrogen can escape from the Earth's surface and out into space, as water it remains Earth-bound, held down by the extreme cold of the tropopause. Geologists too are beginning to see connections between our watery planet and the generation of granite continents, granite being the result of a chemistry that involves the interaction of water and molten magma. Moreover, since the weathering of continents is largely in the hands of life, namely through the draw-down of carbon dioxide, the biota keep the full cycle going, ensuring that enough limestone is subducted to feed the volcanoes and so generate carbon dioxide anew.

Gaia in Action is the outcome of three symposia that were put on by the Wadebridge Ecological Centre at Worthyvale Manor between 1988 and 1990. Certain papers from the first two symposia, namely *Gaia, the Thesis, the Mechanisms and the Implications,* and *Gaia and Evolution* have been brought into the collection. The bulk of the remaining papers in this volume are from the third symposium on *Gaia and Symbiogenesis.* The two exceptions are papers by Jan Sapp, who has surveyed the history of the idea of symbiogenesis, and by Kate Rawles in her questioning of the ethical implications of the Gaia thesis.

The aim of the book is to take the interested reader through some of the fundamental issues associated with Gaia theory. What is the theory? What support does it have and what is the significance of *Daisyworld?* Does the theory offer an explanation of atmospheric and ocean chemistry and therefore of climatic stability and what is the role of life, if any, in maintaining equilibria? What evidence do we have of life acting as a significant player in the regulation of geochemistry? As Lynn Margulis has pointed out, symbiogenesis is a force to be reckoned with in providing life with the requisite biochemical and morphological armoury to have an immense impact on the environment. Physiology emerges out of the structural attributes of the cell. But whereas physiology is usually viewed as simply holding the *milieu intérieur* constant against a fickle environment, Gaia offers a far broader view in that physiology is seen equally to involve regulation of the milieu extérieur. Meanwhile, the two papers on symbiosis and mutualism, one dealing with the deep ocean and the other with soil, show how deeply integrated one life form needs be with another for successful exploitation of the immediate environment. Patrick Lavelle, for instance, shows that mutualism among soil organisms is a *sine qua non* of a rich fertile soil, with benefits that consequently accrue to the entire system.

When Lovelock proposed Gaia as a theory of planetary regulation through the sum of activities of the biota he was not concerned with the social implications of the theory. Yet, just as Darwinism provided the industrialized capitalistic world with a metaphor of competitiveness, as well as of the market acting like natural selection, Gaia conjures up a world that appears to have more to do with cooperation than competitiveness. This idea is taken up by Jan Sapp in his survey of the idea of symbiogenesis while Mae-Wan Ho and Fritz Popp take us into the mysterious world of quantum physics in their proposition that order and coherence are phenomena that emerge naturally out of the living cell. Their claim is that coordination of energy transfer is an emergent property of living cells that behave in the manner of a system of solid state physics. Underlying their research is the pursuit of answers to a range of phenomena from developmental biology, muscle action, long range communication and even consciousness.

Industrialism, the market economy and the rise of the proletariat have led to the alienation of humans from nature and to what Alywn Jones calls 'the fragmentation of reason' in which rational thought becomes dissociated from 'being' and divorced from its roots in culture and community. Likewise, if Darwinism is a theory of the individual engaged in a struggle to survive in an innately hostile environment, Gaia theory, on the contrary, is concerned with a wholesome integration of organisms and their environment. The metaphor of Gaia therefore offers a new way of looking at the Earth. Indeed, it emphasizes our responsibility to maintain a healthy environment in which the cycles of life can operate unimpaired. For Alwyn Jones that means the re-emergence of community such that the individual becomes embedded again in a society of interdependent and mutualistic relationships.

Martin von Hildebrand offers a fascinating example of community relationships in an Amazonian tribe in which the give-and-take economics of reciprocity and exchange mimic what are seen to be comparable processes of interdependence occurring in nature. The parallel with Gaia theory and its notion of holism and interconnectedness is striking and suggests, irrespective of our backgrounds, that we intuitively feel part of nature and its economy. Kate Rawles then discusses the role of ethics regarding our relationship with the natural world and whether Gaia theory brings ethical considerations with it, or on the contrary, whether as a scientific hypothesis, it remains free of any inherent values. In the final paper, Elisabet Sahtouris brings us back to the logical conclusion that the Earth is a super-organism with a physiology that is emergent from the interaction of all the component parts that make up the planet.

Once we accept that Gaia provides a likely explanation of life on this planet we must take note that our actions can no longer be viewed in isolation from their impact on the whole system. Indeed, we must become fully aware that our mindless destruction of natural ecosystems may well in the end threaten our own viability as a species. Gaia theory, therefore, may provide us with the rationale to stop blundering our way across the planet and instead provide us with the insight to forestall irreversible change.

Peter Bunyard

– 1 –
The Gaia Hypothesis

James Lovelock

As I see it there are three principal scientific theories about life on a planetary scale and the first of these is the traditional view and the one to which I subscribe. It goes right back and sees the Earth as a living organism. I suppose probably the first humans that could talk may have discussed this idea long, long ago, but every year, almost every month, I have come across a new statement or I receive a letter in the post, that tells me of an old ancient scientist who had said something about the Earth as a living system on a scientific basis. The earliest I have found so far was the Englishman, James Hutton, who, in a remarkable statement made to the Royal Society of Edinburgh in 1785, concluded: 'I consider the Earth to be a super-organism and its proper study should be by physiology.'

This was not simply an off-the-cuff statement, but based on his own work related to the cycling of the elements in the hydrological cycle. Hutton was much moved by the science of physiology which was almost the whole of biology then, since science had hardly separated at all. Most likely Harvey's work on the circulation of the blood influenced him considerably. This tradition of physiology takes us up to Vladimir Vernadsky (1863–1945) who realized the importance of life in transforming geology. His mentor was the Russian philosopher Corrolenko and, in Bolandin's excellent biography of Vernadsky, the story is told of the young Vernadsky going for walks with Corrolenko in the forests near Kiev, during which the old man would talk about the Earth being alive. Science in Victorian times had fragmented into numerous separate expertises and disciplines and Corrolenko was a kind of link back to the past.

The notion 'alive' bothers many of my scientific colleagues and if any of them are are worried by it, just think of it as no more than the capacity of the Earth to regulate itself and to keep cool when things are changing adversely. It is a characteristic which physiologists refer to as homeostasis. This then is the first tradition, that sees the Earth as a living organism. It is the view to which I subscribe, and I believe it to have a firm scientific basis.

Secondly there is the liberal view which is often called 'the co-evolutionary theory.' In this the organisms are only seen as loosely coupled with their physical and chemical environment. Co-evolutionists accept that organisms may change the composition of the material world but they do not accept that life has a constructive influence by which organisms alter the material world in a way that affects their own selection. I have been able to trace this theory back as far as Lamarck. At the same time I have never been clear whether Vernadsky was of this liberal co-evolutional middle view of the Earth or whether he subscribed to the first, traditional view. I suspect that he would have liked to subscribe to the first traditional view, but the pressures of scientific rectitude in his days, and in particular the political pressures on him in Russia, probably forced him towards more the 'liberal' tendency.

Then lastly we have the scientific theory which we can describe as 'the conventional wisdom.' Now this is something that is neither conventional nor wise. Indeed it has much more in common with trades union politics than with science. In this very Victorian theory of the Earth, the Earth and life sciences exist in separate buildings of the university and meet only to discuss administrative and territorial matters. The life scientists in this kind of theory see the evolution of organisms proceeding according to their personal interpretation of Darwin's great vision. And Darwin, like all other great scientists, suffers the disciple phenomenon. Hence the Earth scientists see the evolution of the material world proceeding strictly according to the rules of physics and chemistry with organisms on the planet merely passengers.

Those then are the three main theories of the Earth in science. In science we are not usually bothered too much about absolute truth; we are much more concerned about having a theory that is useful in predicting experiments and in helping us to pick winners. After all, most working scientists depend on getting grants to fund themselves and it is no use subscribing to theories that pick losers. Let me therefore try to tell you why I think that Gaia theory — hence the traditional theory — offers a sound basis for understanding our planetary system.

Let us go back some twenty years ago to when we first saw those pictures of the Earth from space. We had that vicarious vision of stunning beauty, that dappled white and blue sphere and it stirred all of us, no matter that by now it has just become a visual cliché. I have always thought that our sense of reality comes from matching our personal mental image or model of the world with that we are receiving through our senses and that I think is why that vision — an astronaut's eye view — of the Earth was so disturbing. It showed us for the first time just how much from reality we had strayed.

The Earth was also being viewed from space by the more discerning eye of scientific instruments and it was this view that confirmed James Hutton's vision in the eighteenth century of the Earth as a super-organism. When you see the Earth in infra-red light, rather than visible light it is seen immediately as a strange and wonderful anomaly amongst the planets of our solar system. Our atmosphere, the air we breathe, is revealed to be outrageously out of equilibrium in a chemical sense. It is more like the mixture of gases that enters the intake manifold of your car, with hydrocarbons mixed with oxygen. If that mixture were more concentrated it would be combustible or explosive. In total contrast the atmospheres of our dead partner planets, Mars and Venus, have atmospheres like those gases exhausted by combustion.

This unorthodox composition of the Earth's atmosphere radiates such a strong signal in the infra-red that if there were a space craft right outside the solar system the information received would give *prima facie* evidence that the only planet in the solar system that bore life was the Earth. But much more than this, if the observer stayed there for some time he would see that this very unstable, almost combustible, atmosphere persisted at a steady state and if he were a scientist he would know that this 'stability' required some powerful regulation process operating at the surface that was controlling it and keeping it constant for very long periods of time. It was this kind of evidence from space research that led me to postulate the *Gaia hypothesis* and led me to a long and fruitful collaboration with Lynn Margulis who was at that time the only scientist I could talk to about it.

To sum up the evidence: the presence of life on Earth was revealed by its intensely unusual atmosphere and it was the persistence of this instability for geological periods of time that suggested the presence of the controller, *Gaia.* It is important to recognize that the atmosphere is the smallest compartment of the Earth and yet through it flows most of the elements that go to make up living systems. Thus the carbon, nitrogen, oxygen and hydrogen of living organisms are all flowing through the atmosphere and that is why Gaia was first seen in the atmosphere. The oceans are similarly affected but, as my friend and colleague Mike Whitfield points out, to find and see Gaia in the oceans is a much more difficult task because the effects of life are so diluted by the vast volumes of water and salt that are there.

The theory that life evolved separately and independently of the Earth, although still widely held and the conventional wisdom expressed in many text books, emerged out of nineteenth century science, and is quite wrong. If the physics and chemistry of the Earth were evolving independently of life and if organisms were simply adapting to the changes that took place then there would be no reason whatever to find any marked chemical disequilibria in the Earth's atmosphere. The Earth might have a different composition from the other planets, but there is simply no way that lifeless chemistry could lead to an atmosphere that was rich in reactive gases. According to the third theory we could have, for example, an atmosphere with 21 per cent oxygen, but we could not have methane and hydrogen present at the same time. We could have 90 per cent of hydrogen and methane in the atmosphere, as do the larger outer planets, but we could not have oxygen as well.

It is sometimes said that the eminence of scientists is measured by the length of time that they hold up progress in their field. The Victorians included a great many of these golden 'oldies' and it was inevitable that in the last century, with so many exciting discoveries about the world to be made, such scientists had little time or inclination to think about the total picture, the larger view of the Earth. They were really in the position of the assemblers of a vast jigsaw puzzle and as you know the first task is to collect the pieces into categories: in fact you collect the edges and the blue bits that make the sky, you do not think about the assembled picture until you have got a good chunk of it together.

The second theory that I mentioned, the co-evolutionist theory which perhaps originated with Lamarck is the basis of the modern science of biogeochemistry which Vernadsky founded. It states that life and the environment interact — that gases like oxygen and methane are biological products — but it does not recognize the existence of any tight coupling between the organisms and their environment and does not admit to the active regulation of the chemical composition and climate of the Earth. Most importantly it does not see the Earth as alive. The co-evolutionists recognize the folly of separating the Earth and life sciences but dare not or will not take the full leap to Gaia. They stay with the liberal middle of the road science of biogeochemistry or co-evolution. The second theory also is I think untenable, although it is considerably more difficult to dispose of than was the third theory.

Before I go on to Gaia theory and to show why I think co-evolution is inadequate to explain the facts of the Earth, I think first we need to look at the viewpoint of biologists. Biologists amongst you may wonder why I have not mentioned the biological viewpoints so far in these three theories. I have not done so because, apart from the entertaining criticisms of Gaia by Richard Dawkins and Ford Doolittle, biologists in general have tended to ignore both Vernadsky and Gaia.

Instead they have tended to assume that the physical and chemical world evolves according to the rules laid down in the geology or biogeochemistry department of their university and the details of this material evolution need not be their concern. Accordingly, *if the environment changes then organisms adapt to the change.* They had very good reasons to think this way. There were and still are so many fascinating developments in evolutionary theory and molecular biology that why should biologists bother with controversial matters outside those interests. But the notion of adaptation is all too easily misused to justify ignorance. Somehow both geologists and biologists have failed to note that their separate researches have clearly demonstrated that the world is massively affected by the presence of life. The air we breathe, the ocean and the rocks are all either direct products of living organisms — think of the chalk cliffs of Dover, just one gigantic pile of shells — or else of rocks that have been greatly modified by the presence of life, and this even includes the igneous rocks coming from volcanos. Indeed, organisms are not just adapting to a dead world determined by textbook physics and chemistry alone; they live with a world that is the breath and the bones and the blood of their ancestors and that they themselves are now sustaining.

The abundant evidence that exists of an essentially recursive interaction between life and its environment is fatal to the old conventional wisdom of a completely separate evolution of the Earth and life. It is also destructive to the co-evolutionary argument. Indeed, if organisms are adapting to a world whose material state is determined by the activities of their neighbours then changing the environment becomes part of the game. It would be absurd to suppose that organisms would avoid the act of changing their environment if by so doing they left more progeny.

The Daisyworld model

There are I think three main reasons why Gaia theory has not been taken seriously. First of all it is old-fashioned and goes right back to the Greeks and earlier and must therefore be out of date. Secondly I chose to present it somewhat poetically and unfortunately most scientists, probably as a result of a faulty education have an instinctive distrust of anything of science that is presented without recourse to scientific jargon. And lastly, detail was lacking as to how it worked and very few of us are happy with a theory if we cannot envisage a mechanism. The preliminary nature of the theory led to those entertaining criticisms from Richard Dawkins and Ford Doolittle. Richard Dawkins in *The Extended Phenotype,* expounds at great length and with considerable fluency that Gaia is impossible since planets do not reproduce. Therefore there would be no natural selection of the most fit planet. Ford Doolittle, in Canada, rejected Gaia on somewhat more solid grounds. He said that planetary self-regulation needs foresight and planning by the biota and that there is just no way for global altruism to evolve through natural selection. He was happy with symbiosis and even with Lynn Margulis's endosymbiosis, but he claimed these associations were always between closely connected entities and Gaia would require the existence of a committee of the species to meet annually somewhere to bargain for next year's climate and chemical composition. This global-scale cooperation was out of the question: as equally was the idea of a Panglossian nanny who had looked after the Earth ever since life began.

These criticisms derive from dogma and are absurd. Even so they are hard to answer. For a while I wondered if Gaia was just another one of those untestable notions like the anthropic principle or Rupert Sheldrake's 'morphogenetic fields,' something to be talked about over coffee or a few beers rather than be investigated.

In fact, the feedback loops that link life with its environment are so numerous and so intricate that I could see little hope of ever quantifying or understanding them. Then it occurred to me over Christmas 1981 that you could do in science as both artists and composers do, which is to make an abstraction, an invention that nonetheless captured the essence.

Think of a portrait artist who with a few swift strokes drawn on a canvas, can capture the likeness of his subject and then spend months filling in the details. As scientists we can do the same kind of thing and what I want to try and show you is how we did it. We make our sketch by reducing the environment to a single variable, temperature, and we reduce the biota to a single species, daisies. Now I want you to imagine a planet which is very like the Earth, although in fact it is actually a computer model of a planet that is spinning like the Earth. It has no clouds, and it has an uncomplicated atmosphere without any greenhouse gases or pollutants to complicate its climate. It is also travelling in orbit around a star, the same mass and composition of our own Sun, and like our own Sun it warms up as it grows old. As physicists have discovered it is a property of stars to do this; it is the reverse of a bonfire, the older it becomes the hotter it gets. From straightforward physics it is relatively easy to calculate what would be the mean surface temperature of this imaginary world. Indeed, once we know the colour and hence the albedo of the planet we know its temperature. In the conventional wisdom diagram, we see what happens to that world as its star warms up from the time of the beginning of life to its present luminosity. What we see is a steady warm up of the planet with the temperature rising as the star heats up.

Meanwhile conventional biological wisdom tells us that daisies, like any other mainstream plant, do not grow if the temperature is below 5°C, it is too cold: nor do they grow if the temperature is above 40°C, it is too hot. In fact they grow best in the middle, round about room temperature. Now I think the view that the daisies are passively responding to environmental conditions is replete with nonsense. Instead, if we seeded our imaginary planet with dark and light coloured daisy seeds something different would happen. When the temperature reached 5°C the daisy seeds would germinate, but once they started to grow the darker ones would be at an advantage since they absorb sunlight which makes them warmer, enouraging their growth. The light coloured ones, on the other hand, actually reflect sunlight and are cooler so they do not grow well at all. At the end of the first season many more dark daisy seeds are left compared with light ones, giving dark daisies a head start at the beginning of the next season. By spreading out over an increasing area the dark daisies would soon be warming not just themselves but the region around as well. The result is an explosive positive feedback growth in the dark daisy population, and a sharp rise in the temperature of the planet. However the temperature would not go on rising indefinitely because in time it would become too hot for the dark daisies; moreover once the planet became warm the light coloured daisies would start growing well and begin competing with the dark form. Thus simple competition and natural selection of the two daisy species as the star warms up can be seen to keep the planet's temperature very close to the optimum for daisy growth. That little model, therefore, is a definitive answer to the criticisms of Ford Doolittle and Richard Dawkins. It is a system that has no purpose in it. It does not require committees or anything like that; rather it follows from the process of natural selection tightly coupled into the physical evolution of the planet.

Many of my biological friends are hard-nosed and they said: 'Oh yes, that's a very pretty model but what would happen if there were grey coloured daisies in it? Surely they are not going to waste energy making pigment and they would take over, so that the system would never work.'

It is not very difficult to put another equation in the model for grey daisies and when you do you find that the planet regulates just as well or slightly better than before. The reason is obvious; when it is very cold only dark daisies are fit to grow, the grey ones do not stand a chance and when it is very hot only the light coloured daisies are fit to grow. The only place that grey coloured daisies can grow is in the middle where their growth is not needed, where they are just passengers in a system. So much for that.

When I made the three daisy species model I was quite unaware that I was breaking all of the rules of population biology, since it had been known for sixty years in population biology that you cannot model the competition of more than two species simultaneously. But because I had been brought up in the tradition where you never read the literature before you did an experiment, I had few qualms at making a ten daisy species model. There are no signs of instability, the system works very well. The climate is regulated even better than it was with two daisies; much more smoothly. But the most exciting result is with regard to the ecologist's parameter *diversity.* For the first time we have a theoretical justification for diversity within ecosystems and quite the opposite of what theoretical ecologists have been telling us for 60 years, namely that the more complex an ecosystem gets the more unstable and fragile it becomes. For this little ecosystem, anyway, the more species the more stability.

At this point I went back and read the literature, coming across a scientist who was even more unknown than Vernadsky and yet as important. Alfred Lotka, a contemporary of Vernadsky, was a professor at John Hopkins University and in 1925 he wrote a book called *Physical Biology.* On page 16 he says:

> This fact deserves emphasis. It is customary to discuss the evolution of a species of organisms. As we proceed we shall see many reasons why we should constantly take in view the evolution as a whole of the system, organisms plus environment. It may at first sight seem as if this should prove a more complicated problem than the consideration of the evolution of a part only of the system but it will become apparent as we proceed that the physical laws governing evolution in all probability take on a simpler form when referred to the system as a whole than to any portion thereof. It is not so much the organism or the species that evolves but the entire system, species and environment, the two are inseparable.

Now in Alfred Lotka's time there were no computers and I have calculated to do that model by hand using ordinary analytical mathematics and working an eight hour day and a five day week, but otherwise never stopping, it would take one and a half years. Obviously Lotka was in no position to test his notion but his intuitive insight was immense. Sadly, students of population biology have neglected to follow their founder, Alfred Lotka, and for the past sixty years have got it all wrong.

Daisyworld is just an invention and I do not mean to suggest that the Earth regulates its temperature by growing daisies. The purpose of Daisyworld is to provide insight into the mechanisms of the real world and of Gaia.

That then is how I think it works; at the present stage of its development, as I said earlier, it matters little whether the theory is right or wrong for already it is providing a new and more productive view of the Earth and the other planets. In fact it is not difficult for it to do so, for the conventional theories of ecology and biogeochemistry are crippled by the apartheid that separates the sciences.

Gaia theory provokes us to take on board two principal considerations. The first — the same conclusion as Vernadsky came to — is that life is a planetary scale phenomenon. But I would go farther than Vernadsky in saying that you cannot have sparser life on a planet any more than you can have half of an animal. Living organisms have to regulate their planet otherwise the irresistible forces of physical and chemical evolution will soon render it uninhabitable. And this is very true of our own planet now.

The second thing is that the Gaia theory adds to Darwin's great vision. It does not contradict it, but it is no longer sufficient to consider the evolution of the species separate from the evolution of their environment. The two processes are tightly coupled, as Alfred Lotka said, in a single indivisible process. It is not enough to say that the organism that leaves the most progeny succeeds. Success comes only to the organism that also maintains a benign relationship with its material environment.

A helpful thought I find in connection with the difficult idea of the Earth as alive was put to me by the physicist Jerome Rothstein. He suggested comparing the Earth with a giant redwood tree. Imagine you have gone through a grove of those gorgeous trees on the west coast of America and have come across an old stump. As you step on the stump, standing on 3,000 years of history, it is worth reminding yourself that nearly all of the tree is dead when the tree is alive. In fact the middle of a living tree is dead wood with just a thin skin of living tissue around the circumference and beyond another dead layer, the bark, which protects the tree from the rigours of the environment — although not from the chainsaws of the loggers. Now the Earth is very much like that; you have the middle, molten, dead, incandescent, but around the circumference that same thick skin of living tissue and beyond it the atmosphere which is just like bark on a tree, not formally alive like living tissue, but still a protective layer against the rigours of the environment, which for the Earth is space.

For some time after the Earth was first formed, 4.5 billion years ago, it must have been sterile and evolving quite rapidly in a geological sense through the laws of physics and chemistry alone. However, at some time during that evolution of the Earth as a physical planet a time-window opened when the material conditions of our planet were right for life. The temperature was neither too hot nor cold and the right chemicals happened to be present in the environment.

I am not concerned with whether life originated spontaneously, floated in on a bit of cometary flotsam or was put here by visitors from somewhere else. However, the arrival or origin of life was followed by a period of co-evolution, with life evolving in its own way and the Earth evolving inexorably away from the environmental state that just happened to be favourable for life.

The Earth may thus have passed through a co-evolutionary phase just after life started, but then came a moment when the evolution of the organisms and the evolution of their host planet fused into a single evolutionary process, rather akin to the moment of conception when the sperm and the egg fuse. That moment for me marked the beginning of the system we call *Gaia*.

Theories may be judged useful if they make predictions that stimulate ideas and can be tested by experiment. At first sight it would seem that carrying out planet-scale experiments is likely to be both expensive and reprehensible. Yet, they are happening whether we like it or not as a result of our own activities. Perhaps the largest and most reprehensible of all these experiments is the removal of the forests of the humid tropics, followed by the burning of fossil fuels.

Gaia theory predicts different consequences for these activities than do those of either conventional science or of biogeochemistry. In particular Gaia theory sees the Earth as a responsive supra-organism that will at first tend to resist adverse environmental change and maintain homeostasis. But if stressed beyond the limits of whatever happens to be the current regulatory apparatus, it will jump to a new stable environment where many of the current range of species will be eliminated.

In spite of such excitements as the hurricane-force winds over much of Britain in early October 1987 or the ozone hole over Antarctica, nothing much is yet apparently happening to the environment that suggests an imminent jump to a different state. But even so, such surprises should be looked on perhaps as harbingers of larger non-linearities to come if we persist in our experiments with the planet.

Clouds and the oceans

One recent discovery that illustrates the value of Gaia as a predictor is last year's finding of a connection between cloud cover over the open oceans and algae that live on the surface layers of the sea.

It all began because Gaia theory required the production of large quantities of special compounds able to transfer the elements sulphur and iodine from the sea where they are abundant to the land surfaces where they are depleted, by the wash-off of rainfall and transport by rivers. Curious about this I set sail aboard the research vessel Shackleton in 1971 on its journey from Wales to Antarctica and back, and wherever the ship sailed in the oceans the sulphur compound, dimethyl sulphide, and the iodine compound, methyl iodide, were found. Their abundances in the sea were sufficient to allow a flux to the atmosphere enough to make up the needs of the land surfaces. Had it not been for the predictive value of Gaia theory both of these compounds I think would have remained as curiosities of algal biochemistry rather than be looked upon as major carriers of the sulphur and iodine cycles of nature.

But the story did not end there; with my colleagues, Andi Andreae, Robert Charlson and Steven Warren, we have argued that the output of this sulphur gas, dimethyl sulphide, from the marine algae over the open oceans is the largest if not the only source of the nuclei on which cloud droplets form over the oceans.

Cloud density, if it can be linked with algal growth on the ocean surfaces, can be shown to have as large an effect on global climate as the burning of fossil fuels and that of the CO_2 greenhouse. From the viewpoint of Gaia it is an extremely economic way to manage the climate.

Andi Andreae has found that the output of this compound from the oceans does not much depend upon productivity but on speciation. Indeed it is highest over the desert regions where the ocean is clear, hot and deficient in nutrients. It is likely to be quite a complicated story before it is finally unravelled, but the link between clouds and algal growth as a meteorological one is already becoming established by meteorologists themselves.

The dimethyl sulphide producing algae, by nucleating the water above them and producing clouds, are of course acting just like the white daisies in Daisyworld. Measurements of the onshore breeze coming on to one of the islands of Hawaii show that the mist coming up off the sea is not water vapour mist, but dilute sulphuric acid. Indeed, natural acid rain that is not coming from the burning of fossil fuels is to be found in the middle of the Pacific. The relative humidity close to the surface is much too low for water to condense out as clouds, yet it will do so around the microdroplets of sulphuric acid. This brings me to an incredibly interesting quote which I picked up on the big island off Hawaii from a Polynesian. He told me he had read Captain Cook's journals because he was rather a noted figure on those islands and in Captain Cook's journals, it said 'it is a dispensation of providence that wherever the ship sails in tropic waters there is a golden haze that protects the skins of the men and the rigging of the ship from the fierce rays of the sun.' Now that was long before any pollution and we must assume it was just such an acid haze that he was talking about.

When thinking of the oceans we must bear in mind perhaps the most important point of all: that while water may have been needed for the start of life, the persistence of water on this planet is another of the consequences of the Gaia system. Venus and Mars once had abundant water but, having no life, could not keep it. We have water because of the release of free oxygen through photosynthesis. The oxygen combines with hydrogen to form water and so, in combination with a cold tropopause that freezes out any water, prevents hydrogen escaping into space from the upper atmosphere. Thus life brings us water and water is essential for life.

Geophysiology and the planet

I would now like to introduce Gaia as a geophysiological notion. As stated earlier, Hutton, now known of as the father of geology, was one of the first scientists to think of the Earth in a systems context.

Hutton belonged to the *Circulation Society* which was a group of scientists who were inspired by the discoveries of physiology, like the circulation of the blood, and he applied those kinds of idea to his view of the hydrological cycle and the movement of the nutritious elements through the Earth. Hutton was a polymath; he was a physician, he was a good European who had obtained his degree at Leiden, he was a farmer and a chemist as well and undoubtedly the broad view of life that he had, led to him looking at the Earth as a living system. James Hutton's wholesome view of the planet was discarded early in the last century and this was due partly to a lack of evidence at the time but mostly because there was a growing interest in origins and in evolutionary theories, both of the Earth and of life upon it.

Biologists, meanwhile, had been exposed to Darwin's great vision of the evolution of species by natural selection but too often forgot James Hutton's *uniformitarianism* in which evolution of the material environment was considered to be in a more or less steady state. Now both of those theories, Darwin's and uniformitarianism, were very radical at that time and they appeared in a cultural environment where the scriptural dogma of an active creation was still widely held to be true.

The Earth and life sciences in the nineteenth century were for a time held together by their sharing in a common rejection of the religious idea of creationism, but it was not long before they began to go their separate ways. The divorce occurred, I believe, because more information became available than could easily be digested by the comparatively small number of scientists that there were in the world at that time. Also the techniques for looking at organisms were widely different from those for looking at the physical nature of our planet. Thus, expertises developed and little communication occurred between their practitioners.

In his time Darwin did not know, as we do now, the extent to which the environment is determined by the products of organisms. He did not know, for example, that all of the gases in the atmosphere apart from the rare gases which only add up to about one per cent, are cycled entirely through living organisms and some of them with residence times measured in tens of years. Had he known, his views might well have been different.

So what is geophysiology? Well, like co-evolution, geophysiology rejects the apartheid of Victorian biology and geology while still going much further. Geophysiology is about the evolution of a tightly coupled system whose constituents are the biota, the atmosphere, the oceans and the surface rock; it maintains that the self-regulation of important properties like climate and chemical composition are in consequence an emergence of this evolutionary process. Like living organisms and many closed loop self-regulating systems, the whole system would be expected to show such emergent properties, that is to say the whole would be more than the sum of its parts.

Many biologists find it difficult to understand that geophysiology offers anything new. What they say is that it has been known since the last century that the presence and the abundance of oxygen in the air, for example, is simply a matter of photosynthesis by green plants and the recycling of oxygen and carbon dioxide between the producers and the

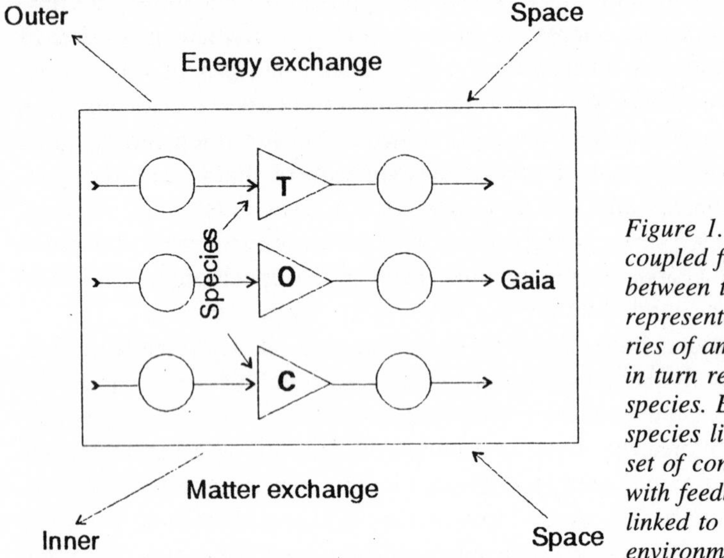

Figure 1.1. A tight-coupled feedback between the biota, represented as a series of amplifiers that in turn represent a species. Each of the species lives within a set of constraints with feedback loops linked to the external environment.

consumers. Now what they fail to understand is the significance that oxygen has remained at its present level for hundreds of millions of years in spite of large changes in the sizes of its sources and sinks. This constancy implies the need for some means for its regulation and this is really what we are talking about and what mainstream biology has missed.

We must also appreciate that when biochemists examine a live animal they know that many of its reactions and processes can adequately be described by simple deterministic physics and chemistry, but they also have to accept the legitimacy of physiology.

Gaia and modelling

Figure 1.1 portrays a system where there is tight-coupled feedback between the biota, represented as a series of amplifiers that in turn represents a species. Obviously there would be *n* of them, but I have put just three on the diagram. The point is to show that each of these species lives within a set of constraints: it may thus be too hot; too cold; too salt; too fresh; too acid; too alkaline; or indeed lacking oxygen or be exposed to too much. That set of constraints is in the feedback loops governing the growth of each set of organisms represented as an amplifier and when any environmental change occurs then natural selection will cause any one of these to bloom and feedback an opposing signal to the environment, if that is necessary, or a positive feedback if there is a need to restore the system to whatever is the *status quo.* The external inputs come from the outside. The only other point I would like to make concerns the practicalities of looking at the Earth as a kind of physiological system. I mentioned that theoretical ecology has spent some sixty years trying to model the species and has now gone into a disastrous mode whereby prominent theoretical ecologists have become prominent mathematicians in a field of chaos. In a sense they have given up theoretical ecology altogether and are claiming to have made great discoveries in the mathematics of chaos. This is not surprising, it is a mathematical generality that if you have systems containing more than three non-linear differential equations without any constraints on them they will frequently go chaotic. Standard population biology models, like the famous Lotka and Volterra one, or more recent ones like that depicting the interactions between spruce budworms and spruce trees, will just about work with two species, but put three into the model and the thing goes mad. Certainly you can't have ten.

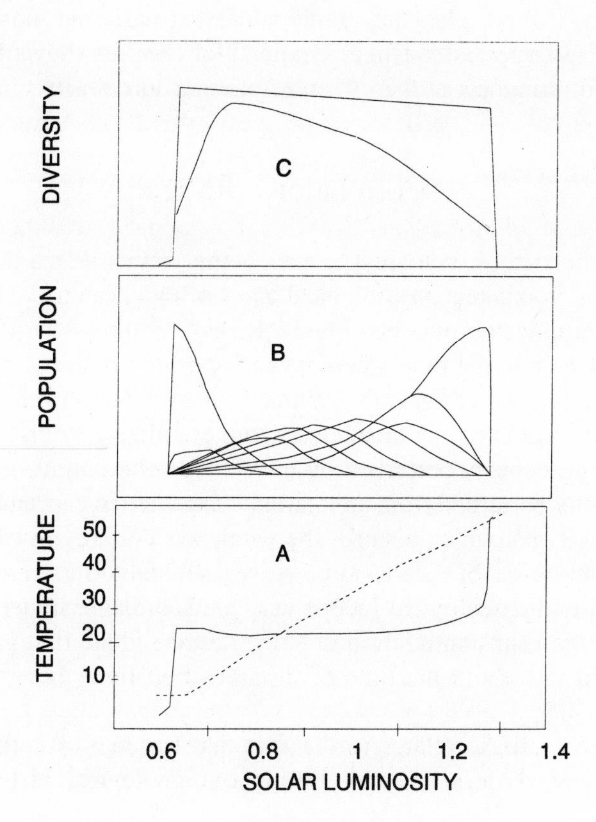

Figure 1.2.

For instance if you make a model using standard population ecology in which grass is being eaten by rabbits and the rabbits are being culled by foxes you will find that the model wanders off and goes into a chaotic mode; indeed, if you perturb it all that happens is that it wanders to a new chaotic behaviour set. By contrast if you feed the environment back into the model by just coupling the growth of daisies to the temperature of the environment in the same kind of way as in the Daisyworld model, the model becomes perfectly behaved. Thus, when time starts daisies grow rapidly followed by the evolution of rabbits which start eating the plants until you come to the point where foxes appear on the scene and start culling the rabbits. The model, meanwhile, moves to a stable point, a single stable track and stays there. If you perturb it by a plague that kills off the rabbits or the grass, the model behaves by making a single loop round, so returning to the stable track. Figure 1.2 depicts the result of incorporating diversity into Daisyworld. The dotted line in **A** shows how the temperature rises were there to be no regulation. **B** shows various population curves of different species, with black daisies represented to the left of the diagram and white daisies to the right. The middle ground — where planetary temperature regulation is most stable — is where most species can live. Graph **C** of the trio shows how diversity rises and plummets at the extremes of solar luminosity.

Correlation with reality

In the same way if you are a biogeochemist rather than a theoretical ecologist and you take a physiological approach you can make the necessary, albeit complicated, models. Figure 1.3 is a graph of the transition from the Archaean to the time when oxygen appeared in the atmosphere in the Protozeroic. The point is that climate, three gases and three species are all being regulated simultaneously and stabilizing whilst the system is being continuously perturbed by increasing solar output. The system too is violently perturbed from an internal contradiction caused by the appearance of oxygen which disturbs the whole system. Yet, always the system moves to its stable state and evolves satisfactorily. Interestingly this model fits the geological record very well, the appearance of oxygen is marked by a substantial drop in temperature and the first great glaciation appeared just about the time of the transition from the Archaean to the Proterozoic.

Another puzzle relates to the fact that the rate of carbon burial has been more or less constant throughout geological history. The only

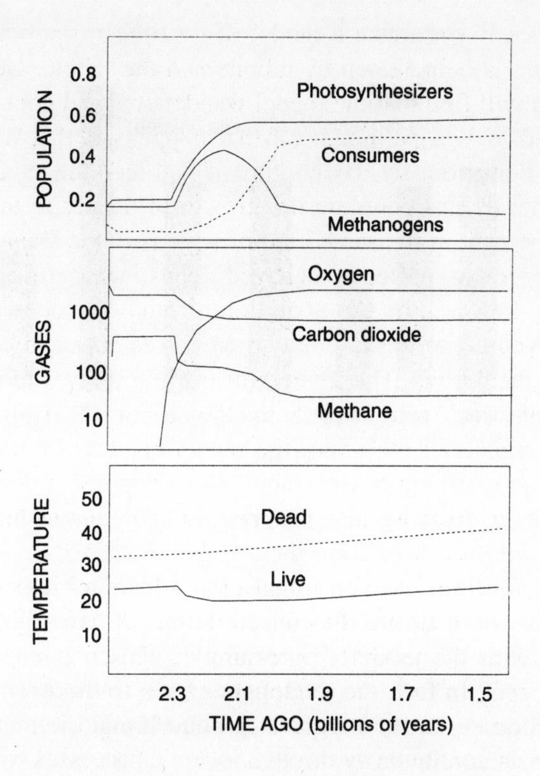

Figure 1.3.

exception is in times of transition, such as we obtain when oxygen appeared. Oxygen was initially a great poison and we would have expected its appearance on the scene as leading to major disaster, yet organisms are very capable of taking advantage of changes of that sort, one consequence of the appearance of oxygen being that it greatly increased the rate of rock weathering and the supply of nutrients. One effect was a substantial increase in the extent of eutrophication photosynthesis, which we would expect from our experience with discharging nitrates into a pond. But what is also surprising is that the methanogens also increase, which leads to more carbon burial. Eventually the consumers picked up and took over the carbon cycling and the methanogens sunk back just to where they were before in accord with the notion that carbon burial is constant. This sort of model you can also do experiments with. I should add, if you do a standard biogeochemical box model just like the theoretical ecology models they will tend to go chaotic or, for them to behave at all, will depend on a careful choice of initial conditions. On the other hand, with the sort of model shown in Figure 1.3, you can put in almost any initial conditions and it just settles down to what is right. Moreover, the values it predicts are all realistic, and the temperatures are not something wild,

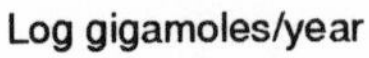

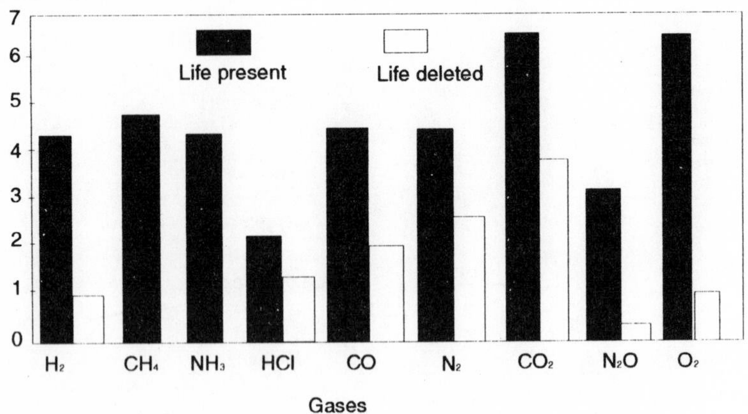

Figure 1.4. The fluxes of gases in the presence and absence of life.

such as minus infinity, as you might obtain from a biogeochemical box model. Equally realistic are the concentrations of gases. You can also do experiments with the model. For example, what happens when carbon burial is stopped? In fact, the model goes back to the Archaean, since, if you stop carbon burial no oxygen is produced and the material entering the environment continuously through tectonic processes will therefore be in its chemically reduced state.

Figure 1.4 demonstrates the fluxes of common atmospheric gases on a planet that has life compared with a dead planet. The last model experiment indicates what happens if you stop methane production. This might be something on the ecological agenda in the near future since methane is a powerful greenhouse gas compared with all the others and there might be cause for some technological fix to stop methane being used. For instance, some genetic engineer could arrange that cattle no longer produce the gas. In fact, if you stop methane production everything comes to a grinding halt and dies quietly. But the point is that you cannot carry out such modelling with a standard biogeochemical box model in which the biota is put in as a box with inputs and outputs but no opportunity to respond, and hence no opportunity to bloom on account of environmental changes.

So what is the message from Gaia for human ecology? First and foremost Gaia forces upon us a concern for the planet and its state of health and offers an alternative to our near obsessive concern with the state of humanity. It is in our own interest anyway to live well with the Earth. If we do not, Gaia will live on but with a new biosphere that may not include humans. The demolition of the forests of the humid tropics and the ever increasing burden of greenhouse gases are real threats to Gaia and humanity alike.

We are in many ways in the same state with regard to the health of the Earth as were the early physicians towards the health of their patients. We have an impressive array of scientific equipment and expertise but so did the nineteenth century physicians. There was microbiology and microscopes and the bacterial theory of disease. There was biochemistry and an understanding of many metabolic disorders. But there was almost nothing a physician could do other than relieve pain or do simple surgery. It was not until after World War II that hi-tech medicine came of age.

So it is with the Earth. We have theories and equipment but there is little that science has to offer for the cure of the ills of Gaia. One thing though we can learn from the physician that is invaluable in our professional practice as planetary physicians is the Hippocratic oath — do nothing that would harm the patient. In our enthusiasm for some new nostrum we should take care that the cure is not worse than the disease.

The other and more optimistic message is that the evolution of Gaia seems to depend upon the activities of individual organisms. If these are favourable for the environment they succeed. If not they are doomed but life goes on. To me this means that it is more important to try to live in harmony with the Earth at a personal level than to allow any of the numerous human collectives and parties to take that responsibility away from us.

– 2 –
Sketch for a History of the Idea of the Biosphere

Jacques Grinevald

> *Until recently the historians and the students of the humanities, and to a certain extent even the biologists, consciously failed to reckon with the natural laws of the biosphere, the only terrestrial envelope where life can exist. Basically man cannot be separated from it; it is only now that this indissolubility begins to appear clearly and in precise terms before us.*
>
> *Vladimir Vernadsky (1945)*

> *Therefore the explanation, which is given of the different phenomena of the Earth, must be consistent with the actual constitution of this Earth as a living world, that is, a world maintaining a system of living animals and plants.*
>
> *James Hutton (1795)*

The emerging ecological perspective which perceives us to be part of the Earth's biosphere is the major cultural and scientific revolution of our time. Yet this perspective has an early precedent. In his 1749 thesis at Leiden entitled *De sanguine et circulatione in microcosmo,* James Hutton (1726–97), the Scots physician who turned farmer and natural philosopher, emphasized the cyclic organic view of the Earth. Hutton's proposition was eventually superseded by the triumphant lifeless mathematical science of *Rational Mechanics.* Hutton often referred to the whole Earth as 'macrocosm' and equivalent to an 'organism.' The parallel between the physiological microcosm of our body and the geological macrocosm of our planet Earth was accentuated in his holistic natural philosophy (Hutton 1788b, 211). In *The Theory of the Earth with Proofs and Illustrations,* James Hutton wrote:

> We live in a world where order everywhere prevails; and where final causes are as well known, at least, as those

> which are efficient. Thus, the circulation of the blood is the efficient cause of life; but, life is the final cause, not only for the circulation of the blood but for the revolution of the globe ... Therefore the explanation, which is given of the different phenomena of the Earth, must be consistent with the actual constitution of this Earth as a living world, that is, a world maintaining a system of living animals and plants. (1795, 11:545f).

Hutton's work, popularized by John Playfair's 1802 *Illustrations of the Huttonian Theory,* is now credited for the discovery of the cyclical nature of geological changes and, together with Buffon, of the immensity of the duration of nature. C.A. Basset, the French translator of Playfair in 1815 pointed out the parallel between Hutton's theory of the Earth and Laplace's stability of the world system. But the first publication of Hutton's theory in 1788 produced no reaction; it was ignored because catastrophism dominated.

Jean-Baptiste Lamarck

Although the term and the modern idea of biosphere does not appear in Lamarck's work, it is relevant here to mention the French naturalist Jean-Baptiste Lamarck (1744–1829), Buffon's protégé. Compared with Lamarck's fame as a botanist and a zoologist or as the debated originator of biological evolution, Lamarck's contribution to geology, biogeochemistry and environmental sciences is more difficult to evaluate because it has been neglected by the historians of Earth sciences and ecology.

Significantly, it is in his little-known but highly original geological treatise, printed at his own expense under the title *Hydrogéologie,* that Lamarck introduced the science of Biology appropriately within the theory of the Earth:

> A sound Physics of the Earth should include all the primary considerations of the Earth's atmosphere, of the characteristics and continual changes of the Earth's external crust, and finally of the origin and development of living organisms. (Lamarck 1802, 7f; trans. by Carozzi 1964, 18).

Lamarck was not a narrow specialized scientist, but, like his mentor Buffon, a philosopher viewing Nature as a whole. Without doubt his

Hydrogéologie was a work of genius. Indeed, prior to Humboldt and more latterly Vernadsky, Lamarck's holistic point of view was a precedent to our global ecological worldview (Jordanova 1984, 45). As a naturalist with an encyclopaedic mind, nurtured by the pre-industrial tradition of the Enlightenment, Lamarck was not only a botanist and a zoologist, but also a mineralogist and meteorologist. Yet the basic concept of the biosphere was still foreign to him and the time was not yet ripe for global ecology.

Lamarck fully realized the enormous importance of the action of living organisms on the changing surface of the Earth's crust. A century before Vernadsky and even longer before the formulation of the Gaia hypothesis, he conceived the planetary role of life, the geochemical importance of the intricate interactions between living matter and the terrestrial environment, and then the links between geology (including mineralogy, petrology, sedimentology), meteorology and evolutionary biology. Independently of Hutton's *Theory of the Earth,* of which he was unaware, Lamarck discovered the grandeur of coevolution and its effect upon the face of the Earth.

For a long time, Lamarck's biogeochemical ideas were ignored. The advancement of science, through scientific institutions and the ideology of industrialization, created compartmentalized and specialized disciplines without paying much attention to the unity of Nature as a whole or biospheric evolution. That Darwin was also a geologist was forgotten: geological sciences and biological sciences advanced separately.

Humboldtian science: a holistic epistemology

Opposition to the fragmentation of knowledge is clearly expressed in the works of Buffon, Hutton, Lamarck, Goethe and of the German romantic natural philosophers. For the Romantics all the sciences of nature were seen within an unique cosmological framework. The Earth, with its inhabitants was considered as a whole, with holism not being considered in opposition to rationality. Such a scientific approach was admirably illustrated by the influential works of the great German geographer and natural philosopher Alexander von Humboldt (1769–1859). Indeed, the 'coevolution' of living organisms, climate, ocean and the Earth's crust is a grand scientific idea deeply rooted in the nineteenth century scientific world-view associated in particular with Humboldt (Worster 1977, 82).

Alexander von Humboldt is now considered a true forerunner of our global ecological view of the Earth in the Cosmos. Vernadsky, in common with his master, Dokuchaev, and the Russian geographers, often quoted Humboldt's *Ansichten der Natur* and others of his works. Written after his famous expedition to the Americas with Aimé Bonpland, Humboldt's *Essai sur la géographie des plantes* (1807) was a classic in early biogeography and ecology. The impact of Humboldt's writings upon Darwin is well documented.

Humboldt, author of a multi-volume synthesis appropriately entitled *Kosmos,* conceived early *l'idée d'une physique du monde* (letter to Pictet of 1796). Here the term *physique* is not equivalent to our standard concept of physics; it is near to the idea of a World Natural History or the old Greek word *Physis.*

This tradition was later shared by Teilhard de Chardin with Helmut de Terra (1900–1981), his German-American fellow-traveller in Asia who, as a geologist and paleontologist, was also author of an important study published in 1955 on Humboldt.

Humboldt, trained as a geologist under Abraham Gottlob Werner (1749–1817) at the famous Freiberg *Bergakademie* where he adopted Wernerian Geognosy, which studies both organic and inorganic bodies in the history of the Earth. *Geognosy,* a term still used in the mid-nineteenth century as in the *Lehrbuch der Geognosie* published by the German mineralogist Karl Freidrich Naumann (1797–1873), has come back into use through the originators of the Gaia theory.

Eduard Suess: geology and biosphere

The Austrian geologist Eduard Suess (1831–1914), first coined the term 'biosphere' in 1875. He was a natural philosopher within the Humboldtian tradition, viewing nature as a whole, with its geological substrate as an integral part of the Earth's surface. In his great book *The Face of the Earth,* Suess imagined a space traveller discovering the face of the planet Earth. It was a striking illustration of the whole-Earth approach. In fact, during Suess's lifetime, several scientists attempted to apply the whole-Earth approach such as Friedrich Ratzel (1844–1904), a German student of the naturalist Haeckel who turned from ecology to geopolitics, and was author of a massive book entitled *Die Erde und das Leben* (Leipzig, 1901–2). The French anarchist and encyclopaedic geographer Elisée Reclus (1830–1905) was the author of many books including *La Terre* (Paris, 2 vols., 1868–69), *Nouvelle Géographie Universelle* (Paris, 19 vols., 1875–93) and *L'Homme et la Terre* (Paris, 6 vols., 1905–8). In this latter book, Reclus declared: *L'Homme est la nature prenant conscience d'elle-même.*

Eduard Suess was born in London of a Jewish merchant family, but after 1845 went to live in Vienna. Partly educated in Prague with French, German and English teachers, he became a great engineer and scholar and also a prominent citizen of Vienna. As a liberal, he achieved a brilliant political career, beginning just after the success of his 1862 book entitled *Der Boden der Stadt Wien,* a pioneering essay in human geology. Two major civil engineering projects brought Suess great fame including an aqueduct that gave Vienna its drinking water supply from the mountains (1873) and the Danube canal (1875).

He had a long and fruitful academic career at the University of Vienna, first appointed as professor of paleontology (1857–62), then for nearly forty years as professor of geology. His long involvement with the Imperial Academy of Science began in 1860. In 1893, he was elected vice-president and in 1898 president of the Academy. He died in April 1914, just before the Great War.

In 1981, the 150th anniversary of Eduard Suess's birth was commemorated by the *Österreichischen Akademie der Wissenschaften,* which in its special publication, completely ignored Suess's idea of the biosphere. Indeed, although the entry 'Suess' in the *Dictionary of Scientific Biography* rightly declares that 'emphasizing the unity of the living world, in 1875 he created the concept of the biosphere,' many statements about the origins of the term biosphere neglect the name of Suess. For instance, the widely-read unofficial 1972 Stockholm UN Conference publication: *Only One Earth* declared that it was 'the Soviet physicist, Vladimir Ivanovich Vernadsky, who invented the word biosphere' (Ward and Dubos 1972–76). Yet, in his book *La Biosphère,* Vernadsky (1929, 93) commented:

> It was only in 1875 that E. Suess, one of the most eminent geologists of the last century, introduced into science the notion of biosphere, as the idea of a particular envelope of the terrestrial crust penetrated by life.

Published in Vienna, just three years before the first International Geological Congress in Paris, Suess's 1875 book must be considered as a milestone in the development of geotectonics. But the title, *Die Entstehung der Alpen,* which provided the 'theoretical basis of much of Suess's later work' and in itself was 'influential out of all proportion to its size' (Greene 1982, 148), was rather misleading. The book is clearly not only about the development of the Alps. In the final chapter of *Die Entstehung der Alpen,* Suess presented his holistic view of the development of the Earth. He explained that the Earth consisted of several concentric structures, with a core and a mantle. In addition to the *atmosphere,* a term that had already been in use for a long time in the scientific literature, Suess coined the terms: the *hydrosphere* and the *lithosphere.* The idea of the Earth as made up of and surrounded by different spheres was not new, it was part of an intellectual tradition derived from Aristotle's *Meteorologica* and the Greek view of the Earth as a globe in the sky.

However, as Suess emphasized, 'one thing seems strange on this spheres-built celestial body, namely organic life.' The plant, which deeply roots in the soil to feed and at the same time rises into the air to breathe, wrote Suess, is indicative of how life interacts between the atmosphere and the lithosphere. The German word Eduard Suess used for this zone of interaction was *eine selbstandige Biosphäre,* a sustainable biosphere (1875:159) .

French and Swiss Alpine geologists were deeply impressed by Suess's 1875 book. This impact is emphasized in several memorial books by the French geologist Pierre Termier (1859–1930), a friend of Teilhard and the uncle of Henri Termier who together with his wife eventually published a *Histoire géologique de la biosphère* in 1952. In his *A la gloire de la Terre,* which contains many pages on the life and work of Eduard Suess, Pierre Termier (1922) notably described the enthusiasm of his master Marcel Bertrand (1847–1907), a Corps des Mines engineer working with the Geological Survey of France, on discovering *Die Entstehung der Alpen.*

Suess's work owed a great deal to the rise of mountaineering, of which Horace-Benedict de Saussure was a founding father. The early alpinists were not only part of the Romantic movement, but also of the scientific development of physics.

Parallel to ocean discoverers like James Cook or George Forster, early mountaineers were scientific explorers interested in geology, mineralogy, botany, zoology, meteorology, calorimetry, physics and the chemistry of gases. Scientific instruments like thermometers and barometers played their part in de Saussure's ascent of Mont Blanc.

Suess's *The Face of the Earth* was a massive international publishing enterprise and a scientific work of art. His aesthetic approach was a typical result of Viennese culture in old Austria. In the mind of Pierre Termier (1922), it was 'a sumptuous temple,' an 'extraordinary book,' a 'poem,' a 'work of genius.' In German, the first volume appeared in

1883; the others appeared in 1885, 1888, 1901, and the final volume in 1909.

The English translation, *The Face of the Earth* (5 vols., 1904–24), was made under the direction of William Johnson Sollas (1849–1936), a versatile scientist who combined geological investigations and biological research. In English-speaking countries Suess's concept of biosphere was not apparent and it was generally ignored by those following the history of ideas. It is even excluded from the recent Macmillan *Dictionary of the History of Science* (Bynum *et al.* 1981).

Suess's great book had the deepest influence on geological thought since the publication in the 1830s of Charles Lyell's *Principles of Geology.* It was not an original revolutionary work as was Alfred Wegener's controversial book *Entstehung der Kontinente und Ozeane* first published in 1915, but the final synthesis of an epoch, comparable with Humboldt's *Kosmos.* In fact, Suess's work is a classical description of the globe's surface before the rise of the concept of continental drift of Wegener. As argued in particular by Brouwer (1981) and Sengör (1982), the work of Eduard Suess provided the intellectual background for the promoters of 'mobilism' (1924, 290), and was a pivotal and decisive scientific source for the Swiss, Emile Argand, the German, Alfred Wegener, the American, Frank B. Taylor and the South African, Alexander Du Toit.

Suess's biosphere and Teilhard de Chardin

In Suess's opinion, the idea of the *biosphere* as the unity of flora and fauna covering the Earth's face emerged out of the revolution in natural history introduced by Lamarck and Darwin: 'it is thanks to Lamarck and Darwin that we succeeded in coming to this conclusion,' he remarked.

In France, whereas establishment geologists were sceptical of Wegener's ideas on continental drift, considered by Pierre Termier (1928) as 'the dream of a great poet,' a 'seductive,' 'unnecessary' and excessively 'convenient' hypothesis, they more readily accepted the term 'biosphere' proposed by the respectable Austrian master. Among this scientific circle of Earth scientists was the Jesuit father, Pierre Teilhard de Chardin (1881–1955), then professor of geology at the Institut Catholique of Paris. In the 1920s, the close friend of Teilhard was the mathematician-turned-philosopher, Edouard Le Roy (1870–1954), Bergson's interpreter and successor at the Collège de France. Together, the two unorthodox Catholic thinkers discussed the new scientific idea of the biosphere and, in collaboration with the Russian scientist, Vladimir Vernadsky, then in Paris, developed the notion of the noosphere (Teilhard 1956, Vernadsky 1945).

Teilhard first used the term biosphere in a laudatory review of *The Face of the Earth,* in 1921. He then used it in all his philosophical essays, particularly in *Le Phénomène humain,* written in 1938–40 in China, and only published after his death in 1955. As we know, the biosphere is a very important concept in Teilhard de Chardin's philosophical work.

According to Teilhard, the biosphere (a term he credited to Suess and never to Vernadsky) is only the organic totality of living beings, forming a continuous thin layer around the face of the Earth, distinct and in addition to the other geospheres. That concept is similar to what Vernadsky called living matter, and others biomass or biota. Problems with terminology and conceptual confusion still persist.

Thus, in 1969 Gillard proposed a new term, namely 'ecosphere,' for that part of our sphere in which there was life together with the living organisms it contained. In the same way as the 'biosphere' was the rough total of all living organisms, the 'ecosphere' was the rough total of all ecosystems (of the hydro-ecosphere, the litho-ecosphere and the atmo-ecosphere). Gillard had quoted Professor Marcel Florkin (1900–1979), an eminent Belgian biochemist, who introduced the Vernadskian biogeochemical concept of 'the biosphere' in his 1943 textbook *Introduction à la biochimie générale.*

Teilhard's evolutionary cosmic philosophy became an inspiration to many people all over the world, including some in Marxist circles. Indeed the Teilhardian idea of the biosphere (and of the noosphere) is still accepted by many, as for instance by the New Age Movement. Nevertheless, Teilhard's extreme anthropocentric views, impregnated with ideas taken from the Western philosophy of progress and development, are now rejected by radical thinkers, including deep ecologists.

Indeed, because of its strong anthropocentrism, the Teilhardian philosophy or theology of the Earth does not accept the idea of the biosphere as a global ecological system. On the contrary, Teilhard disregarded the stability of the self-regulating planetary ecosystem, being instead obsessed with his discovery of time and the irreversibility of the evolutionary process. Moreover, Teilhard apparently never understood Vernadsky's teachings on biogeochemical cycles. Thus, although the Teilhardian biosphere is a living force, with a geological significance and a time's arrow essentially opposed to the processes of entropy, it is not an ecological concept.

Vladimir I. Vernadsky (1863–1945)

Like Teilhard, Vernadsky recognized the great contribution of naturalists such as Buffon and Lamarck. He also paid homage to the profound influence that Goethe and Humboldt exerted over him. Our ignorance of Vernadsky remind us of our lack of knowledge of the history of ecology in Russia and the part played by Vernadsky's biosphere concept in the rise of the Soviet tradition of environmental studies and global ecology.

To investigate further the Soviet scientific tradition following Vernadsky's biospheric perspective, I refer you to Kamshilov (1976), Budyko (1980; 1984), Fortescue (1980), and especially Lapo (1987), author of a book first published in 1982 and entitled *Traces of Bygone Biospheres.* These authors link Vernadsky's scientific heritage and the Gaia hypothesis with its emphasis on the transformation of the Earth's environment by living organisms and notably by microorganisms.

In 1963, the Soviet Academy of Sciences, celebrated the centenary of the birth of the Academician V.I. Vernadsky. On that occasion, the Soviet biogeochemist and oceanographer Alexander P. Vinogradov (1895–1975), a former pupil and collaborator of Vernadsky, declared:

> Much time will have to pass before the historian of science will be able to review the vast scientific legacy of Vernadsky and fully detail the depth and many-sidedness of his influence.

Significantly, in a book review of the recent first English translation of Vernadsky's *The Biosphere,* James E. Lovelock declared:

> When Lynn Margulis and I introduced the Gaia hypothesis in 1972 neither of us was aware of Vernadsky's work and none of our much learned colleagues drew our attention to the lapse. We retraced his steps and it was not until the 1980s that we discovered him (Vernadsky) to be our most illustrious predecessor. *(New Scientist,* 17 July 1986).

Born in St Petersburg on 12 March 1863, to a liberal learned family, Vladimir Ivanovich Vernadsky graduated from the University of his native city, where the famous chemist Dimitri Ivanovich Mendeleev (1834–1907) and the geographer and soil science pioneer Vasili Vasilevich Dokuchaev (1846–1903) encouraged him to study the Earth sciences. He became an internationally reputed mineralogist, one of the founders of modern geochemistry and a pioneer in radiogeology. He placed great emphasis on the need to study Precambrian formations with the aim of finding the oldest rocks of the Earth's crust in relation to the idea of life as the most powerful geochemical agent. But, above all, Vladimir Vernadsky is now considered the creator of biogeochemistry and the founding father of the contemporary conception of the biosphere.

The most interesting period of Vernadsky's life was the 1920s, after the October Revolution and the First World War, especially his fruitful stay in France from July 1922 to December 1925. He had been invited there by the Rector of the University of Paris, the mathematician Paul Appell, to deliver lectures on geochemistry at the Sorbonne.

Meanwhile, at the Paris Museum, Vernadsky worked again with his old friend Alfred Lacroix (1863–1948), whom he had met many years before, in 1888, at the Collège de France laboratory of mineralogist Ferdinand Fouqué (1828–1904). Lacroix was also a friend of Teilhard and as a result Vernadsky met Teilhard and his friend Edouard Le Roy, as well as the Abbé Christophe Gaudefroy (1878–1971), mineralogist at the Institut Catholique.

Vernadsky adopted Suess's term biosphere after the First World War in his early biogeochemical studies, but it was only during his stay in Paris that he developed a theory of coevolution which he called the 'living matter' and the planetary environment of life, partly created and controlled by life, the biosphere. He may well have derived some of his ideas from his uncle Yevgraf Maximovich Corrolenko, an amateur philosopher familiar with the works of great naturalists. According to Balandine (1982, 24), Corrolenko believed the Earth to be a living organism. A precedent for the Gaia thesis!

Many interesting ideas belong to the prehistory of the Gaia hypothesis. In particular, Vernadsky pointed out the contribution of the founders of organic chemistry, Justus von Liebig (1803–73) in Germany, Jean-Baptiste Boussingault (1802–87) and Jean-Baptiste Dumas (1800–1884) in France as to how chemical cycles connected all organisms, including microorganisms, soils and the atmosphere.

The physiological concept of metabolism, appeared in mid-nineteenth-century Germany under the term *Stoffwechsel* and later in the French literature, being applied not only to individual living organisms, but also to the vast organism of nature, that comprised a geophysiology of the biosphere. Inspired by a recent paper on 'Boussingault and the nitrogen cycle' (Aulie 1970), James Lovelock and Lynn Margulis cited Dumas and Boussingault:

> The atmosphere, therefore, is the mysterious link that connects the animal with the vegetable, the vegetable with the animal kingdom. (Margulis and Lovelock 1975a; Margulis 1981, 347).

Vernadsky was the first scientist to be concerned with the boundaries of the biosphere as 'the domain of life' and he devoted a special article in 1937 to 'the limits of the biosphere.' Yet, solving the question concerning the upper boundary of the biosphere was as complicated as that concerning the lower boundary (Lapo 1987, 59). Thus, he was interested in atmospheric ozone,* notably in the work of the physicists Fabry and Buisson and he considered the stratospheric ozone shield as the upper limit of the biosphere, created by the biota for biota:

> La vie créant l'oxygène libre dans l'écorce terrestre, crée par là même l'ozone et protège la biosphère des rayonnements pernicieux des ondes courtes des astres célestes. (Vernadsky 1929, 147).

Ozone was the subject of a first international congress in 1929, in Paris, the principal convener of the conference being the physicist Charles Fabry (1867–1945). In 1929, ozone was not seen as threatened as it now is with the discovery of the Antarctic ozone hole.† Yet, we must remember it was Vernadsky who discerned the interactive link between the ozone shield and the biosphere.

Vernadsky, Hutchinson and ecology

G.E. Hutchinson was born in Cambridge, England, in 1903.‡ His father, Arthur Hutchinson, F.R.S., was a mineralogist and a friend of the

* Ch. Fabry, 1950, *L'ozone atmosphérique,* préface de J. Cabannes, Paris: CNRS. See J. Lecomte *et al.* Charles Fabry, 1973, *Applied Optics,* 12(6):1117–29. A brief review is given in G. Brasseur, 1987, 'The endangered ozone layer,' *Environment,* 29(1):6–11.

† The scientific and 'ecologist' literature is becoming immense. See John Gribbin (ed), 1986, *The Breathing Planet, A New Scientist Guide,* London: Blackwell. J. Gribbin, 1988, *The Hole in the Sky, Man's Threat to the Ozone Layer,* London: Corgi. R. Clarke, 1987, *The Ozone Layer,* Nairobi, UNEP\GEMS Environment Library No. 2.

‡ In 1962, Hutchinson received the Eminent Ecologist Award of the Ecological Society of America, and in 1979 the Franklin Medal of the Franklin Institute for the development of the scientific basis of ecology. See 1971, *Limnology and Oceanography,* 16(2), issue dedicated to G. Evelyn Hutchinson, including a Bibliography and notably a paper

Norwegian, Victor M. Goldschmidt, another great name in the rise of modern geochemistry. Hutchinson was a great naturalist, limnologist, zoologist, population ecologist and an interdisciplinary scientist, who developed the circular causal systems thinking in ecology with applications to 'the large self-regulatory cycles of the biosphere' (Hutchinson 1948a).

Hutchinson, as Frank Egerton notes (1983, 262f) founded 'a significant school of ecology at Yale University.' The school included such famous ecologists as Howard T. Odum, Robert MacArthur, Lawrence B. Slobodkin, John Vallentyne and Ramon Margalef, a Spanish ecologist who later published his book *La Biosfera entre la termodinámica y el juego* (Margalef 1980).

Hutchinson, a man of unusual foresight, was instrumental in the publication in America of two of Vernadsky's works on the biosphere, George, Vernadsky's son, then at Yale, being the translator. The first work, 'Problems of Biogeochemistry,' dated from 1938, was under the editorship of Hutchinson himself and was published in 1944 in the *Transactions of the Connecticut Academy of Arts and Sciences* (Vernadsky 1944); the second, more diffuse entitled 'The biosphere and the noosphere,' was published in *American Scientist* in January 1945, a few days after Vernadsky's death on January 6, 1945, in Moscow.

In a foreword the Editor (inspired by Hutchinson, I presume) wrote this laudatory presentation: 'The two contributions together present the general intellectual outlook of one of the most remarkable scientific leaders of the present century' (Vernadsky 1945a). At the time, Vernadsky's ideas made no impression, but later these two references were included in the standard bibliography of Eugene Odum's (1971) *Fundamentals of Ecology.* In a paper of 1943, Hutchinson credited 'Academician V.I. Vernadsky' for the term biogeochemistry (Vernadsky 1939).

In several papers by Lovelock and Margulis on the Gaia hypothesis, as well as in Lovelock's first book on Gaia (1979), Hutchinson's inspiration is clearly recognized, as in an early paper on Gaia entitled 'Homeostatic tendencies of the Earth's atmosphere.' Other contributions to the Gaia concept have been acknowledged by Lovelock and Margulis, notably those of the Swedish geochemist Lars Sillen, the German-born American paleontologist Heinz A. Lowenstam and Alfred Redfield, the latter being a life-long member of Harvard University and Woods Hole

by Yvette H. Edmondson, 'Some components of the Hutchinson legend,' pp.157–72; and E.S. Deevey (ed), 1972, *Growth by Intussusception, Ecological Essays in Honor of G. Evelyn Hutchinson,* Hamden, Conn: Archon Books. See also Saarinen (1982); McIntosh (1985).

Oceanographic Institution. Redfield's 1958 paper entitled 'The biological control of chemical factors in the environment' became a classic, partly reedited in *Readings in Ecology* by Edward J. Kormondy (1965).

The theme of the biosphere threatened by Man's activities began to emerge during the 1960s. The very term of biosphere gained currency at the international level with the so-called 'Biosphere Conference' convened by UNESCO in Paris in September 1968 (the Proceedings being published in Paris by UNESCO in 1970).

The first International Conference on the Environmental Future was held in Finland during the summer of 1971 (see *The Biosphere Today,* by Polunin 1972), while the widely read *Only One Earth* (Ward and Dubos 1972) became the unofficial report to the 1972 Stockholm Conference. However neglect of the Gaia hypothesis and Vernadsky's work illustrated a vast ignorance concerning the fundamental holistic concept of the biosphere.

In 1965, the first chapter of Hutchinson's book *The Ecological Theatre and the Evolutionary Play* was entitled 'The biosphere or volume in which organisms actually live' (Hutchinson 1965). Later, in introducing the September 1970 issue of *Scientific American* on 'The Biosphere,' Hutchinson wrote:

> It is essentially Vernadsky's concept of the biosphere, developed about 50 years after Suess wrote, that we accept today.

In the early 1970s, Hutchinson's writings on Vernadsky's tradition were still largely ignored, even by the scientific community in the United States, including ecologists Paul Ehrlich and Barry Commoner. But, since the early 1980s, the situation has changed. In *Carbon Dioxide Review,* 1982, edited by William C. Clark (1982, 22), we therefore read:

> The last several years, however, have brought a growing recognition of the critical role played by the oceans' biological processes in determining the effects of increasing CO_2. This trend is part of a wider resurgence of the biogeochemical perspective of life on Earth, sketched almost half a century ago by Vernadsky and now elegantly remodeled by Lovelock as the *Gaia hypothesis.*

William C. Clark, systems ecologist educated at Yale University and coeditor of *Environment* magazine, member of the US National Academy of Science's Board on Atmospheric Sciences and Climate and its Committee on the Applications of Ecological Theory to Environmental Problems, was to be leader of the first phase, during 1983–87, of the interdisciplinary research project on 'Ecologically Sustainable Development of the Biosphere' at the International Institute for Applied Systems Analysis (IIASA), Laxenburg, Austria. There, Vernadsky's perspective is considered as 'prophetic' (Clark and Munn 1986, 10) and the Gaia thesis is taken seriously.*

In an important report entitled Atmospheric Carbon Dioxide and the Global Carbon Cycle published by the U.S. Department of Energy in December 1985, we read the following 'concluding comments':

> The system comprising the Earth's surface, atmosphere, and the biota might be viewed as if in homeostasis so that the chemical composition of the atmosphere and the climate are both regulated by biota to its preference. No intricate planning, foresight, or cooperation appears to be needed. Regulation can arise as a simple colligative property of life and its environment. One such view, after Vernadsky (1926) and Hutchinson (1954), was recently restated as the Gaia hypothesis (Hitchcock and Lovelock 1967; Lovelock 1979; 1983). It offers a challenging perspective on the natural cycles of the elements.

Global ecology: the Earth as a living planet

What is the difference between Gaia and the biosphere? And first of all, what is the definition of our concept of the biosphere bearing in mind that Vernadsky referred to 'the living organism of the biosphere?' (Vernadsky 1929, 21) The notion of Gaia indicates a self-regulatory biogeochemical mechanism with the capacity to keep the planet Earth living by controlling the global environment of the face of the Earth. Gaia is synonymous with the Earth as a planetary living being. But the geosphere is not the biosphere. If the basic idea of the Gaia hypothesis is that the atmosphere is an extension of the biosphere, this revolutionary idea was already stated by Vernadsky and embodied in his biogeo-

* See also Rafael Serafin, 'Vernadsky's *Biosphere,* Teilhard's *Noosphere,* and Lovelock's Gaia: Perspectives on Human Intervention on Global Biogeochemical Cycles,' Laxenburg, Austria, International Institute for Applied Systems Analysis, 1987; and his paper entitled 'Noosphere, Gaia and science of the biosphere,' *Environmental Ethics,* 1988, 10(2).

chemical conception of the biosphere. Consequently a closer view including a historical perspective is now necessary to understand the affiliation between the Gaia concept and Vernadsky's concept of the biosphere.

The year 1970 marked the emerging recognition of our global ecological crisis and the adoption of a cosmic perspective on the ecology of the whole Earth. In this new context, Vernadsky's *La Biosphère* must become a classic, within environmental education as well as scientific learning.We should also credit Vladimir Vernadsky with the title of father of the global ecology of the biosphere. Indeed he is the most illustrious precedent for the current Gaia theory. And because we have neglected his biospheric message, and the early warnings of ecologists, we are in the midst of a grave planetary crisis. That situation is well captured by the dramatic historical shift from Eduard Suess's *The Face of the Earth* to Jonathan Schell's *The Fate of the Earth.*

References

Abram, D. 1985. The Perceptual Implications of Gaia. *The Ecologist.* 15(3):96–103.

Bailes, K.E. 1978. *Vernadsky and the Biosphere.* Irvine: Univ. of California, History Department.

Balandine, R. 1982. *Vladimir Vernadsky.* Trans. from the Russian. Moscow: Mir.

Batisse, M. 1975. Man and the biosphere. *Nature.* 256:156–58.

Bergson, H. 1907. *L'Evolution Créatice.* Paris: Alcan. p.271. (English trans. by A. Mitchell. 1911. *Creative Evolution.* London: Macmillan. p.271).

Blum, H.F. 1965. Evolution of the biosphere. *Nature.* 208:324–26.

Bolin, B. 1979. Global Ecology and Man. *Proceedings of the World Climate Conference.* Geneva: WMO. 537:27–56.

—— 1980. *Climatic changes and their effects on the biosphere.* Geneva: WHO.

Bolin, B. and R.B. Cook (eds). 1983. The Major Biogeochemical Cycles and their Interactions. *SCOPE.* Report 21. Chichester: Wiley.

Bolin, B. and B. Boos (eds). The Greenhouse Effect, Climate Change and Ecosystems. *SCOPE.* Report 29. Chichester: Wiley.

Botkin, D.B. 1982. Can there be a theory of Global Ecology? *Journal of Theoretical Biology.* 96:95–98.

Budyko, M. 1980. *Ecologie globale.* trans. from Russian. Moscow: Progrès.

—— 1984. *Evolution of the biosphere.* Trans. from Russian 1986. Dordrecht: Reidel.

Caldwell, L.K. 1985. Science will not save the biosphere but politics might. *Environmental Conservation.* 12(3):195–97.

Castri, F. 1985. Twenty years of international programmes on ecosystems and the biosphere: an overview of achievements, shortcomings and possible new perspectives. pp.314–31 in T.F. Malone and J.G. Roedere (eds). *Global Change.* Cambridge University Press.

Clark, W. and R.E. Munn (eds). 1986. *Sustainable Development of the biosphere.* Cambridge University Press.

Cloud, P. 1983. The biosphere. *Scientific American.* 249(3):176–89.

Cole, L.C. 1958. The ecosphere. *Scientific American.* 198(4):83–96.

Commoner, B. 1972. *The Closing Circle: Nature, Man and Technology.* New York: Bantam.

Cook, R.B. 1984. Man and the Biogeochemical Cycles: Interacting with the Elements. *Environment.* 26(7).

Cowen, R.C. 1986. The biosphere and the atmosphere: a global picture. *Technology Review.* (3):17.

Dasmann, R.F. 1972. *Planet in Peril: Man and the Biosphere Today.* New York/Harmondsworth: Penguin.

Davis, C.B. 1984. Imperatives, Strategies, and the World Campaign for the biosphere. *Environmental Conservation.* 11(4):291f.

Day, W. 1984. 2 ed. *Genesis on Planet Earth. The Search for Life's Beginning.* New Haven: Yale University Press.

Dickinson, R.E. (ed). 1987. *The Geophysiology of Amazonia. Vegetation and Climate Interactions.* New York/Chichester: Wiley.

Dubos, R. 1969. The biosphere: a delicate balance between man and nature. *Unesco Courier.* (January).

—— 1972. *A God Within.* New York: Scribners.

—— 1979. Gaia and creative evolution. *Nature.* 282:154f.

Dumas, J.B. and J.B. Boussingault. 1841. *Essai de statique chimique des êtres organisés.* Paris: Fortin et Masson. (Recent ed. 1972. Bruxelles: Culture et Civilisation.)

—— 1842. Essai de statique chimique des êtres organisés. *Annales de chimie et de physique.* 4:115–126.

Duvigneaud, P. 1974. *La Synthèse écologique. Populations, communautés, écosystèmes, biosphère, noosphère.* Paris: Doin.

Egerton, F.N. 1983; 1985. The History of Ecology. *Journal of the History of Biology.* 16:259–310; 18:103–43.

Ehrlich, P.R., C. Sagan, D. Kennedy, W.O. Roberts. 1984. *The Cold and the Dark. The World after Nuclear War.* New York: Norton.

Evans, F.C. 1956. Ecosystem as the basic unit in ecology. *Science.* 123:1127f.

Florkin, M. 1965. Approches moléculaires de l'intégration écologique. Problèmes de terminologie. *Bulletin de l'Académie Royale de Belgique, Classe des Sciences.* 5th series. 51:239–56.

Forey, P.L. (ed). 1981. *The evolving biosphere.* Cambridge University Press.

Fortescue, J.A.C. 1980. *Environmental Geochemistry: A Holistic Approach.* New York/Berlin: Springer. *(Ecological Studies* 34).

Gates, D.M. 1971. The flow of energy in the biosphere. *Scientific American.* September. (Incorporated in 1971. *Energy and Power.* San Francisco: Freeman. pp.41–52).

Georgescu-Roegen, N. 1976. *Energy and Economic Myths.* New York: Pergamon.

Gillard, A. 1969. On terminology of biosphere and ecosphere. *Nature.* 223:500f.

Goody, R. (ed). 1982. *Global Change: Impacts on Habitability: A Scientific Basis for Assessment, A Report by the Executive Committee of a Workshop held at Woods Hole, Massachussets, June 21–26, 1982.* Pasadena: CalTech, JPL, NASA.

Gribbin, J. (ed). 1986. *The Breathing Planet. A New Scientist Guide.* Oxford: Blackwell.

Grinevald, J. 1986a. Biosphere et politique internationale: de la guerre froide à l'hiver nucléaire. In B. Jurdant (ed). *Senses of Science. European Association for the Study of Science and Technology, IVth meeting, 29 Sept–1 Oct 1986.* Strasbourg: Conseil de l'Europe, Université Louis Pasteur, GERSULP.

—— 1986b. The biosphere, by V.I. Vernadsky. *Environmental Conservation.* 13(3):285f.

Heintze, C. 1977. *The Biosphere: Earth, Air, Fire and Water.* New York: Thomas Nelson.

Henderson-Sellers, A. 1981. The Earth's environment — a uniquely stable system? *Geophysical Survey.* 4(3).

Hughes, C.J. 1985. Gaia: a natural scientist's ethic for the future. *The Ecologist.* 15(3):92–95.

Hughes, J. Donald. 1983. Gaia: an ancient view of our planet. *The Ecologist.* 13(2):54–60.
Humboldt, A. de. 1805. *Essai sur la géographie des plantes, accompagné d'un tableau physique des regions équinoxiales.* Paris: Levrault, Schoell.
—— 1847–59. *Cosmos; essai d'une description physique du monde.* Trans. from German by H. Gaye and Ch. Galusky. Paris: Gide.
—— 1866. *Tableaux de la Nature.* Trans. by M.C. Galusky. Paris: Guérin.
Hutchinson, G.E. 1940. Bio-Ecology. *Ecology.* 21(2):267f.
—— 1954. The biochemistry of the terrestrial atmosphere. pp.371–433 in Gerard P. Guiper (ed). *The Earth as a Planet.* University of Chicago Press.
—— 1965. The biosphere or volume in which organisms actually live. In *The Ecological Theater and the Evolutionary Play.* New Haven: Yale University Press.
—— 1970. The Biosphere. *Scientific American.* 223(3):45–53.
—— 1979. *The Kindly Fruits of the Earth: Recollections of an Embryo Ecologist.* New Haven: Yale University Press.
Hutton, J. 1788a. Theory of Rain. *Transactions of the Royal Society of Edinburgh.* 1(2):41–86.
—— 1788b. Theory of the Earth; or investigation of the laws observable in the composition, dissolution, and restoration of land upon the globe. *Transactions of the Royal Society of Edinburgh.* 1(2):209–304.
—— 1795. *Theory of the Earth with Proofs and Illustrations.* Edinburgh: William Creech/London: Cadell & Davies. 2 vols. (New ed. 1959 New York: Stechert-Hafner).
Hutzinger, O. (ed). 1980–85. *The Natural Environment and the Biogeochemical Cycles, The Handbook of Environmental Chemistry.* Berlin/New York: Springer. Vol.1, A–D.
Huxley, T.H. 1863. *Man's Place in Nature.*
Imshenetsky, A.A., S.V. Lysenko, G.A. Kazakov. 1978. Upper boundary of the biosphere. *Applied and Environmental Microbiology.* 35(1):1–5.
Ingersoll, A. 1983. L'atmosphère. *Pour la Science.* 73:122–36.
International Council of Scientific Unions (ICSU). 1986. *The International Geosphere Biosphere Programme: A Study of Global Change, Final report of the Ad Hoc Planning Group, prepared for the 21st General Assembly, Berne, September 14–19, 1986.* Paris: ICSU.
Jaworski, H. 1928. *Géon ou la Terre vivante.* Paris: Gallimard.
Jessop, N.M. 1970. *Biosphere: A Study of Life.* Englewood Cliffs, NJ: Prentice Hall.
Jones, R.L. 1980. *Biogeography: structure, process, pattern and change within the biosphere.* Amsterdam: Hulton Educational.
Kamishilov, M.M. 1974. *Evolution of the biosphere.* Trans. from Russian 1976. Moscow: Mir.
Khozin, G. 1976. *Biosphere and Politics.* Trans. from Russian 1979. Moscow: Progress.
Kovda, V.A., *et al.* 1970. Contemporary scientific concepts relating to the biosphere. pp.13–29 in *Use and conservation of the biosphere.* Paris: UNESCO.
Le Roy, E. 1927. *L'Exigence idéaliste et le fait de l'evolution.* Paris: Boivin.
—— 1928. *Les Origines humaines et l'évolution de l'intelligence.* Paris: Boivin.
Lorenz, E.N. 1967. *The Nature and Theory of the General Circulation of the Atmosphere.* Geneva: WMO.
Lotka, A.J. 1925. *Elements of Physical Biology.* Baltimore: Williams & Wilkins. (New ed. 1956. *Elements of Mathematical Biology.* New York: Dover).
Lovelock, J.E. 1972. Gaia as seen through the atmosphere. *Atmospheric Environment.* 6.
—— 1979. *Gaia: A New Look at Life on Earth.* Oxford University Press.
—— 1985. Are we destabilising world climate? *The Ecologist.* 15(1–2).
—— 1986a. Geophysiology: A New Look at Earth Sciences. *Bulletin of the American Meteorological Society.* 67(4).
—— 1986b. A New Look at Earth Sciences. In Robert E. Dickinson (ed). *The Geophysiology of Amazonia: Vegetation and Climate Interactions.* Chichester: Wiley.

—— 1986c. The Prehistory of Gaia. *New Scientist.* 17 July: p.51.
—— 1986d. Gaia: The world as living organism. *New Scientist.* 18 Dec: pp.25–28.
Lovelock, J.E. and S.R. Epton. 1975. The Quest for Gaia. *New Scientist.* 6 Feb: pp.304–9.
Lovelock, J.E. and L. Margulis. 1974. Atmospheric homeostasis by and for the biosphere: the Gaia hypothesis. *Tellus.* 26:1–10.
—— 1986. Gaia and geognosy: towards a science of the biosphere. In M.B. Rambler (ed). *Global Ecology: Towards a Science of the biosphere.* Boston: Jones & Bartlett.
Lovelock, J.E. and M. Whitfield. 1982. Life span of the biosphere. *Nature.* 296:561–63.
Lowenstam, H.A. 1981. Minerals formed by organisms. *Science.* 211:1126–31.
Malone, T. 1984. Biogeochemical Cycles: A New Research Agenda. *Environment.* 26(7):4f.
—— 1986. Mission to Planet Earth: Integrating Studies of Global Change. *Environment.* 28(8).
Margalef, R. 1980. *La Biosfera entra la termodinámica y el juego.* Barcelona: Omega.
Margulis, L., and J.E. Lovelock. 1974. Biological modulation of the Earth's atmosphere. *Icarus.* 21.
—— 1975. The atmosphere as circulatory system of the biosphere — the Gaia hypothesis. *The CoEvolution Quarterly.* 6:30–40.
—— 1978. The Biota as Ancient and Modern Modular of the Earth's Atmosphere. pp.239–43 in H.U. Dutsch (ed). *Influence of the Biosphere on the Atmosphere.* Basel/Stuttgart: Birkhauser.
—— 1981. Atmosphere and Evolution. pp.79–100 in John Billingham (ed). *Life in the Universe.* Cambridge, Mass: MIT Press.
Meyer, F. 1985. Temps, devenir, évolution. *Communications.* 41:111–22.
Moisseiev, N.N., *et al.* 1985. Biosphere Models. pp.493–510 in R.W. Kates *et al.* (eds). *Climate impact Assessment: Studies of the Interaction of Climate and Society.* SCOPE Report 27. Chichester: Wiley.
Myers, N. (ed). 1985. *The Gaia Atlas Planet Management.* Pan Books.
National Research Council. 1983. Toward an International Geosphere-biosphere Program. *A Study of Global Change, Report of a National Research Council Workshop, Woods Hole, Massachusetts, July 1983.* Washington: National Academy Press.
Odum, E.P. 1971. *Fundamentals of Ecology.* Philadelphia: Saunders.
Odum, H.T. 1971. *Environment, Power and Society.* New York: Wiley-Interscience.
Oparin, A.I. 1957. 3 ed. *The Origin of Life on the Earth.* Trans. from Russian. New York: Academic Press/Edinburgh: Oliver & Boyd.
Polunin, N. 1972. The biosphere today. pp.33–52 in N. Polunin (ed). *The Environmental Future.* London: Macmillan/New York: Barnes & Noble.
—— 1980. Environmental Education and the Biosphere. *Environmental Conservation.* 7(2).
—— 1984. To Battle for the Biosphere. pp.1–9 in T.N. Veziroglu (ed). *The Biosphere: Problems and Solutions.* Amsterdam: Elsevier.
Redfield, A.C. 1958. The biological control of chemical factors in the environment. *American Scientist.*
Riedl, R. 1973. Die Biosphäre und die heutige Erfolgsgessellschaft. *Universitas.* 28(6):587–93.
Rosnay, J.E. 1975. *Le Macroscope. Vers une vision globale.* Paris: Seuil.
Russell, P. 1984. *The Awakened Earth. The Global Brain.* London: Ark.
Sagan, C. 1973. *Cosmic Connection, An Extraterrestrial Perspective.* New York: Doubleday. p.60.
Sagan, D., and L. Margulis. 1983. The Gaian perspective of ecology. *Ecologist.* 13(5):160–67.
Schell, J. 1982. *The Fate of the Earth.* New York: Knopf.

Schneider, S.H. and R. Londer. 1984. *The Coevolution of Climate and Life.* Sierra Club Books.
Schopf, J.W. (ed). 1983. *Earth's earliest biosphere. Its Origin and Evolution.* Princeton University Press.
Senise, F. 1972. *Biosfera in agonia.* Roma: Barone.
Siever, R. 1983. The Dynamic Earth. *Scientific American.* 249:46–55.
Sillen, L.G. 1966. Regulation of O_2, N_2, and CO_2 in the atmosphere: thoughts of a laboratory chemist. *Tellus.*
Snyder, T.P. (ed). 1986. *The biosphere catalogue.* Oracle, Ariz./London: Synergetic.
Suess, E. 1875. *Die Entstehung der Alpen.* Wien: Braunmuller.
—— 1904–24. 5 vols. *The Face of the Earth.* Trans. by Hertha B.C. Sollas. Oxford: Clarendon Press.
Sukachev, V. and N. Dylis. 1964. *Fundamentals of Forest Biogeocenology.* Trans. from Russian by Dr J.M. Maclennan. 1968. Edinburgh/London: Oliver & Boyd.
Taube, M. 1985. *Evolution of Matter and Energy on a Cosmic and Planetary Scale.* Berlin: Springer.
Teilhard de Chardin, P. 1925a. L'Hominisation. Introduction à une étude scientifique du phénomène humain. In 1957 *Oeuvres.* Paris: Seuil.
—— 1925b. L'Histoire Naturelle du Monde. pp.201–31 in 1959. *Oeuvres.* Paris: Seuil.
—— 1956a. *Le Groupe Zoologique humain. Structures et directions évolutives.* Paris: Albin Michel.
—— 1956b. The Antiquity and World Expansion of Human Culture. In W.L. Thomas (ed). *Man's Role in Changing the Face of the Earth.* University of Chicago Press.
—— 1959. *The Phenomenon of Man.* London: Collins.
—— 1966. *Man's Place in Nature.* London: Collins.
Thomas, L. 1974. *The Lives of a Cell. Notes of a Biology Watcher.* New York: Viking.
Vallentyne, J. 1960. Geochemistry of the biosphere. In *Encyclopedia of Science and Technology.* New York: McGraw-Hill.
Vernadksy, V.I. 1924. La Géochimie. In Félix Alcan. *Nouvelle collection scientifique.*
—— 1925. L'autotrophie de l'humanité. *Revue générale des sciences.* 36:495–502.
—— 1926. *Biosfera.* Leningrad: Nauchnoe Khimikoteknicheskoe Izdatelstvo. (New ed. 1967. Moscow: Nauka).
—— 1930. *Geochemie.* Leipzig: Akademische Verlagsgesellschaft.
—— 1932. L'étude de la vie et la nouvelle physique. *Revue générale des sciences.* 43.
—— 1934–35. Le problème du temps dans la science contemporaine. *Revue générale des sciences.* 45:550–58; 46:208–13,308–12.
—— 1944. *Problems of Biogeochemistry.* Trans. by George Vernadsky, Ed by G.E. Hutchinson. *Transactions of the Connecticut Academy of Arts and Science.* 35:483–517.
—— 1945. The biosphere and the noosphere. *American Scientist.* 33:1–12.
Veziroglu, T.N. (ed). 1984. *The biosphere: Problems and Solutions.* Amsterdam: Elsevier.
Vinogradov, A.P. 1960. The origin of the biosphere. pp.15–29 in Marcel Florkin (ed). *Aspects of the Origin of Life.* Oxford: Pergamon.
—— 1963a. The development of V.I. Vernadsky's ideas. *Soviet Soil Science.* 8:727–32.
—— 1963b. Centenary of the birth of V.I. Vernadsky. *Geochemistry.* 3:211–13.
—— 1966. The scientific legacy of V.I. Vernadsky. In A.P. Vinogradov (ed). *Chemistry of the Earth's Crust: Proceedings of the Geochemical Conference Commemorating the Centenary of Academician V.I. Vernadsky's Birth.* Trans. from the Russian by N. Kaner. Israel Program for Scientific Translations. Vol.1.
Wallen, C.C. 1973. *A brief survey of meteorology as related to the biosphere.* Geneva: WMO.
Ward, B. and R. Dubos. 1972. *Only One Earth.* Harmondsworth: Penguin.
Watson, L. 1985. *Heaven's Breath. A Natural History of the Wind.* London: Hodder & Stoughton.

Weiner, D. 1988. *Models of nature: ecology, conservation and cultural revolution in the Soviet Union.* Indiana University Press. p.80.

Westbroek, P. 1983. Life as a geologic force: new opportunities for paleontology? *Paleobiology.* 9:91–96.

Whittaker, R.H. and G.E. Likens (ed). 1973. The Primary Production of the Biosphere. *Human Ecology.*

Woodwell, G.M. 1970. The Energy Cycle of the Biosphere. *Scientific American.* 223(3):64–74.

Worthington, B. Barton. 1982. World Campaign for the Biosphere. *Environmental Conservation.* 9(2).

– 3 –
James Lovelock's Gaia

Lynn Margulis

My plan is to state 'Gaia'as a scientific hypothesis. Having recognized the Gaian phenomenon I would like to explain where I think Gaia comes from and ask for how long this Gaia phenomenon has persisted on the surface of the Earth. And then I would like to raise some of the objections to the Gaia hypothesis. We have now come some thirty years. For the first ten years or so it was known as 'Life as seen through the atmosphere' — and other phrases. It was not called the Gaia hypothesis until, as you all know, Jim (with the help of William Golding) found a good four letter word to focus the attention of his colleagues on his idea.

The Gaia hypothesis is the offspring of Jim Lovelock's fertile imagination and the US space programme. The hypothesis is concerned primarily with the lower atmosphere that is, the trophosphere. With respect to the chemical composition of the reactive gases of the lower atmosphere, the oxidation/reduction state and the pH (i.e., acidity and alkalinity), the Gaia hypothesis states that these attributes of the atmosphere are actively maintained by the activities of the biota. 'The biota' refers to the sum of all living organisms: flora, fauna and especially microbiota. At current estimates we are talking about thirty million or so species.

I reject Jim's statement 'The Earth is alive;' this metaphor, stated this way alienates precisely those scientists who should be working in a Gaian context. I do not agree with the formulation that says 'Gaia is an organism.' Firstly in this context noone defines 'organism.' Nor do I think that Gaia is a singularity. Rather Gaia is an extremely complex system, a set of interacting ecosystems, with identifiable regulatory properties which are very specific to the lower atmosphere.

Equally I think there are no fundamental inconsistencies between the Gaia hypothesis and the basic tenets of Darwinian evolution, despite some neo-Darwinian latter-day saints. Yet, Gaia is a hypothesis that can be tested just as Darwinian evolution is a testable scientific hypothesis. Gaia definitely falls within the realm of science even though scientists themselves may be ignorant or small-minded in denying that the hypothesis is testable. Like evolution as a hypothesis, it is testable but complex and requires many observations.

Why do so many people disagree, why do they tend to reject the Gaia hypothesis? My reading of the reasons are as follows: they ask how possibly can the mere biota regulate the planet Earth? How on this gigantic scale, can the temperature and the reactive gases of the planet be maintained? How does some little organism that is just trying to 'maximize its fitness' i.e., increase its rate of reproduction in a thoroughly 'selfish' way, possibly contribute to global regulation in a Panglossian sense? Since no mechanism for regulation appears to exist these investigators deny the existence of the Gaian phenomenon. Lack of evidence of control mechanisms is the usual kind of complaint. Thus, our critics argue first that Gaia has not been stated properly as a scientific hypothesis and second that we lack a tangible mechanism of environmental control.

Both of these objections can be countered. As scientists, we cannot deny the existence of phenomena simply because we have failed to see mechanisms. The response the Gaia hypothesis is encountering is very much like the reception, in the 1920s, of the ideas of Swiss meteorologist Alfred Wegener. He saw a phenomenon, 'continental drift' as he called it, but it was not until the early sixties, that many scientists — those dragging magnetometers behind ships, those studying deep earthquakes, those recovering deep-sea drilling cores — discovered a mechanism that brought about the acceptance of Wegener's phenomenon. Together, through the impetus of great minds such as Harry Hess, Daniel Mackenzie and Fred Vines, the concept emerged of plate tectonics as the mechanism of continental drift. Today the phenomenon of 'drift' is generally believed because the mechanism 'plate tectonics' has been revealed.

The other serious objection to the Gaia hypothesis has to do with time scale, argue the neo-Darwinists of this world. The question is posed more or less like this: since living organisms are only interested in their immediate survival and the leaving of more offspring, how can the Earth have been regulated for more than 3,000 million years? How indeed can fast-acting organisms contribute to some million years of regulation and stability?

One of the major tools of the Gaia hypothesis is the intrinsic global level of observation it employs. Let us compare planetary phenomena of the Earth with those of the 'sister' or flanking planets, Mars and Venus. Let us start with Venus. A view of the surface of Venus from the Soviet Venera space flight 9 (which was launched on October 27, 1975 and landed on the planet in January 1976) indicates some relevant features.

The camera had just 45 seconds to operate, because conditions on Venus were so highly acidic and hot. The major features of the atmospheres of Venus as detected by the Soviet Venera space shots merely confirm what astronomers had detected using telescopes. The Venus surface is littered with rubble, composed primarily of ejecta material from meteorite impact or volcanic debris. Conspicuously missing are the sedimentary rocks, the open bodies of water like those on Earth, and the atmosphere of Venus is far richer in carbon dioxide.

The Russians are now taking direct meso-scale measurements using orbiters and they have confirmed that Venus is an extremely dry planet. The clouds are extraordinarily acidic because they are composed of sulphate particles. To sum up Venus has a carbon dioxide-rich atmosphere with fewer than 3 per cent nitrogen and with high temperatures of about 400°C.

The other 'sister,' the planet out just beyond Earth, is Mars, with its polar ice caps. We know there is some water on its surface. In the late 1960s the US planned the Viking spacecraft, with its two orbiters and its two landers. Launched in 1975, Viking reached its target in 1976 and made two landings, one at Chryse and one at Utopia. The dedicated reason for the mission was to find out if the planet Mars harboured life. Lovelock had already predicted there was no life on Mars, but NASA hardly wanted to hear about his theories when they were spending a 1,000 million dollars on the 'biology package' to detect life on the red planet. Jim was correct, employing the Gaia hypothesis, he predicted no life would be found on Mars at a time when none of us, myself included, understood what the Gaia hypothesis was.

What was the logic behind his assertions? As we approach Mars we see what Jim meant; many features from the orbiter look as if they should be interpreted as riverine, and as having once contained flowing water. These features have since been cratered through impacts which means that the water-related features are even more ancient than the meteorite craters. Most water was probably out-gassed from Mars over 2,000 million years ago; that which remains is frozen as ice and permafrost. Today there is no liquid water, although most agree that the evidence suggests there once may even have been Martian oceans. Like Venus, the atmosphere of Mars is primarily composed of carbon dioxide, 95 per cent of the gas. Like Venus, Mars is very dry. On Mars too, sulphur, conferring acidity, is thought to be present although the surface temperature of Mars is very cold whereas that of Venus is very hot. Professor Toby Owen calls it the 'Goldilocks syndrome': one planet, Venus, is too hot, the other Mars, is too cold. The Earth is just right.

PLANETARY ATMOSPHERES			
	Venus	***Earth***	***Mars***
Carbon dioxide (%)	98	0.03	95
Nitrogen (%)	1.7	79	2.7
Oxygen (%)	trace	21	<0.13
Methane	none	0.0000015	none
Water (m*)	0.003	3000	0.00001
Pressure (atm)	90	1	0.0064
Temperature (°K)	750	290	220

* Depth of water in metres over the planet if all water vapour precipitated out of the atmosphere. (Table derived from *GSA Today,* 1993 3(11).

Table 3.1

In contrast to the naive but complex 'chicken-soup' and photosynthesis experiments that NASA scientists set up to test for life on Mars is Lovelock's concept. He stated his request very clearly: just give me the gas exchanges, just tell me how much of each gas is produced over what period of time; just measure the endogenous Martian surface gas fluxes. If NASA had provided Lovelock that information for the surface of Mars he could have tested for life directly. The rates of removal and production of various gases on Mars and Venus can be explained completely on the basis of physics and chemistry alone. But neither NASA nor the Russian space programme undertook a serious chemical analysis of either the Martian or Venus surface nor of their unperturbed gas fluxes. Perhaps, for the intellectual climate at the time, it was premature to ask for those sorts of measurements.

If we interpolate what to expect of an Earth placed right between Mars and Venus in a 'gedanken' experiment we should see a carbon dioxide rich atmosphere, fewer than 3 per cent nitrogen, and a surface temperature somewhere betweeen that of Mars and Venus. We should expect a very acidic planet. The Apollo mission has provided us many pictures of the Earth taken from the Moon. If we had an orbiter that landed in the middle of the Colorado desert, we may well not find evidence of life on

Earth. Even in Colorado we cannot expect giraffes or elephants to signal the existence of life by walking in front of the camera. So what is here on Earth to tell us about the ubiquitous surface distribution of life? Just as on our flanking planets, to detect life on Earth we would need gas exchange measurements telling us which gases were to be found and in what amounts.

In Table 3.1 (see p.57) we compare the atmosphere of Venus with those of the other planets. Note it is composed of some 98 per cent carbon dioxide. Mars' atmosphere at 95 per cent has roughly the same composition as Venus, while each of these planets has about 2 per cent nitrogen. Regarding gases such as argon that are inert, and 'noble,' they behave more or less as expected for unreactive substances and the concentrations are similar in all three instances. Thus, the planetary reactive gas behaviour is best understood by the Gaia hypothesis. On Venus and Mars we have barely detectable amounts of water and oxygen. Then, when we look at the Earth as if we are equilibrium chemists, we are incredulous, totally flabbergasted. The atmospheric composition of gases on Earth is like a mixture that goes into an automobile, not like the 'spent' gas mixture that comes out. Indeed the Earth's atmosphere is composed of a reactive mixture of gases. For instance nitrogen plus oxygen reacts to form nitrogen oxides which in the presence of water become nitrite and nitrate ions. Yet the Earth is composed of nearly 80 per cent gaseous nitrogen (N_2) and more than 20 per cent oxygen (O_2). What is worse is that a whole suite of gases — hydrogen, methane, ammonia, all of which react directly with oxygen — can always be detected in air samples. Finding hydrogen and oxygen together that have not reacted to produce water reflects some active and dynamic phenomenon that is generating those reactive gases. The same can be said for nitrogen in the presence of oxygen.

The Earth has far too much oxygen. Oxygen appears to have been around at approximately 20 per cent for at least 600 million years. The other striking difference between the Earth and her neighbours is that the carbon dioxide on Earth has virtually disappeared. Only 0.03 per cent is left. To the chemist and physicist the Earth is a planetary anomaly. Meanwhile the Gaia hypothesis states that this anomalous situation is generated and maintained by life, that the reactive aspects of the atmosphere are products of the evolution of life.

The next question is, for how long has the Earth been a planetary anomaly? I want now to show you why I think the Gaian phenomenon has been going probably for 3,500 million years. Gaia hardly requires man. As we discuss in *Microcosmos* (Margulis and Sagan 1991), we are just another one of these mammalian 'weeds;' species that come and go every million years or so.

A prime question is, where did the carbon dioxide go? Many people think that the carbon dioxide is in the biota, within the bodies of animals, trees and plants, but in fact fewer than one part per million is found in the bodies of such organisms. An astounding observation, made also by Toby Owen, is that if we converted all the limestone deposits of the sediments into carbon dioxide gas of the air then our planet's atmosphere would have ratios of oxygen and carbon dioxide just like Mars and Venus.

The rocks we find in the Northwest territories represent what Dorion Sagan and I have called in *Microcosmos* 'a bacterial skyscraper.' The rocks were made by communities of bacteria around 2,300 million years old. To keep a time perspective, any kind of animal, including those like ancient trilobites or brachiopods that make chitinous or limestone shells, are only 570 million years old. Indeed the tropical forests and African elephants that are so dear to our hearts are just latter-day epiphenomena of the effects of life on the planet. They are the Bachs and Beethovens of an orchestrated system that has been playing for 3,500 million years. Fundamentally the crucial Gaian mechanism is a bacterial system. The bacteria-made rocks are analogous to coral reefs of the much later Phanerozoic Aeon. They follow a similar pattern of growth, precipitation, and subsidence so that a gigantic reef is formed that reaches the sea surface. Such rock-making phenomena took place at certain localities over thousands and even tens of thousands of years. The area of Northwestern Canada that today is the Canadian Arctic was tropical or semi-tropical when the rocks first formed. These bacterial rocks, ancient reef-like systems, are called stromatolites. The oldest stromatolites known are 3,400 million years old. The communities of cyanobacteria and other organisms that formed these rocks were at the high point of their expansion just before 700 million years ago. From then on they were eaten back by animals, faced competition from algae and were subjected to other factors that altogether led to their demise. The important point to realize is that these stromalitic structures tell us that bacteria have been removing carbon dioxide from the atmosphere from some 3,500 million years ago to the present. Such really huge stromatolite deposits are no longer being made; they have become extinct. How do we know that stromatolites were made by bacteria? Because we are lucky. In western Australia, in places such as Shark Bay, 800 miles north of Perth, the salt content is very high. In Hamelin Pond of Shark Bay we find scenes that we imagine are quite smilar to ancient ones and bacterial calcium carbonate structures being made today are remarkably similar in detail to those of 2,000 million years ago.

What are they? Primarily composed of limestone, the blue-green sheen on top is due to carbonate-precipitating oxygen-producing bacteria. We need to remember that the action of the whole Gaian phenomenon may be on the micron and sub-micron level (10^{-6} m). Yet there is so much action in so many dynamic populations that the phenomena are actually detectable on a planetary scale. We are extending ourselves from microns to kilometres in scale. Today the largest living stromatolites we know of are about two metres high. Nevertheless the site where the carbon dioxide is actually removed from the atmosphere, is a membrane which is thinner than one tenth of a micron. It is this the membrane through which salt is pumped. The concept here is that microscale actitivies result in macro-scale phenomena — which Jim Lovelock calls the colligative (collective) properties of life.

We have two major reservoirs of carbon at the surface of the planet; one is the much larger reservoir found in rocks and the other is the carbon in the cell material as well as that in fossil fuels. As the deposits are laid down simultaneously free oxygen is produced. The same process — oxygenic photosynthesis — gives us both deposited carbon and atmospheric oxygen. Probably many different types of cyanobacteria are involved, these bacteria being the heroes of a saga in which they have been truly responsible for global change. Take an organism called *Microcoleus:* it looks like a bunch of insulated telephone wires, made of long thin fibres encased in a sheath. The organisms move rapidly towards the light; if impeded by sediment, they trap particles together. They will 'trap' carbon dioxide precipitated by other cyanobacteria as sediment clasts. Layer upon layer of rocky sediment is produced. *Microcoleus* never lives entirely alone; it is always found in a community.

In addition to the lack of carbon dioxide in Earth's atmosphere and over-abundance of oxygen we have too much free hydrogen, too much methane and too much ammonia. All of these are extremely hydrogen-rich gases that react with oxygen. The reason for their presence is simple. Methane comes exclusively from anaerobic methanogenic bacteria which produce some million tonnes per year. The only way we can explain the presence of 1 to 2 parts per million of methane in today's atmosphere is by realizing it is bacterial excrement. Some of these methanogenic bacteria are found in huge numbers in the guts of ruminants such as cows, which Sir David Smith has called '40-gallon fermentation vats on four legs.'

Hydrogen is a well-known product from photosynthetic fermenting bacteria, microorganisms that always grow under anoxic conditions. Every one of such reactive gases (e.g. hydrogen, methane, ammonia, hydrogen sulphide) is a product of life. Almost all are the products of microbial life. Even when these gases are produced by animals or plants the fundamental metabolism is either due to associated microorganisms or is represented in the bacteria. Hence animals and plants do no more than add to that which bacteria do and have been doing for aeons. Thus, although trees can photosynthesize to much greater heights compared to bacteria, they are essentially photosynthesizing using the same biochemical mechanisms. Furthermore, major cycling like the production of methane or hydrogen sulphide, or the fixation of inert atmospheric nitrogen, cannot be carried out at all by animals and plants. These gas emissions require bacteria either alone or in symbiotic concert. The vast complex and diverse metabolisms that run the Earth system are all found in bacteria. Occasionally some of them were amplified by the later evolution of animals and plants. Already in the Archaean aeon (3,500–2,500 million years ago) we have direct evidence of bacteria's oxygenic ability, methanogenic ability, sulphate reduction and oxidation ability, nitrogen fixation ability. This diversity of pathways is found in seaside communities of microorganisms, like that dominated by *Microcoleus*.

Because the ancient limestone has been infiltrated with chert flint in the formation of rock some microbial communities became silicified. Under favourable conditions the rocks can be sliced and examined with the light microscope. Just the kind of organisms that today reside in the intertidal zones and are laying down the calcium carbonate can be found trapped in ancient cherts. On the basis of microfossils we say that these organisms flourished at least 2,000 million years ago and probably as much as 3,500 million years.

If we had found laminated '*Microcoleus*-like' sediment on Mars or Venus we might have an incentive to ask if Gaia had ever occurred on these planets. Indeed these bacterial communities — only a few of which preserve as stromatolites — are surface structures: the skin tissue of the Earth. Evaporites are on top and sometimes carbonate is found underneath. The quantity of carbonate depends on the weathering of local rocks. Salts (sodium chloride, magnesium chloride) including gypsum (calcium sulphate) are also found. Right beneath the evaporite layer is the community of microorganisms, the 'telephone-wire community' that carries out much of the oxygenic photosynthetic activity. A given modern mat only a few centimetres thick may be a hundred or more years old. They are totally organized, packed with diversity, and it is through them that the essential gas exchanges take place, contributing to the Gaian phenomenon by growth and metabolism. Yet we walk over them as if they were dirty sand. We must recognize this continuous covering of the Earth as living; the Earth's living surface coat has been responsible for the global-level regulation and exchanges of reactive gases. Particular organisms, for instance, take in hydrogen sulphide and carbon dioxide and produce sulphur globules which are later metabolized and become aerosol sulphate particles. The mat layers go on and on, extraordinarily complicated, with bacterial cells arranged in organized communities.

A disastrous storm during the winter of 1979 destroyed the *Microcoleus* mats in an area we had been studying in Baja California. Jim Lovelock, Claude Monty and I went to visit those mats the following spring, but all we found were huge puddles. Desperately, I said 'the mats must be here, they have got to be here.' Claude Monty quipped that if I expected such communities to have been around for 3,500 million years a little spring flood was hardly going to bother them! For two years *Microcoleus* mat communities failed to get the intertidal exposure required yet, unbeknown to us, their remnants survived under water. Instead of seeing the *Microcoleus* community we witnessed a total change, with a preponderance of orange and red bacteria. The flood experience was informative; it was like a local extinction and was followed by colonization with all kinds of new organisms that had not been seen before. Many were anaerobic bacteria. The mud laid by the storm, to a bacterium in the community, was equivalent to dumping twenty metres of débris on New York City. Yet, starting in 1981 conditions returned to what they had been before: normal intertidal conditions.

When we returned we first noticed that a mud layer with the capacity to preserve the microbes had been laid down. Probably this kind of cover accounts for why we have preservation of mat communities in the fossil record. Today that particular microbial community of Baja California Norte, Mexico, is back in the recovery stage. Here we see exemplified at the local microscale the kind of discontinuities that we find in Jim Lovelock's 'Daisyworld model.' We have a carbon dioxide removal-oxygen release system, followed after the catastrophe by sulphur-colonizing bacteria and then back again to what I call the normal condition: oxygenic photosynthetic mat-building communities.

The Gaia hypothesis was invented for the atmosphere-trophosphere's chemical and temperature regulation. We (John Stolz, Betsey Dyer, Peter Westbroek, Greg Hinkle, Ricardo Guerrero and I) are beginning to believe that Gaian regulation must be considered a property of the Earth's surface sediments too.

I conclude with just one more example of sedimentary Gaia: enormous guano nitrate and phosphate deposits on the islands off the coast of Peru. These rock piles were laid down, as you well know, by generation after generation of sea birds. Such a sedimentary feature is wholly impossible on lifeless Mars or Venus. Surely guano islands are Gaian features that are completely out of equilibrium from the 'chemistry and physics of planets' point-of-view. These rock islands are produced because of an upwelling in that part of the world. Phosphate and other minerals lead to phytoplanktonic blooms. The fish then eat the phytoplankton, predatory fish eat smaller fish. Birds eat the larger fish and year after year these guano birds nest in the same place. The guano mountains represent thousands of years of accumulation of bird droppings. This particulate matter here on the surface of the planet, extremely phosphorus rich, from the Gaian point of view, is something entirely unknown on Mars and Venus. Other atmospheric particulates too would be impossible without Gaia. Some people call them sea birds, some people call them albatrosses. Whatever they are called they are clearly metre-wide phosphorus-nitrogen-sulphur-rich locomotory volatiles in the atmosphere. Until the geologists, geophysicists and atmospheric chemists realize that these volatiles cannot be modelled by equilibrium chemistry or Newtonian physics but require an understanding of exponential growth potential (a feature of all the components in the surface layer called life) they will not succeed in intellectual comprehension. Indeed until they become Gaian in outlook these physical scientists will not have a proper model for climate or temperature or atmospheric composition. Until the neo-darwinists come up with solid knowledge of metabolic and atmospheric chemistry they will not have a proper model for the evolutionary history of life.

In 1664 Sachs von Lewenheimb wrote a book entitled *Oceanus Macromicrocosmicus.* He was a champion, as I understand it, of Harvey's physiological view of the cycling of the blood. He said that when the blood cycles it does not mean that it makes a 'perfect circle' rather it is part of a closed system phenomenon. He rejected the idea of open systems in which the blood just seeped out of the heart, as previously thought. Von Lewenheimb used 'meteoric' water (rain, fog, snow) taken from a weather example to defend blood physiology. He pointed out that when the water runs off it does not just vanish but it forms a circle, not in a geometric sense but in a figurative sense. Thus it evaporates and then precipitates over the mountains, collecting into rivers and then into lakes and more rivers until it collects in the ocean.

Now Lovelock has the Harvey–von Lewenheimb problem in reverse.

Today we all accept that our blood circulates in our bodies. Everybody realizes that we are not 'being teleological' when we say that bicarbonate has a function in the blood, that mechanisms exist which keep our blood temperature constant, that mechanisms maintain calcium, chloride, and potassium ion concentrations within physiologically appropriate bounds. The means by which the blood is regulated is not a philosophical or teleological issue; it is a scientific matter. What are the mechanisms that maintain the physiology of circulating blood? Here Jim and I are in the reverse of the situation in which Harvey and von Lewenheimb found themselves. We ask what mechanisms maintain the methane in the atmosphere, or dimethyl sulphide; indeed what physiological mechanisms maintain these and so many other phenomena of Gaian planetary control? Like those enlightened scientists of three hundred years ago we find we are being criticized by the geophysical scientists for our inability to produce precise physiological and biochemical explanation. We are accused of teleology. But like the modern physiologists and plate-tectonic geologists we shall overcome. That the air is regulated by life will soon seem obvious to all biologists and geologists, including climatologists. Scientists will feel compelled to read Lovelock's works. Jim Lovelock will be recognized as the latter day William Harvey, and the science of planetary biology and global medicine will begin.

– 4 –
The Gaia Hypothesis: Mechanisms and Tests

Andrew J. Watson

To investigate whether Gaian homeostasis may be a natural consequence of an intimate 'close-coupling' between the biota and the global environment we have developed *Daisyworld,* an imaginary planet where the environment has been simplified to a single variable, planetary temperature, and the biota consists of only one or two species of daisies.

From the Gaia hypothesis one may make predictions about the evolution of the global environment and its present stability, and these may be used to test the hypothesis according to the scientific method. In particular, an environment which evolves by long periods of stasis punctuated by short periods of change would be consistent with Gaia, whereas a history of rapid and continuous fluctuation would not. Major changes in the environment should occur simultaneously with sudden changes recorded in the fossil record.

The Gaia hypothesis as originally stated by Lovelock and Margulis (1974) was this: the environment at the surface of the Earth is actively kept in homeostasis by the biota for their own benefit. At the time that it was first proposed, most Earth scientists thought of life (when they thought of it at all) simply as an opportunist adapting to the global environment. Life rarely had any actual influence on the environment, let alone controlled it in any sense. During the past fifteen years this perception has changed greatly, and most scientists today would probably agree that it was the emergence of life on Earth, more than any other single factor, which caused our planet's evolution to diverge from that of Mars, Venus or the Moon.

However while acknowledging that life has influenced the environment, mainstream science still stops well short of accepting the Gaian notion of homeostasis by and for the biota. This idea, it has been argued, is teleological, implying that life has some underlying purpose which was designed into it at the beginning — a notion which belongs to philosophy and religion, not science. My purpose here is to show that some form of regulatory behaviour may actually follow as a natural consequence of the close relationship between the biota and the global environment which scientists already accept, and that the hypothesis is in fact open to test using the classical scientific method.

More than anything else, it is the composition of the atmosphere which shows us that life is a global geological force. Table 4.1 lists the major sources of the most abundant atmospheric gases, rare gases excepted. With the exception of water vapour they all derive either directly or indirectly from the organized activity of life. (In this context, the products of industry may legitimately be regarded as 'life processes.') This conclusion is not altered if the table is extended to include trace gases at lower and lower concentrations; on the contrary, it is reinforced.

There is nothing controversial about this table; it reflects the established scientific wisdom regarding the sources of atmospheric gases, and it clearly shows that on Earth organisms have a profound influence on the environment. Now, the converse is also true and has been recognized since the time of Darwin; that is, organisms are influenced by the environment. To take atmospheric composition as an example again, plants and animals are obviously dependent on the oxygen, carbon dioxide and nitrogen in the air. In other words, life and the global environment are two parts of a close-coupled system, where the two components are arranged in a feedback loop (Figure 4.1). Perturbations of one will affect

Gas	Major source	Biological/industrial
Nitrogen	Denitrification	Yes
Oxygen	Photosynthesis	Yes
Water vapour	Evaporation	No
Carbon dioxide	Respiration	Yes
Methane	Methanogenesis	Yes
Hydrogen	Natural hydrocarbon Oxidation/anthropogenic	Yes
Carbon monoxide	Methane oxidation/ anthropogenic	Yes
Nitrous oxide	Nitrification/denitrification	Yes

Table 4.1. Sources of abundant atmospheric gases.

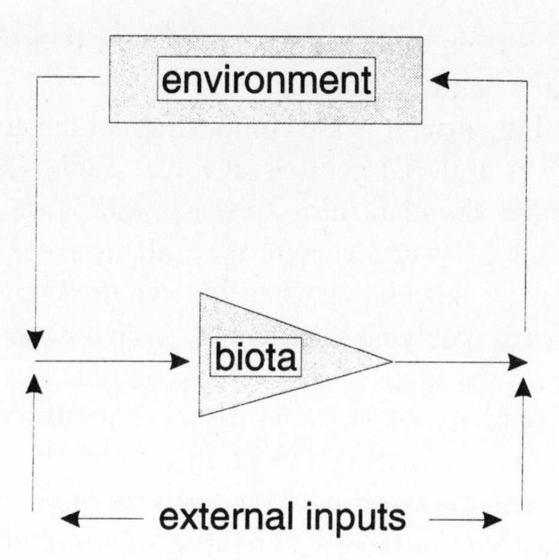

Figure 4.1. Schematic illustrating the biota and the environment as a closed loop.

the other and this will in turn feed back on the original change. The feedback may be positive or negative, but it will not in general be non-existent. Figure 4.1 includes provision for external variables to be taken into account, because the system is not completely closed. Examples of external perturbations might be changes in the solar output, meteorite impacts and orbital wobbles.

We would like to know what properties this close-coupling between life and the environment might confer on the system. Might it, for example, confer increased stability? The difficulty here is that the diagram is too simplistic: in reality both the biota and the environment are vastly complex entities, multiply interconnected, and there is hardly a single aspect of their interaction which can as yet be confidently described by a mathematical equation. To make progress, and as an exercise to illustrate the possibilities, we must make some drastic simplifications. We shall reduce the environment to a single variable, say temperature, and the biota to a single species, namely daisies.

Daisyworld

Daisyworld is a cloudless planet with a negligible atmospheric greenhouse on which the only kind of life is daisies, which for the moment we will assume to be white. Because the daisies are lighter than the ground they cover, they tend to increase the albedo of the planet and thus to cool it. The mean temperature of the planet as a function of the area covered by daisies will have a form like Figure 4.2a. The dotted line shows how

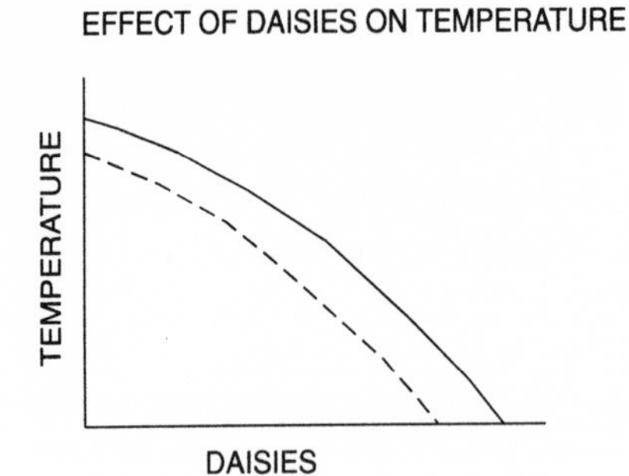

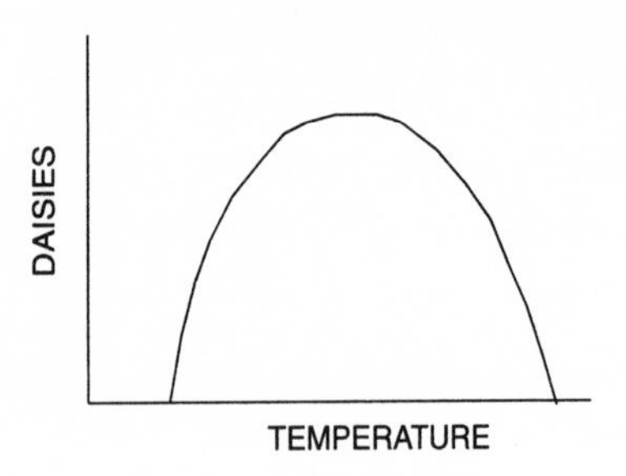

Figure 4.2a. Dependence of mean planetary temperature on the number of white daisies. Decreasing the solar luminosity shifts the curve to the dotted line. Figure 4.2b. Dependence of daisy population on temperature.

the curve might shift following a change in some external variable which influences the temperature. As an example of such a variable we will take the luminosity of Daisyworld's Sun.

Now, let us assume that the daisies grow best over a restricted range of planetary temperatures. The temperature-versus-growth curve peaks at 20° Celsius say, and falls to zero much below 5° or much above about 40°. As a function of temperature, the steady-state population of daisies will look like Figure 4.2b. Figures 4.2a and 4.2b both relate the temperature to the daisy population at steady state, so that the steady state condition of the system as a whole must be specified by the intercepts of the two curves. In Figure 4.3 they are superimposed, and it can be seen that there are two possible steady-state solutions for the particular case drawn here. It turns out that the solution where the derivatives of the two curves have opposite signs is unconditionally stable, whereas the other solution tends to instability so that the system will normally come to rest at the stable solution.

Consider now what happens to the stable solution when some change in the external environment alters the planetary temperature. Suppose for example that Daisyworld's Sun warms up, as ours is supposed to be doing. If the daisy population is held constant, we get a much larger change in the planetary temperature than if we allow the daisies to change to their new steady state. In the stable configuration, the daisy population alters so as to oppose the original change.

Notice that here we have made very few assumptions: we have assumed that the daisies can affect the temperature, but the mechanism works equally well whatever direction they affect it. That is, they could

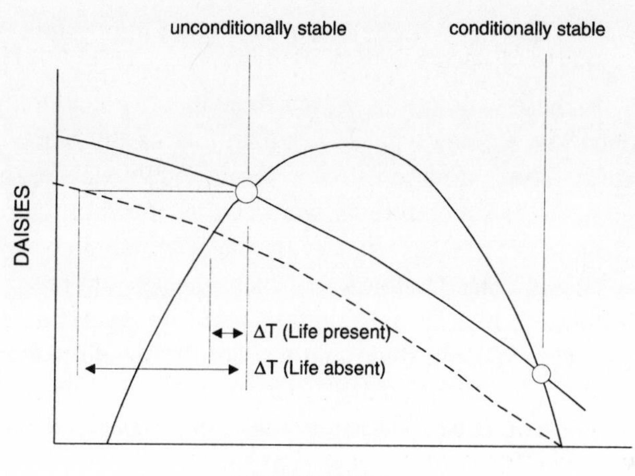

Figure 4.3. Simultaneous solution of these functions.

just as well be black daisies. We have assumed that they can only grow within a restricted range of our environmental variable, but all mainstream life requires temperatures above freezing and below about 50° Celsius, and indeed the general picture of a peaked growth curve is common to a number of environmental variables besides temperature, for example pH.

Lovelock and I discussed this model in some depth in a paper in *Tellus* (Watson and Lovelock 1983). We emphasized there that the exercise was being conducted, not because we believe that daisies, or any other plants, regulate the Earth's temperature by this mechanism, but because it provides an easily understood model of close-coupling between the biota and the environment. The daisy populations were modelled by differential equations borrowed directly from population ecology, and we considered also the case of competitive growth of white and black daisies. Figures 4.4a, 4.4b and 4.5 show the results of a few computer calculations for the mean temperature of the planet, for varying assumptions. In each case, the mean planetary temperature at steady state has been plotted as a function of the luminosity of Daisyworld's Sun.

For the case illustrated in Figure 4.4a only one species of daisy (black in this case) was allowed to grow. Some regulation of the planetary temperature is apparent, though in this case over a rather limited range of luminosity. When both black and white daisies are included (Figure 4.4b) we get good regulation over a much wider range of input luminosities. The regulation has the peculiar characteristic that the mean temperature actually tends to decrease as the luminosity increases. This type of behaviour is not unusual for a multiple loop, non-linear system such as we are dealing with here, but it is quite impossible in simple single loop feedback systems.

In these simulations we assumed that the local temperature of the white daisies was somewhat lower than that of the black daisies because they absorb less radiation. As a result, white daisies grow best when the planetary temperature is warmer than the optimum temperature of the growth curve. Black daisies on the other hand grow best when the planet is cooler. The feedback on each species of daisy is in this case self-limiting: white daisies 'prefer' a warm planet, but if they grow to cover too much ground they tend to cool the whole planet and thereby inhibit their own growth. Black daisies are similarly self-limiting. It is not however necessary to set up the system in this civilized configuration for it to exhibit homeostasis. We can if we like contrive to make the feedback on one or both types self-reinforcing. In the calculations for Figure 4.5 we retained the assumption that black daisies prefer colder conditions but pretended that a white cloud formed over each black daisy. Thus

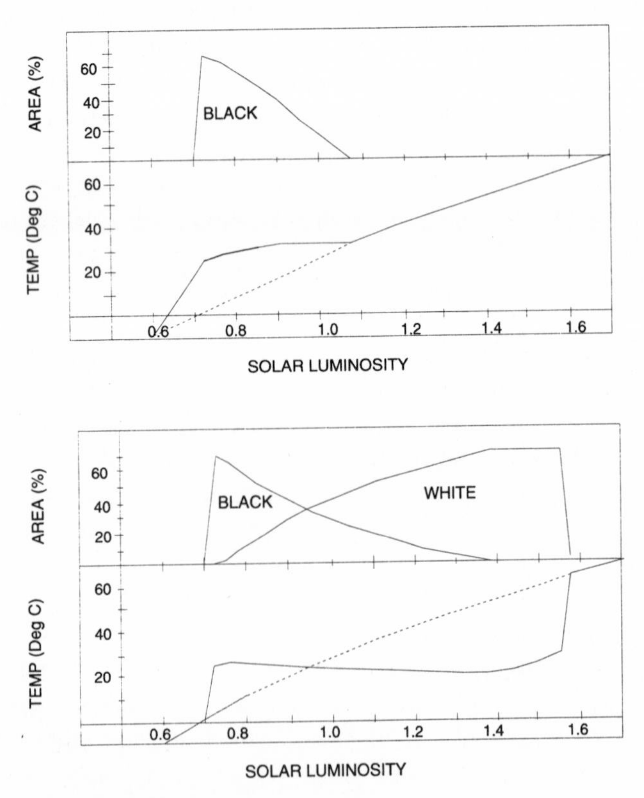

Figure 4.4a. Black daisies only.
Figure 4.4b. Black and white daisies in competition.

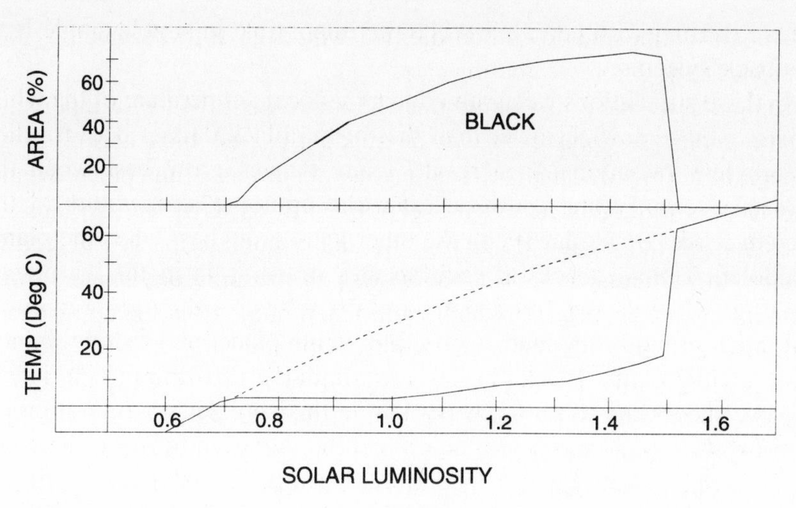

Figure 4.5. Same as Figure 4.4b, but with black daisies covered by white cloud.

more black daisies mean more white cloud which tends to cool the planet, which further stimulates the black daisies and inhibits the white. The result is again excellent homeostasis over a wide range, but the black daisies, which now push the temperature in the direction that they themselves favour, out-compete the whites which always go extinct in this model. The moral is that if we try to set the system up in a way which is unstable, it simply adjusts itself by deleting unfit species until it is stable again.

What relevance does this contrived, idealized world have to the Earth? That depends on how general are our assumptions and how strong are the postulated feedbacks between organisms and their environment. To illustrate, we can sketch out the elements of a feedback loop, analogous to that on Daisyworld, which might conceivably have helped to stabilize the Earth's temperature over geological time.

First, it is necessary to assume that the biota have a net effect on the temperature of the Earth. For the purposes of this argument the direction of this effect is immaterial, but we have argued that the net effect of life on Earth may be to depress the planetary temperature by 'pumping down' atmospheric carbon dioxide considerably, thus reducing the efficiency of the atmospheric 'greenhouse' (Lovelock and Watson 1982). The reasoning goes as follows. Over geological time, the main removal process for carbon from the biosphere is by the chemical weathering of silicate rocks in the soil (Walker *et al.* 1981). In soils the partial pressure of carbon dioxide is much higher than in the atmosphere because of the decay of organic matter by soil microbes (Holland 1978). In the absence of life, presumably atmospheric carbon dioxide would have to be much higher to produce the same weathering rate.

Secondly we have to assume that there is a net effect of temperature on the biota. A good case can be made that the biosphere is low-temperature limited. That is to say, a general cooling of the planet would lead to less biological activity over the Earth as a whole, perhaps an extension of the barren polar regions and a contraction of the fertile tropics. In particular it would lead to less soil respiration, hence slower removal of carbon dioxide, which would then build up in the atmosphere and tend to oppose the original change. Although in detail this mechanism is quite unlike that on Daisyworld, the principle is really the same. One needs only to assume that the biota affect the temperature and that the temperature in turn affects the biota in a consistent manner, to be led to the conclusion that the net effect of these interactions will be regulatory. Positive, destabilizing feedback loops can also exist. However, if the biota-environment is a strong interaction these states will be highly unstable and will therefore be transitory; most of the time the system will reside in the stable configurations where negative feedback dominates. The Gaia hypothesis of global regulation by the biota may follow as a natural consequence of the intense and vital interaction between the Earth and the organisms which inhabit it.

Tests for Gaia

According to Karl Popper (1963), science proceeds by logically unjustified and unjustifiable conjectures, theories or hypotheses. These generate predictions which are open to refutation, or testing. One problem with the Gaia hypothesis is that, in common with other conjectures in the field of Earth history, its subject matter is remarkably difficult to test by direct experiment. However it is certainly possible to gain some insight as to the course of Earth history through applying a gaian perspective. We are all the time adding to our knowledge of the environment in the geological past, so these suggestions do have a fighting chance of being tested.

1) Stasis the norm:
If there is any truth in the idea of Gaian homeostasis, it follows that stasis must be the norm of affairs on Earth. This applies equally to the biota and to the environment in which it resides, for a substantial change in one will provoke a response by the other. However, there is no doubt that major changes have occurred in the past and that the system is not im-

movably frozen in one state. There are for example, several major extinctions in the fossil record (e.g. Raup and Sepkosky 1982) and there is one generally agreed major change in atmospheric composition; that is, the appearance of free oxygen. Following Gaia we would expect that these changes would be relatively rapid episodes where the system 'flips' from one stable state to a new one, accompanied by a temporary failure of the regulatory mechanisms. Similar behaviour can be seen on Daisy-world at the extreme limits of regulation, where a slight increase in solar luminosity causes the sudden extinction of the daisies. We therefore suggest that the atmosphere should have evolved by a kind of punctuated equilibrium, long periods of stasis being interrupted by short periods of rapid change. Furthermore, the shifts should occur at the same time as major changes in the fossil record. For example, there is not much evidence to constrain speculation about the history of atmospheric oxygen after its appearance about two billion years ago. There are indications that it had reached a level comparable to that of today by the time of the Carboniferous, (Watson 1978) but there appears to be no geological reason why oxygen should not have varied widely and quite rapidly over the intervening 1,700 million years.

But that is not what we would predict from Gaia. Gaia would regulate the oxygen level most of the time, with major changes occurring only at crisis points in the history of the Earth. If, as we piece together the history of the atmosphere, it becomes clear that atmospheric components typically vary widely and continuously over geological time, this will be evidence against Gaia. But if the major changes occur in synchrony with a punctuated fossil record, then we should take this as evidence consistent with the hypothesis. Sometimes it may be possible to pinpoint an event which caused the initial change, but it is probably irrelevant to ask whether these punctuations are caused by changes in the environment, or in the biota, since the two components are intimately linked together.

2) Mars:

There is increasingly good evidence that Mars was once a much warmer planet with running water on its surface. This has led some scientists to speculate that, although Mars is now definitely a dead planet, it may have supported a thriving biosphere in the distant past. If a future Mars mission found evidence for fossil life on Mars, we should regard this as evidence against the Gaia thesis, unless we could also find evidence for a really cataclysmic planetesimal impact which might have sterilized the planet. A biosphere that was 'in control' of the planet's geochemistry would not have succumbed quietly to a slow cooling of the planet.

3) Gaia and pollution:

We can also describe the response of Gaia to the relentless exploitation and pollution of the biosphere by our own species. At first the system will tend to respond so as to minimize the changes we are inflicting. In a global sense, little harm will therefore be done, providing we do not stress the present state too far. But suppose that we apply so much stress that we push the system beyond the limits of regulation; it may then begin to change of its own accord to a new state. If that occurs we will find ourselves powerless to reverse the changes. Eventually the system will come to rest in a new stable state, but that state may not include most of the animals and plants that enrich our present Earth; it may not even include *Homo sapiens.* Given our present ignorance of how much stress the present configuration of the biosphere can take, the Gaia thesis should warn us to be wary of inducing global-scale changes in the environment. The danger is not so much that we will kill Gaia and hence wipe out any planetary regulation; rather by unbalancing such regulation we may find not only our own species threatened with extinction but just about everything else we care for.

References

Holland, H.D. 1978. *The chemistry of the atmosphere and the oceans.* New York: Interscience.

Lovelock, J.E. and L. Margulis. 1974. Atmospheric homeostasis by and for the biosphere: The Gaia Hypothesis. *Tellus* 26:2.

Lovelock, J.E. and A.J. Watson. 1982. The regulation of carbon dioxide and climate: Gaia or geochemistry. *Planet. Space Sci.* 30:8.

Popper, K.R. 1963. *Conjectures and Refutations.* London: Routledge & Kegan Paul.

Raup, D.M. and J.J. Sepkosky. 1982. Mass extinctions in the marine fossil record. *Science.* 215:1501.

Walker, J.C.G., P.B. Hays, J.F. Kasting. 1981. A negative feedback mechanism for the long term stabilization of Earth's surface temperature. *Journal Geophys. Res.* 86:976–82.

Watson, A.J. 1978. *Consequences for the biosphere of forest and grassland fires.* PhD thesis. Reading (UK) University.

Watson, A.J. and J.E. Lovelock. 1983. Biological homeostasis of the global environment: the parable of Daisyworld. *Tellus* 35B:284.

– 5 –
Daisyworld and the Future of Gaia

Peter Saunders

Daisyworld is a mathematical model devised by James Lovelock in response to criticism of the Gaia hypothesis by Doolittle (1981) and Dawkins (1982). The objection was on theoretical grounds: they claimed that however much the Earth may appear to be regulating itself, it cannot actually be doing this. Self-regulation, they argued, cannot evolve except by natural selection, and natural selection cannot act on a whole planet. Lovelock's reply was to construct a counter-example, a hypothetical planet which regulates its own temperature simply and effectively and whose ability to do this arises out of ordinary physical processes without any selection at all (1982; see also Watson and Lovelock 1983).

The model not only proves the critics were wrong, that self-regulation does not require selection, it also strongly suggests both that the Earth really does regulate itself and also how. For while Daisyworld is a highly simplified model of the Earth, it is an abstraction, not fiction. The few processes that occur on it are standard: absorption of light from the Sun at a rate dependent on the colour of the surface, radiation of energy into space according to the Stefan–Boltzmann law, growth and death of daisies, with the former depending on the temperature and the amount of space available. Nothing more, certainly no inexplicable foresight or tendency towards altruism.

The simplicity of the model is not only necessary for it to be tractable, it also makes it more convincing. The alternative would have been to undertake a massive computer simulation, but even if there were tens or even hundreds of variables this would still be far fewer than on the Earth, so it would not be a complete model. And if self-regulation appeared it would be hard to decide whether this was characteristic of the real world or only an artefact of the particular choice of equations and parameters. In contrast, because Daisyworld is a simple model with only a very few variables, we can see exactly how the self-regulation comes about, and why we should expect it to occur in the real world as well.

Briefly, all that is needed is a suitable combination of negative and positive feedback. Linear systems generally have at most one or the other and are accordingly stable or unstable, respectively. (Unstable systems seldom survive for long, so we don't usually think of them as systems at all. This is why negative feedback is a more familiar concept). Non-linear systems can have both, and this, as Lovelock demonstrated, can readily lead to self-regulation, which implies far more resilience than ordinary stability. As for the Earth, we know that both positive and negative feedback exist, so we should not be at all surprised to find self-regulation.

While Daisyworld is not a detailed model of the Earth, it illustrates the sort of regulation that the Earth almost certainly has. Hence although it does not predict such things as how long it will be before the fossil fuels run out or what precisely will happen if the polar ice caps start to melt, we can use it to discover some of the properties that the Earth shares with any system that is regulated in this way. Above all, it suggests what is likely to happen as the regulation breaks down. It predicts that this may come about rapidly and with comparatively little warning, and that even if recovery is possible, it may be unexpectedly difficult.

By demonstrating how self-regulation can arise without selection, Daisyworld shows that competition is less important in evolution than is commonly believed. Thus science does not oblige us to believe that the world and indeed we ourselves are fundamentally selfish. Cooperation is at least as natural as competition, and our own interests can often be best served by fitting into our natural place in the order of things, rather than striving for an apparent advantage which may turn out to be against our best interests in the long run.

The model

The mathematical model of Daisyworld consists of a small number of simple equations describing the few processes which are taken into account. The fundamental equations and choice of constants are due to Watson and Lovelock (1983). Most of them are standard, and where they are not, the details are not crucial to the results. The solutions, which are easily found, are omitted here but can be found in Saunders (1994).

Daisyworld is a hypothetical planet in orbit around a sun very much like our own. It receives solar energy at a rate proportional to $L(1 - A)$ where L is the luminosity of the sun and A is the albedo (reflectivity) of the planet and $1 - A$ therefore its absorptivity. (It is customary to work in terms of the albedo because astronomers are naturally more interested in the amount of light that is reflected.) We suppose that the surface of

Daisyworld is a medium grey, so that $A = 0.5$. Daisyworld also radiates energy into space, and by the Stefan–Boltzmann Law it does this at a rate $\sigma(T + 273)^4$ where $\sigma = 5.75 \times 10^{-5}$ is Stefan's constant and T is the surface temperature of the planet in degrees Celsius.

Now while the solar luminosity is not necessarily constant (main sequence stars like our Sun become brighter in time) it is hardly likely to change rapidly. Daisyworld will therefore be at equilibrium, which means that its temperature will be just at the point at which the energy lost by radiation exactly balances the energy received from the sun. Hence T must satisfy the equation

$$\sigma(T + 273)^4 = SL(1 - A) \tag{1}$$

where S is a constant which depends on, for example, the radius of Daisyworld's orbit. We can adjust the units of L by absorbing a factor into S and for convenience we do this so as to arrange that when L is approximately equal to one the surface of Daisyworld is at a reasonable temperature for daisies, i.e. about 20°C.

We therefore set $S = 9.17 \times 10^5$ and then, with $A = 0.5$, equation (1) becomes

$$T = (298.8L)^{1/4} - 273. \tag{2}$$

This simple relation between the solar luminosity and the planetary temperature is shown in Figure 5.1a (see p.79). The lifeless planet responds passively to the sun, becoming hotter or colder in straightforward response to changes in the rate of energy supply.

We now introduce life on to the planet, and to keep the model simple we suppose that the entire biota consists of two species of daisies, one black and one white. Both species grow fastest at 22.5°C and less well at higher or lower temperatures. Below 5°C or above 40°C they cannot grow at all. They are also sensitive to crowding, and grow more slowly as they occupy a greater proportion of the area of the planet. We represent all this by using the following expressions for the rates of spreading of the two species of daisy:

$$da_w/dt = a_w(x\beta_w - \gamma)$$
$$da_b/dt = a_b(x\beta_b - \gamma) \tag{3}$$

Here a_w and a_b are the areas occupied by white and black daisies, respectively, γ is the death rate which is taken to be constant and the same for both species (and for the calculations is set equal to 0.3) and $x = 1 - a_w - a_b$ is the area of the planet not covered by daisies. The factors β_w and β_b, as the growth rate per unit area for the white and black daisies, express the temperature dependence:

$$\begin{aligned} \beta_w &= 1 - 0.003265\,(22.5 - T_w)^2 && 5 < T_w < 40 \\ &= 0 && \text{otherwise} \\ \beta_b &= 1 - 0.003265\,(22.5 - T_b)^2 && 5 < T_b < 40 \\ &= 0 && \text{otherwise} \end{aligned} \quad (4)$$

where T_w and T_b are the temperatures at which the daisies are growing.

If Daisyworld were completely covered in black daisies it would have a lower albedo, say 0.25, and if it were covered in white daisies it would have a higher one, say 0.75. If some of it is covered in daisies and the rest of it is bare, the albedo of the whole planet will be the weighted average:

$$A = 0.25a_b + 0.5x + 0.75a_w. \quad (5)$$

Because black daisies absorb more heat than bare earth, the areas covered in black daisies will be warmer than the average temperature of the planet. Similarly, areas covered in white daisies will be cooler. We model this by the equations:

$$\begin{aligned} (T_w + 273)^4 &= q(A - 0.75) + (T + 273)^4 \\ (T_b + 273)^4 &= q(A - 0.25) + (T + 273)^4 \end{aligned} \quad (6)$$

where q is a parameter that represents the degree to which the energy from the sun is redistributed over the planet. (These particular equations were chosen because they are the simplest that ensure that the energy balance equation [1] is still satisfied, but apart from that the form is not crucial.) If $q = 0$, all local temperatures are equal to the mean temperature T, whereas if $q = SL/\sigma$ there is no heat flow at all. Here we use an intermediate value, 2.06×10^9.

This completes the model. To see how it works, we suppose as before that any changes in solar luminosity are slow enough that Daisyworld is always at or very near equilibrium. The areas covered by daisies will therefore have reached constant values, i.e. the derivatives da_w/dt and da_b/dt will both be zero. The differential equations (3) therefore reduce to a pair of algebraic equations:

$$a_w(x\beta_w - \gamma) = 0 = a_b(x\beta_b - \gamma). \quad (7)$$

When there are no daisies, we can find the value of the planetary temperature T as a function of the solar luminosity L from a single equation, (2). Now there are more variables to find and correspondingly

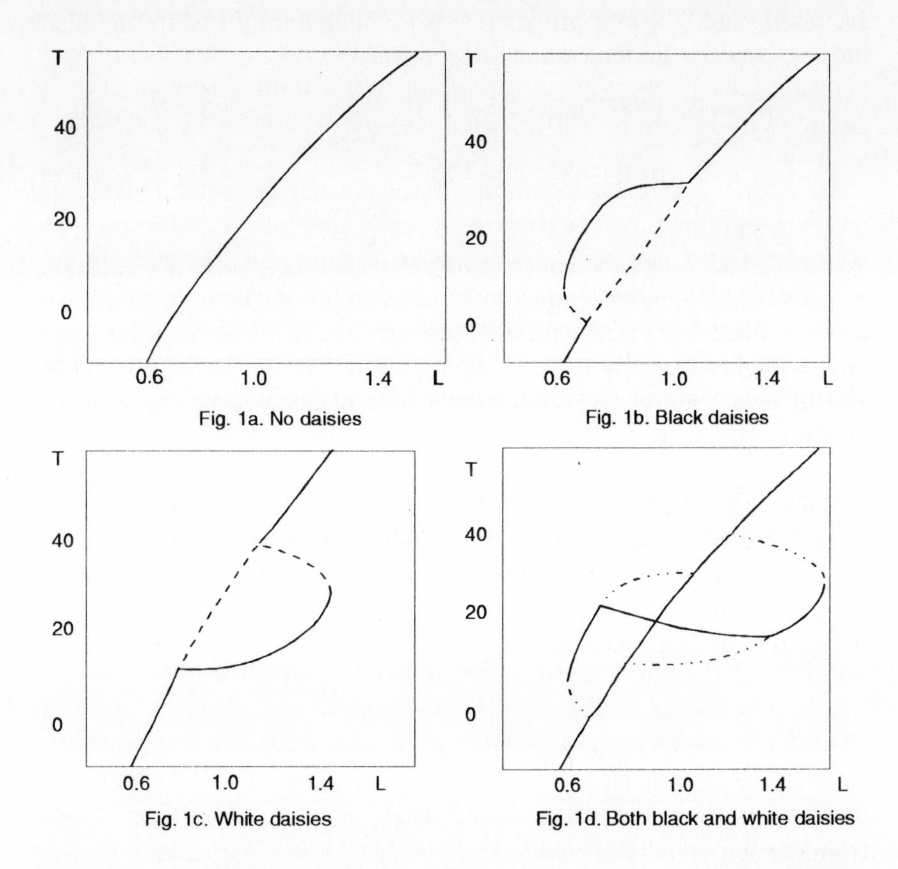

Figure 5.1. The temperature (T) *of Daisyworld as a function of solar luminosity* (L) *with: (a) no daisies, (b) only black daisies, (c) only white daisies, (d) both black and white daisies. In all cases there are ranges with no daisies and in (d) ranges with only black or only white. Dotted lines denote unstable equilibria.*

more equations to solve, but the problem is the same in principle and not much harder in practice.

The solutions (Saunders 1994) are illustrated in Figure 5.1. In all cases except Figure 5.1a (no daisies) there are ranges of L for which more than one equilibrium value of T is possible. This is because the relation between L and T is highly nonlinear, and nonlinear equations typically have multiple solutions: even the familiar quadratic equation has two.

The figures show all the combinations of L and T for which Daisyworld is in equilibrium, with the energy received from the sun equal to the amount lost into space, and the areas occupied by daisies at constant values. Not all of these correspond to states in which we would actually expect to observe Daisyworld, because not only must it be in equilibrium but the equilibrium must be stable. Otherwise the slightest disturbance, and slight disturbances are always occurring, will drive it away from the equilibrium, like a tiny puff of wind blowing over a needle balanced on its point.

In Figure 5.1 stable equilibria are indicated by solid curves and unstable equilibria by dotted curves. For any given *L* we can read off the corresponding value of *T* exactly as in Figure 5.1a. If there are two possible stable equilibria, then either value of *T* is possible, and, as we shall see, this has important consequences.

We may think of Daisyworld as a point in the *L*–*T* diagram moving slowly along one of the solid curves. This makes it easy to see how *T* changes with *L*. Even when curves branch (or, as mathematicians say, bifurcate) it is easy to see what will happen, as only one of the branches is stable. The exception is when the solid curve ends, either by bending back or by becoming unstable. In that case, the point jumps to the other stable equilibrium, which corresponds physically to large changes in *T*.

The mechanism of self-regulation

Now that we have the model, let's see what it does. We begin with the simple case of no daisies. We can immediately read off from Figure 5.1a that the response to an increase in solar luminosity from 0.7 to 1.5 will be a steady rise in temperature from 0°C to 52°C.

Imagine the same change in *L*, but this time suppose that there are seeds for black daisies. When $L = 0.7$ Daisyworld is at freezing point, and it is too cold for daisies to grow. Even if some appear, perhaps because they are on a sunny slope which is warmer than the surroundings, they cannot spread.

When $L = 0.72$, however, the temperature rises to 2°C. If any black daisies do appear then by equation (5) they warm their surroundings to above 5°C. At this temperature they grow faster than they die on all kinds of terrain, not just on the slopes, so more daisies appear. This increases the area of Daisyworld that is covered in black, which increases the rate of absorption of solar energy, which makes Daisyworld even warmer, which makes the daisies grow faster, and so on. This is an example of positive feedback: when the system is perturbed its response increases the effect of the initial perturbation.

The process does not go on forever because eventually the daisies get overcrowded and the resulting negative feedback limits their growth.

There is, however, a dramatic increase in the number of daisies, from zero to covering about 70 per cent of the planet.

As L increases further, the temperature increases, and soon Daisyworld is so warm that the temperature of areas with daisies rises above the optimum for growth. The daisies now grow less rapidly and the area they occupy starts to shrink. This cools the planet, so the temperature rises only very slowly. The feedback here is negative because the reduction in the number of daisies improves the conditions for growth and so acts against the reduction. There is consequently no runaway effect, and the daisies disappear slowly, until when L is about 1.1 there are none left. From then on the temperature increases with L according to equation (1).

All this is illustrated on Figure 5.1b. There is always an equilibrium with no daisies, but between $L = 0.72$ and $L = 1.10$, it is unstable. This means that the appearance of only a very few daisies will very rapidly result in the growth of a much larger number. In particular, we can read off directly how if L is increased from a low value, T will increase slowly until $L = 0.72$ and then rise very rapidly from 2°C to 24°C.

The difference between Figures 5.1a and 5.1b illustrates a very important point. In many situations, especially those that have to do with the future of the environment, we especially want to know whether a given situtation is stable. There are well established mathematical techniques for doing this, and they can give valuable insights into what is going on. On the other hand, almost all the results we obtain are only about what would happen if there were a small perturbation in one of the variables of the model. We are not told what to expect if something new is added. Now one can hardly model the unknown, but we usually assume that we have thought of everything that has a significant influence and that any small factor that we have ignored won't make much difference. More often than not this is true; otherwise there would be little point in mathematical modelling. If, however, we are discussing the stability of a highly complex system, it is precisely the possibility that a small perturbation will have a large effect that we are concerned with. As we have seen, all it takes to make the equilibrium at $L = 1.0$, $T = 25.8$ unstable is a packet of daisy seeds.

What is more, adding extra variables is more likely to destabilize a stable system than the reverse, essentially because a stable system has to be stable with respect to perturbations in every variable separately and in combinations of variables as well. It is thus predictions of stability, i.e. of safety, that are the more likely to be wrong.

Let's go back to Figure 5.1b. We have seen that if L is increased from a low value to 0.72 then the temperature rises slowly to 2°C and then very rapidly to 24°C. What happens if the luminosity then drops below 0.72? This is easy to deduce from the diagram. The point representing the state of Daisyworld is now on the upper curve, and when L is reduced it follows this curve back. Hence T decreases, but only gradually. When $L = 0.70$, for instance, the temperature is still 21°C, whereas on the way up it was zero. Only when L falls to 0.63 is there a sudden drop in temperature, from 9.6°C to –6.8°C.

This is an example of *hysteresis,* a phenomenon which is very common in non-linear systems (i.e. in almost all real systems of any complexity) but not in the simple models encountered in elementary textbooks. It often happens that the path a system follows in the transition between two states depends on the direction of the change. Typically there is a sort of delayed reaction (as the term suggests, since it comes from the Greek word *hysteros,* a delay): the system tends to remain close to the state it began in. Where there are sudden jumps they do not occur at the same point along the way, and this has the important consequence that if a small change in a parameter brings about a large change in a system, reversing the change in the parameter will not reverse the effect it brought about. We shall return to this point later, but its importance for ecology should be obvious.

Figure 5.1c illustrates what happens if the daisies are white rather than black. The situation is much the same except that because white daisies cool the planet instead of warming it everything is reversed. If the luminosity is increased then T increases steadily until $L = 0.84$, when the daisies first appear and start to spread slowly. The temperature remains relatively low until $L = 1.58$, when the daisies suddenly vanish and the temperature rises from 31°C to 62°C. The sudden appearance of daisies and accompanying drop in temperature occurs at $L = 1.22$ if the luminosity is decreasing.

In the full Daisyworld model (Figure 5.1d) there are seeds for both black and white daisies so either or both will grow if conditions are right, i.e. if the local temperature is between 5°C and 40°C. This represents a significant change in the model, because there is now interaction within the biota as well as between organisms and environment. It turns out that this adds considerably to the properties of the model.

Let us consider the same sequence as before. L begins at a low value and then increases steadily. Then T also increases steadily until suddenly at $L = 0.72$ there is a population explosion of black daisies and an accompanying rise of temperature. As L increases further so too does T, but only until $L = 0.75$. Then white daisies start to grow, and the result is that the average temperature of Daisyworld actually decreases, which it continues to do while L almost doubles.

During this time the area occupied by daisies remains constant at 67 per cent although the black ones are gradually being replaced by white. There are almost always more daisies than there would be if only one kind could grow. *What is more, the area covered by either species is never much less and often significantly greater than the area that it would occupy if the other were not present.* Each species also survives at luminosities at which it cannot exist by itself. Thus even though the two species compete for space, the presence of each is generally beneficial for the other.

Eventually, though only after the luminosity has risen to 1.38, the last black daisies disappear. The temperature then starts to rise, first slowly and then more rapidly. The white daisies spread slightly, but then at $L = 1.58$ they suddenly vanish and the temperature rises abruptly from 31°C to 62°C.

To see how this behaviour relates to real environmental problems, imagine that there are intelligent beings on Daisyworld, and that they have discovered how to control the luminosity of their sun. This is difficult and expensive, so they are reluctant to do anything unless they absolutely have to. The Daisyworlders are aware that the sun's luminosity has been increasing for a long time, but the planet is still comfortable. It has actually been getting cooler. While black daisies are becoming less common they are being replaced by white ones so that the total area covered by vegetation is constant. All in all, there seems to be nothing to worry about.

As L gets to 1.5, the inhabitants notice that the temperature is beginning to rise and some of them agitate for appropriate measures to be taken. Will they succeed? Perhaps not, because there will be others arguing that the effect is only small, that it is probably part of some long term cycle (after all, it has been getting cooler for some time now) and besides, the climate is still perfectly comfortable. As for the black daisies, well, it's a pity they've gone extinct, but there are still lots of white daisies left and they're the important ones that cool the planet. There is no particular virtue in biological diversity, certainly not enough to justify doing anything about the sun.

If, however, the warning signs are ignored, and the luminosity reaches 1.58, the consequences will be catastrophic, in both senses of the word. The white daisies will suddenly vanish and the temperature will rise to 62°C. Even if the Daisyworlders survive, to get the daisies back and restore a comfortable climate they will have to reduce the solar luminosity not to just below 1.58 but all the way down to 1.22, a much more expensive undertaking.

While the details of this story are about the imaginary Daisyworld, I think the moral is real enough. If a system that has seemed resistant to changes in conditions starts to respond to them, that may be a warning that it is reaching the limits of its regulative capacity, and that a catastrophic change will soon occur. If that happens, the hysteresis which is typical of systems with this sort of self-regulation may make recovery difficult or even impossible. To quote an early but anonymous systems theorist, an ounce of prevention is worth a pound of cure.

Daisyworld and evolution

Daisyworld was originally created in response to criticisms of Gaia based on the theory of evolution by natural selection. It is therefore not surprising that in addition to helping us understand some of the problems of global ecology, Daisyworld can also throw some light on the study of evolution.

The first point is that it shows how easily we can be misled into seeing adaptation where none exists. Imagine that an interplanetary expedition was sent from the Earth to Daisyworld. The astronauts would report that they had found a planet with a mean temperature of about 22.5°C and that its entire biota consisted of two species of daisies. Since there was no other life on the planet they would have plenty of time to study the daisies in detail and they would find that both species grew fastest at a temperature of 22.5°C. They would be very likely to conclude that here was a clear example of natural selection, that the daisies had adapted to the prevailing conditions on the planet.

But we know that isn't what happened. It is Daisyworld that adjusted its temperature to suit the daisies, not the other way round. Above all, the temperature of about 22.5°C is a property of the daisies, not of the planet or the Sun. The adaptationist account is, as such accounts quite often are, logical and plausible — it is also wrong.

Let's now go on and see what happens if we do put some selection into the model. The two species grow in separate patches and it is warmer where there are black daisies than where there are white ones. In fact, as long as both species are present, the local temperatures are always 17.5°C for white daisies and 27.5°C for black ones. The change in mean planetary temperature as L increases is due to a change in the black/white ratio.

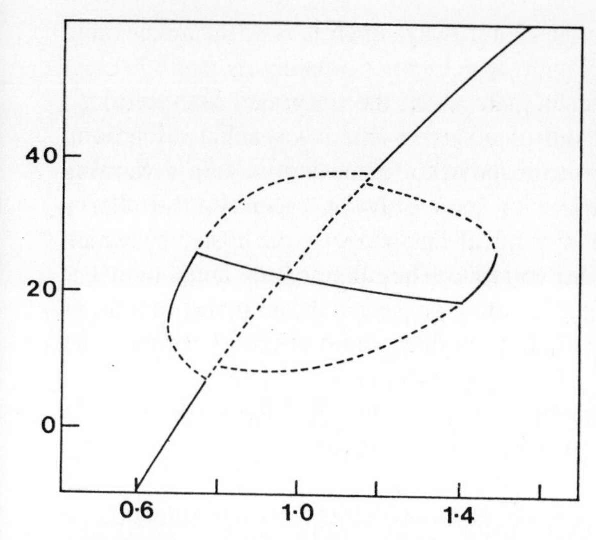

Figure 5.2. The temperature of Daisyworld as a function of solar luminosity (L). *Both black and white daisies are available and each species has its maximum growth rate at the local temperature. Dotted lines denote unstable equilibria, and the cases of no daisies or one species can be read off by comparison with Figure 5.1.*

Since each species will exist for a long time at a fixed temperature, we might expect them to evolve so as to make these their optimal growth temperatures. We can model the effect of this by altering equation (3) slightly to

$$\beta_w = 1 - 0.003265\,(27.5 - T_w)^2 \qquad 10 < T_w < 45$$
$$\beta_b = 1 - 0.003265\,(17.5 - T_b)^2 \qquad 0 < T_b < 35 \qquad (8)$$

with both functions β taken as before to be zero outside the stated ranges.

The general picture is not much changed (see Figure 5.2). The local temperatures remain the same. The total area covered by daisies is only slightly greater: 70 per cent of the planet instead of 67 per cent. Significantly, however, the range of luminosities over which Daisyworld is stable is reduced, from 0.63 to 0.68, by about 16 per cent.

Since we understand how the regulation works, it is not hard to see why natural selection should have this effect. The black daisies, which do the regulating at low temperatures, now grow at slightly higher temperatures than before. And conversely for the white daisies. There is consequently more overlap and less coverage of the ends of the range.

The phenomenon might, however, puzzle the imaginary astronauts. Suppose that while they are investigating Daisyworld (the original version) they realize that because both black and white daisies have the peaks in their growth functions at 22.5°C the regulation of the planetary temperature (and with it of course the survival of the daisies themselves) is more effective than it would be if the daisies had evolved to maximize their growth.

The astronauts would be very hard put to explain how the daisies had been able to show such foresight, which is not possible by natural selection. The answer, of course, is that natural selection had nothing to do with it. The fit between organism and environment was achieved in quite a different way. In fact, it was precisely the absence of selection that was crucial, for if mutant daisies which grew better at the local temperatures were to appear, their short term advantage would mean that they would replace the original stock and so reduce the range of self-regulation.

Thus the effect of natural selection is to reduce the ability of the planet to regulate itself. This is no more than might have been anticipated. The critics of the Gaia hypothesis are right to doubt that natural selection can produce self-regulation, and by the same token we may expect that if self-regulation does arise, by whatever mechanism, natural selection is likely to weaken it.

The famous geneticist R.A. Fisher once called natural selection 'a mechanism for generating the improbable.' Another way of putting it is that natural selection produces organisms which are unnatural, because they are not the sort of thing that we expect from Nature. They are in a very real sense artificial, and have often been written of as having been designed just as watches are, whether by the Creator (Paley 1802) or by natural selection as *The Blind Watchmaker* (Dawkins 1986).

Artificial objects, especially those that are the most unnatural in that they are the most cleverly designed to suit a particular purpose, tend to be less stable than natural ones. Animal breeders are well aware of the problems that can arise through intensive selection for some desired character. Engineers understand that striving too hard for optimization tends to produce structures with potentially dangerous instabilities (see, for example, Thompson and Hunt 1973).

The more something arises through natural processes, the more it is what we would expect Nature to produce, the more robust we may expect it to be. In a modern society we cannot avoid creating environments which are to some extent artificial, but we must seek a balance between the advantages this may bring and the dangerously unstable situation it may lead us into.

When we create something by piecemeal optimization we are likely to prejudice long-term suitability for the sake of small short-term gains. We might call this the *Esau effect,* after the man who traded away his birthright for a mess of pottage, just to satisfy an immediate need. This poses a considerable problem for society, since it implies a need for planning which may fit awkwardly into our political and economic systems. Fortunately this is sometimes acknowledged — surely no one believes that uncontrolled market forces can reduce the use of CFCs or the pollution of our air and water — but it is by no means certain that we are capable of acting quickly enough or decisively enough.

Conclusion

Daisyworld was designed to show how the Earth could have the property of self-regulation simply on account of the way that natural processes work, and in this it has succeeded. As a simple example of the sort of control mechanism the Earth may well have, it suggests several other important ideas as well.

In the first place, it warns us that we cannot afford to be in the least complacent about threats to the environment. Perhaps the most important thing to realize about a regulated system is that the regulation can break down. Daisyworld illustrates how when that happens the transition to intolerable conditions can be quite abrupt. The first warning may be that a system that has previously seemed insensitive to changing conditions starts to respond in the expected direction. The time between the first indication that something is going wrong and the complete breakdown of the system may be uncomfortably short. Once the disaster occurs, even if it is possible to retrieve the situation, the hysteresis that is typical of systems like this means that it will require far more time and effort than would have been needed to save it in the first place.

While these results have been obtained only for the simplified model, they must be taken seriously. As Watson and Lovelock (1983) point out, we only have to assume that the biota are affected by the global temperature (which is obvious) and conversely (through, for instance, altering the proportion of carbon dioxide in the atmosphere) and we can see how a temperature-regulating mechanism similar to that of Daisyworld can exist on the Earth. We now understand how such a system is likely to behave, and in particular what some of the dangers are. Of course a complex system like the real Earth may behave somewhat differently from the highly simplified Daisyworld, and detailed modelling is needed to predict what is likely to happen in any particular situation, but the warning is there. We can no longer confidently assume either that everything will remain all right or at least that there will be ample time to adjust.

Daisyworld demonstrates how self-regulation, an important property shared by all organisms and one which clearly contributes to their survival, can arise without selection. Indeed, if selection does act, it makes very little difference to the daisies and is significantly worse for the planet. This is an example of how natural systems tend to be more robust than artificial ones, including those created by selection. Piecemeal optimization can lead to the Esau effect because only short term advantage is taken into account. Natural systems, in contrast, are stable because they are part of, not inherently in conflict with, the environment.

The theory of evolution by natural selection leads to a exceedingly dismal view of the world. If every organism ultimately owes its existence to a principle of universal selfishness, how can selfishness not be fundamental to the nature of every living creature, ourselves included? Even apparent altruism has to be explained (through kin-selection) as a form of selfishness. (See for example Wilson 1975.) In contrast, Daisyworld shows how an important organismic property, self-regulation, can arise not through competition but by ordinary physical laws.

Daisyworld is not a utopia where everything and everyone always places the general good above individual desires. For all its simplicity there is more to it than that. There is competition (for space) but cooperation (in regulating the temperature) turns out to be more important. And the cooperation comes about not by the subtle action of selfishness or even by some special principle of altruism. It is simply a matter of the daisies doing what it is natural for them to do according to the conventional laws of Nature. Lovelock and Watson (1983) describe the Daisyworld model as a parable. Perhaps the real moral of the parable is that our interests are best served by fitting in with Nature instead of struggling against her.

References

Dawkins, R. 1982. *The Extended Phenotype.* Oxford: Freeman.

—— 1986. *The Blind Watchmaker.* Harlow: Longman.

Doolittle, W.F. 1981. Is Nature really motherly? *CoEvolution Quarterly.* 29:58–63.

Lovelock, J.E. 1972. Gaia as seen through the atmosphere. *Atmospheric Environment* 6:579f.

—— 1979. *Gaia: A New Look at Life on Earth.* Oxford University Press.

Paley, W. 1802. *Natural Theology.* London: F.C. & J. Rivington.

Saunders, P.T. 1994. Evolution without Natural Selection: Further Implications of the Daisyworld Parable. *Journal of Theoretical Biology.* 166:365–73.

Thompson and Hunt. 1973. *A General Theory of Elastic Stability.* London: Wiley.

Watson, A.J. and J.E. Lovelock. 1983. Biological homeostasis of the global environment: the parable of Daisyworld. *Tellus* 35B:284–89.

Wilson, E.O. 1975. *Sociobiology.* Cambridge, Mass: Harvard University Press.

– 6 –
Mechanisms or Machinations? Is the Ocean Self-regulating?

Michael Whitfield

Could Gaia be at work in the oceans? First, I would like to put the oceans into perspective so that we can get a feel for the context of the oceans and why they are important in the Gaia hypothesis, and then to look at their biology to show that there is indeed some relationship between the biological requirements of the organisms that live in the oceans and the composition of the oceans. Second, I would like to look at the role of the Gaia hypothesis to see whether a Gaian mechanism can be found in the ocean.

The belief is that the oceans were actually the cradle of life and that life evolved in the oceans in the first three million years of the Earth's history. That being so, if a Gaian mechanism has developed, even if it is a Gaian mechanism that relates to the atmosphere, it must first have developed within the oceans. And so it is to the oceans that we must look in the first place for the components of any such mechanism. When we look at the oceans they seem to be vast, a tremendous expanse of water to depths of five miles, but if you think of the Earth as a mass of rock about the size of a football, the oceans would be seen as a film of moisture on the surface. Yet it is that thin film of moisture and very thin atmosphere above it that is actually the site of life on Earth.

Other aspects to take into account are external forcing functions — those events outside the control of life — that might be impinging on life and that thin film of moisture. In addition we must consider the weathering process, powered by the Sun, which in the early days of the Earth's history poured material into the oceans and actually was responsible to a large measure, before life began, for setting the recipe for the chemical soup in which the biota evolved. We also have to consider the planetary motions, orbital wobbles, and the impact of planetesimals.

These phenomena are clearly outside the control of the biota, as is the distance of the Earth from the Sun, and that sets the context within which the biota must work. Extremely important too are the processes that work within the centre of the Earth — the convective processes within the mantle that move the Earth's crust and shape and reform the ocean basins. Clearly if they are within the control of the biota it is at several steps removed.

The Earth day

One way is to think of the whole of the Earth's history as compressed into one day. On that basis prokaryotic cells were first seen in the fossil record at about eight o'clock in the morning; then at about eight o'clock at night came the first nucleated cells; at about ten o'clock at night colonization of land took place; so for all that time life was fixed in the oceans. On that timescale the oceans are seen to be very dynamic, for example they are stirred by convective motions at 3,000 revolutions per minute, while the water in the oceans is renewed once a second and the sediments at the bottom of the ocean about once every hour and a half. Most of the elements in the ocean and certainly all the elements important to life have a residence time of less than a minute and some of the elements like iron and manganese have residence times of micro- or milli-seconds on that timescale. Thus this thin film of moisture on the surface of the Earth is subject to considerable forces. Meanwhile, the present episode of continental drift was initiated maybe an hour and a half ago on that timescale. What we need to ask is how could life have evolved and maintained itself within that exceedingly dynamic system?

In looking at the dynamics in terms of the residence times of common indicators such as iron, aluminium and other minerals, one of the first facts to strike us is that the more concentrated the element the longer in general it stays in the oceans: hence the ocean appears to be acting as an accumulator. The major components have residence times of several hours on the Earth-day timescale, but the elements that are really important to life, elements such as nitrogen and phosphorus, have residence times of maybe less than a minute in the oceans. In fact, we have discovered considerable correspondence between the requirements of the biota and the composition of sea water.

We also see that the elements not required by life are at very low concentrations, of less than 10^{-9} molar in sea water and therefore they turn round very rapidly. What life has done is to take on board for its own purposes the elements that tend to stay in sea water for relatively longer and if you look at a concentration plot it is the more concentrated elements in the ocean that are the ones biologically required. Even so some of these are at low concentrations: recent measurements of iron for example indicate levels of down to below 10^{-9} molar.

Thus we find through a brief look at the oceans that although it is very dynamic there has been a certain correspondence between the composition of sea water and the requirements of organisms. In terms of the Gaia hypothesis and in terms of the stability of the oceans, what mechanism could be responsible for this accommodation? A number of possibilities present themselves which can be illustrated by a tank of water model. The first is that there could be a level fixed by the steady state; hence material is being added to the oceans at a very rapid rate, but equally it is also being moved. Once the two balance, we find a concentration in the ocean fixed by the clocks-in and the clocks-out. Perhaps the steady state has been fortuitously fixed over the past 3,000–4,000 million years at a level that the organisms require, that is one possibility. Another possibility is that for every element that goes into the oceans an equilibrium is reached resulting from a feedback which enables a level to be maintained by an active process. This kind of feedback is like a ball valve on a cistern, keeping the level constant. However such regulation would require a separation reaction and a separate mechanism for every element in the periodic table. In summary that system does not work: thus when tried for a number of elements a reasonable equilibrium may be obtained despite changes in the input and output, but that system does not work for all of the elements and certainly not for some of the more important ones involved in life.

That leads us to another possibility: that there is a feedback involving active mechanisms that either controls the supply or else controls the rate of removal from the oceans. That is one kind of feedback. Another kind is one that has an effect on the internal husbandry of the element to make sure the elements are where they are required and in the required concentration. It is important to assess the oceans on such a basis before looking for more complicated mechanisms. In a typical chemical engineer's model of the oceans — basically a bucket in which the contents are stirred — we can put some numbers to the flux of mass going in. For instance, the flux over 18 seconds on the Earth day shows that some 200 x 10^{20} grammes of suspended solids have gone in — enough to fill the bucket. One of the important points about this kind of model is that life is not involved: we simply add material to the oceans.

What sort of an ocean will that give you? Some clues can be derived from looking at the ratio of the concentration of the elements in the ocean to that in crustal rock — hence the partitioning between the two. Should we then finish up with a simple steady-state model then that is probably the consequence of a straightforward partitioning of the elements between the solid phases that are pulled into the ocean and the solution phases within the oceans themselves — that is, a distribution between the rocks and water and a following of simple chemical rules. We can check on this by taking another parameter, that of electronegativity, which gives an idea of the tenacity with which an element remains either in solution or attached to the surface of rock. Should there be a simple geochemical mechanism controlling sea water composition then there should be a simple relationship between the ratio that you can currently observe between crustal rock and sea water. In fact, for a whole range of elements including a number of biologically important ones such as nitrogen, phosphorus or iron, we find such a simple relationship, all lying on a fairly convincing straight line in the plot. Several elements lie above the line, these being the volatiles that come from volcanoes and are put in by another mechanism.

The major sea salt elements have a different correlation because they are not removed by a simple geochemical mechanism. The scale is in fact logarithmic, indicating a spread plus or minus of two orders of magnitude, and giving a hundred times or a hundredth of the concentration that would be determined by simple geochemistry. Indeed, it would make an enormous difference if the seas were a hundred times more salty than they are, since then we would be seeing crystals of sodium chloride deposited on our beaches. What that means therefore is that for some elements geochemical ground rules prevail but for others, specifically those involved with the existence of life, they do not seem to work.

Before invoking a Gaia hypothesis we need to try and see what the ground rules are because otherwise we might be arguing a point which could be explained much more simply. The traditional view is that there is a relationship between the external forcing functions and the biota, with such functions giving an input to the environment which itself then influences the biota so that the biota must adapt to compensate for any change. The tremendous difference the Gaia hypothesis puts into our thinking is that this may no longer be the case and that there is actually a feedback loop with the biota being able to control and influence their environment. There is even a suggestion that in some instances the biota may be able to modify the external forcing functions, for instance a modification of the climate or even of continental drift.

Three questions have to be asked. The first is do the biota influence the composition of the oceans on a global scale? It seems unlikely at first sight because of the vastness of the oceans and the notion that the brown microbial slime could influence anything seems far fetched. The second question is whether any changes brought about by the biota could constitute the components of a regulatory system? Thus if you look at the influence of the biota on the environment, can you see feedback loops sufficient that the biota could stabilize or manipulate their environment to satisfy their own requirements? The third question is to what extent does the biological manipulation of the environment predominate over external forcing functions? Clearly if Gaia is going to work it has to be quantitatively effective, it is not sufficient to say that it can work; it has to be shown to work. Here we are just beginning to make some steps towards getting the necessary information.

Coming to the first question, whether the biota influence their environment, we are already aware that through photosynthesis carbon is taken out of the atmosphere and oxygen released. Some of the carbon sinks, either because the plankton die or because they are eaten by grazing animals which then defecate and their pellets fall down to the ocean floor. Indeed, it would appear that the main Gaian mechanism in the ocean takes the form of a continual rain of droppings from the surface. We must bear in mind that the material fixed on the surface by the biota is not just the carbon but includes trace metals and other essential elements such as nitrogen, phosphorus, iron, manganese.

The process depends on a number of factors, in particular the supply of nutrients. Clearly when plants grow they will strip out the nutrients and if the material all falls to the bottom then very quickly the ocean would become a desert because there would be no nutrients left on the surface. Hence, for life to continue in the oceans it is vital that this material is recycled from the bottom layers of the ocean. That release from the bottom can be either through organic matter decaying through the action of bacteria or it can be the dissolving of shell material, calcium carbonate or silicate. Another important aspect is that plankton should be able to stay in the sunlit zone for photosynthesis to be able to continue. We therefore find a very close link between the physics of the ocean, for instance the way it circulates, and the biology of the ocean, because the physics of the ocean will stir back the nutrients released in the deep waters to the surface layers as well as enable stabilization of the surface layers to occur in the spring when the surface is warm and so provide the conditions for the growth of plankton.

There are two important links in this process; one via the volatiles to the climate because it is the climate including the winds and the temperature differential that stirs the ocean; the other via the particle flux to the deep ocean that dictates the distribution of the elements within the ocean. A sample of the plankton taken from the ocean comes out as brown slime and if we put that slime into a box by which we can follow the pathways we find that the material that drops out from the surface is almost entirely biologically produced. Some 25 per cent by weight is organic, 70 per cent minerals and the remaining 5 per cent consist of wind-blown dust and debris from the land. Hence the biota drive the particle cycle in the ocean sending material down into the depths at a tremendous rate. We are talking of 10^{12} moles of carbon per day.

To summarize we find that by biological means we obtain fixation of carbon in the surface layers giving exchange of oxygen, carbon dioxide and other gases while carbon, nitrogen, phosphorus, silicon and a range of other elements go into the particles that drop down into the deep ocean. Some of the soft material, the organic material, is recycled by biological processes and the elements are released and available for mixing back to the surface. Some of this material accumulates in the sediment where there are biological processes also taking up elements from the oceans. In general the biological requirements of the surface dictate the kind of material that is deposited in the deep ocean. One result of this, as ascertained over the last decade through taking a series of samples of water from the water column down to depths of up to five miles, is that elements involved in this biological pumping get depleted in the surface layer but enriched in deep water. Thus we are seeing a signal of biological activity that indicates that the biology of the oceans has had a tremendous impact on its chemistry.

Certain elements show up in large concentration on the surface and a much lower concentration in deep water. Here we find that the material has been put in through weathering processes and the transport of dust rather than being derived from biological sources. Once such material gets into the ocean it is stripped out onto particle surfaces that are themselves biologically controlled. Indeed the size, distribution and character of the particles are dependent on biological processes.

As examples we can follow what happens to silicon and phosphorus down to depths of some 4,000 metres. We find a rapid recycling of the nutrients with the soft parts of the organisms being preferentially broken down just below the density discontinuity that is stabilizing the surface layers, with the result that a very rich layer of nutrients is formed which can easily be recycled back. Elements that regularly fall into this recycling category include biologically essential carbon, nitrogen, phosphorus, iron, copper, zinc, iodine, vanadium and sulphur.

A look at the oceans overall as a global system indicates that there is a process of transport from one region to another, as if on a conveyor belt. Cold water with a high salinity forms in the North Atlantic and drops to the bottom of the ocean from where it follows a long journey passing via the Indian Ocean to the Pacific. During that process the oceans gradually age and within that ageing water we find an accumulation of all the biologically important elements. Nitrogen concentrations for instance are much higher in the Pacific than they are in the Atlantic because they have accumulated. Another important consequence of this finding is that the concentration of elements in the various oceans follow similar ratios, as for instance of phosphorus and nitrogen. Again the steadiness of such ratios, despite changing concentrations, suggests that the process is entirely driven by biological entities.

The biology of the oceans affects the nature of the atmosphere, particularly through influencing carbon dioxide levels. Over the past thousand years the levels of carbon dioxide in the atmosphere have increased by a factor of two or three, therefore if a Gaian mechanism is at work we would expect there to be increased fixation in the oceans and deposition in the form of carbonate to the depths. Another important gas emanating from the oceans is dimethyl sulphide, which as Lovelock has shown not only closes the feedback link between the movement of sulphur from land to the oceans but also may be critical to the formation of rain-bearing clouds over the oceans.

Recent work suggests that growth of plankton in the oceans is limited by the availability of nitrogen. Even though some phosphorus may be left in the surface waters, growth may slow down once nitrogen has been stripped out of the surface layers. One might expect nitrogen fixation to make up for any shortfall in readily available nitrogen, however, nitrogen-fixing organisms require considerable quantities of iron for the enzymes to function. Iron is in very short supply in the contemporary ocean and the main route for the addition of fresh iron to the oceans is by means of atmospheric precipitation. We can therefore imagine a benefit to any organism that can generate rain-bearing clouds to wash iron out of the atmosphere. Observations on phosphorus concentrations indicate that nitrogen fixation is occurring in the older waters as a result of more iron being made available.

We find that the major impact of the biota on the oceans is to modify the distribution of elements in the oceans, a kind of parsimonious recycling of the elements and there clearly is a strong relationship between the presence of life in the oceans and the distribution of elements. The recycling delays the fall-out of any important nutrient, phosphorus for instance after entering the ocean will on average recycle ten times before it drops out to the bottom.

We therefore have an answer to our first question, whether the biota can influence the composition of the oceans: indeed we find that they can markedly and dramatically. But how might Gaia work in the oceans? Here we are on weaker ground simply because we only have the barest quantitative information. Nevertheless the feedback of phosphorus to the surface layers of the ocean may provide us with a working example. Basically the cycles of the biologically important elements are all interrelated so that when one cycle is influenced it will affect another cycle as well. One such feedback mechanism is based on the relationship between phosphorus and oxygen. What happens is that phosphorus is trapped in particulate matter and drops to the deep ocean but as it falls it is attacked by bacteria which themselves require oxygen. In taking up oxygen the bacteria regenerate the phosphorus which therefore returns to the surface layers. Imagine that the quantity of phosphorus input increases by a factor of ten with phosphorus being the controlling nutrient. That influx of phosphorus would therefore increase the flux of particulate matter to the deep ocean. Meanwhile the demand for oxygen by the bacteria would increase and oxygen levels in the deep ocean would fall. Therefore the efficiency with which the particles are regenerated would also fall and more particles would reach the deep ocean. Here indeed we have a simple feedback mechanism which controls the quantities of phosphorus available for planktonic growth.

A simple assay of the concentrations of particular elements does not indicate its availability for biological use. Indeed the total concentrations in water are not necessarily as important as whether it is present in an available form. Thus if zinc is trapped in organic complexes or stuck on particles then it may not be available for biological use. We are now beginning to discover that for many important elements such as iron, manganese, zinc, copper, the availability is controlled by organic complexes in the water that are formed by interactions of the elements with material released from the plankton. Hence the plankton is actually controlling the availability of such elements in its vicinity.

This process of control is found even in the open ocean where the source of the metal is from the deep water where the organic material has been produced in the surface layers. Again we are discerning the likelihood of a feedback loop: the organisms are dependent on the availability of certain trace metals whose availability they control. What we need at this stage are the actual quantities involved to be able to say whether such mechanisms are predominant.

The next major question for a Gaian machination is whether there is an impact of the oceans on climate which itself will be reflected in a change in the circulation patterns of the oceans which in turn will affect gravity. Again the data is scant but it is clear, for example, that changes in the climate in the North Pacific have been changing the productivity of the biomass over the last decade. Such situations must make us wary when we try to predict such phenomena as the effect of increasing carbon dioxide on the atmosphere. Thus, if there are positive feedbacks in the system, changes are likely to occur very rapidly, as they have done during previous ice ages.

The photochemistry of the oceans clearly has an important impact on nutrient supply. Iron, for example, is readily available in anoxic water into which it easily dissolves. During the first one to two billion years of the Earth's history there was little free oxygen present and the waters were anoxic. However, once the oceans became oxygenated, iron converted to a different form which was extremely insoluble and difficult to get at. We now find some interesting aspects of iron availability in the surface layers that suggest that again either accommodation or manipulation of the environment has taken place. Thus iron can be converted to the readily available form by the photolytic breakdown of organic matter in water, that organic matter being derived from living organisms.

The transparency of the ocean is also linked to the breakdown products of photosynthesis. Indeed, many of the condensation products from the detrital organic matter will themselves trap light, hence where there is an accumulation of these breakdown products the water gradually becomes brownish and photosynthesis becomes difficult. For instance those organisms which produce non-photodegradable breakdown products will quickly shade themselves out. There will therefore have been selection pressure on the organisms to produce products that do not disturb the transparency of the surface, again suggesting an interaction between the organism and the environment.

With regard to the third question it has to be stated that the Gaia hypothesis must alter fundamentally our perceptions. To my mind there have been four changes in my thinking. First, Gaia puts life at the centre. We intuitively feel that life should be at the centre, particularly where it concerns our own species. We therefore feel that life must have a formative influence on the environment and in that respect the new way of thinking makes us look for feedbacks and links within the system. The other important change is that we have to look globally, we have to think big, because to show whether such mechanisms are dominant we have to see quantitatively whether they can provide the necessary feedback to stabilize the environment as well as to discover what the positive feedbacks may be. An important source of carbon dioxide, for instance, is in the tropical oceans whereas the sinks, separated by thousands of miles from the source, are in the North Atlantic. This is the kind of broad scope we have to keep in mind.

The fourth impact of Gaia on our thinking has been that it forces us to focus on the inadequacies of the way scientists think of the world as being divided into disciplines; that there is a physics, a chemistry and a biology and that these can be pursued independently by people who do not communicate with each other and work in different buildings. Thus, if we want to get at the problems of interaction between the biota and the environment we must look at the interaction between these disciplines, because chemistry affects the viability of organisms, physics affects the productivity of organisms and they themselves affect the physics and the chemistry. Although I have to admit it is not yet under the flag of Gaia, what we are trying to do at the moment is to start a series of studies of the ocean which will relate what we can see in the surface layers to global changes. This is all part of a joint global ocean flux study with half a dozen or more countries involved. Initially we are looking at the North Atlantic but later the intention is to spread our interests further. It is important that we get quantitative information that will enable us to decide on any feedbacks. Even though the work is not being carried out under the guise of Gaia a number of people working on it are already thinking in the context of Gaia. At least the Gaia hypothesis will have begun to make us ask the right questions.

– 7 –
Marine Salinity: Gaian Phenomenon?

Gregory J. Hinkle

Salt composition and total salinity in the oceans have been constant over geological periods of time (at least the 570 million years since the beginning of the Phanerozoic Aeon). Analysis of sedimentary rocks has provided geological evidence that the concentrations of the major ions have not changed appreciably for hundreds of millions of years (Garrels, *et al.* 1971). Mass extinctions owing to changes in salt concentrations have not occurred despite the very limited salinity fluctuation tolerance of virtually all marine organisms. Attempts to determine the physico-chemical reactions responsible for salt concentration stability in marine systems are underway (e.g. Whitfield 1981). Although many models have been proposed, none have sufficiently detailed the dynamic mechanisms by which the concentration of all the marine ionic species has been maintained. Attempts to model steady state salinity solely on the basis of chemistry and physics have universally failed.

The Gaia thesis, as proposed by James Lovelock, considers the long-term geological effect of everyday biological activity, and provides an alternative perspective from which to view phenomena of salt dynamics. Using laboratory-contained microbial ecosystems and abiological controls we are testing the hypothesis that evaporite-associated microbial communities (i.e., cyanobacterial mats) actively regulate their environment and in the process contribute to the Gaian phenomenon of ocean salinity regulation.

Gaia and salt

Is ocean salinity under active, dynamic biological control? Have the biota regulated the salt composition of the oceans for at least 2,000 million years? Before the advent of the Gaia hypothesis these unasked questions would have been greeted with cries of derision by leading oceanographic and geological authorities. Against the backdrop of our ever-increasing understanding of the forces that shape and build planets, the Gaia hypothesis has provided a paradigm within which these questions take on scientific meaning (Lovelock 1987).

One of man's oldest questions was, and still is, 'Why are the oceans so salty?' The simple and essentially incorrect answer was that salts, released through the weathering of rocks and transported by rivers, accumulated in the oceans. The concentration of salt in the ocean was said to increase as a function of time and the process had been going on for so long that the oceans were now very salty. If one calculates how long it takes to accumulate an 'ocean's-worth' of salt, one finds that in relation to the age of the Earth (over four thousand million years), accumulation to present salinities occurs within a very short time (fewer than 60 million years, Whitfield 1982). From a Gaian point of view this old question must then be rephrased as 'Why aren't the oceans even saltier?' The two ions comprising 90 per cent of the salts in sea water, sodium (Na^+) and chlorine (Cl^-), are both below saturation by a factor of 10! (Holland 1978). In other words the present concentrations of sodium and chlorine ions in the world's oceans would have to be 10 times higher for NaCl to precipitate in the open ocean. If salt is added at a rate of approximately one 'ocean's-worth' per 60 million years, and if the two ions accounting for 90 per cent of total salinity are a factor of 10 below saturation, then the concentration of salts in the oceans should increase with time. Yet this conclusion is completely at odds with both geological and biological evidence pointing to a constancy of composition and of total salinity in the oceans for well over 500 million years (Whitfield 1981: Garrels *et al.* 1971).

Once again we return to the question 'Why aren't the oceans saltier?' If the oceans have remained very nearly constant in both composition and total salinity for so long given the rapid input of riverine salt, then the many ions making up sea water must also be removed at an equally rapid rate. Many attempts have been made to model the evolution of marine chemistry and much has been learned (Holland 1978; 1984). However these models have failed to provide a rational explanation (on the basis of the laws of chemistry and physics) for either the composition of the oceans or the constancy of that composition over geological periods of time. All the models to date lack an understanding and appreciation of the effect of biological activities on geological processes. While acknowledging the effects of the environment on the evolution of organisms, the models have ignored the equally important and reciprocal effect of life on the evolution of the environment. The effects of biological activity, the accumulation of wastes and biomass and the use of metabolites within the environment, cannot be predicted solely from the laws of chemistry and physics. In fact most geochemists take great pains to remove any and all traces of life in their experiments for the very reason that 'contamination' (i.e. metabolic activity and its by-products) yields unpredictable and inconsistent results. Until these models see living processes as something greater than an inscrutable, undescribable 'black box' they are likely to remain ineffective tools.

Much recent work has pointed to the crucial role of the biota, in particular microorganisms, in understanding the unexpectedly low concentrations of many biologically important elements in sea water (Whitfield 1981; 1982; Whitfield and Watson 1983). Elements required by or toxic to the biota tend to be anomalously low in concentration. The possibility of active biological regulation of salinity has been considered only a few times and then rejected for lack of a plausible mechanism relating rapid biological processes to long-term geological salt removal (Whitfield 1981). Within a Gaian framework this distinction between geology and biology becomes increasingly blurred.

The control of ions across an ion-selective permeable membrane is a central principle of any contemporary definition of life (e.g. Wilson and Maloney 1976). Intricate and energetically demanding ion pumps (i.e. salt pumps) in the membranes of all cells maintain a consistent osmotic milieu within which proteins and nucleic acids interact. In a Gaian framework the control of salinity is then the sum ionic control of the individuals in a community or ecosystem. The small size of bacteria often belies their ecological significance. For instance, although bacteria typically make up just 10–40 per cent of the biomass in a typical open ocean sample, because of their high surface to volume ratio they represent 70–90 per cent of the biologically active surface area (Azam 1987). The realization that just one millilitre of sediment can contain up to 100 million salt-pumping bacteria illustrates the enormous influence the biota necessarily have on global salt fluxes. The abundance, metabolic diversity and rapid turnover rates of bacteria point to their central role in maintenance of all gaian phenomena, as does that these phenomena must have been occurring long before the evolution of eukaryotes. That organisms control the salinity of their internal environment is indisputable. That organisms or groups of organisms can control the salinity of their external environment is the thesis of this work.

The limited ability of all marine organisms to survive changes in the salinity of their environment puts biological constraints on how severe fluctuations in total salinity might have been in the past. The contemporary oceans contain approximately 3.4 per cent salt (100 grams of ocean water completely dried would yield 3.4 grams of salts). If the concentration of salts in the ocean were to increase above 5 to 6 per cent only halophilic bacteria characteristic of evaporitic basins would survive. A barrier exists in the range of 4–7 per cent salt above which osmotic stress becomes overwhelming and basic cellular functions such as ion-pumping and the maintenance of membrane potential fail (Khlebovich 1969). And since the rate at which salts are transported to the ocean is so rapid, the time required for such a change in salinity is geologically very short. The lack of evidence for mass extinctions through changes in global salinity, despite the potential for dramatic changes in total salinity owing to episodes of glaciation, planetismal impacts, changes in weathering rates and other planet-scale perturbations, demonstrates the stability of the oceans for at least the last 570 million years.

Composition of rocks deposited in paleo-oceans permits geologists to determine with considerable accuracy the composition of the principal ions and total salinity at the time of deposition. The evidence suggests that neither composition nor total salinity has changed appreciably for hundreds of million years and puts a geological constraint on the degree of salinity fluctuations in the ancient past (Garrels 1971).

Experimental approach

Inherent in the Gaia hypothesis is the idea that reciprocal relations between the biota (the sum of all living things on the planet) and the environment maintain homeorrhetic conditions on Earth. Salt (i.e. NaCl) is ultimately removed from the oceans via the formation of evaporite basins in the sun-drenched tropical regions of the world (Holland 1978). An evaporite flat looks like a lifeless geological setting. The conspicuous absence of plants and animals only furthers our perception of an inanimate environment. But intimately associated with all known evaporite basins are communities of bacteria (prokaryotic organisms lacking a nucleus) thriving in waters too saline for most eukaryotic organisms (i.e. the nucleated organisms — plants, animals, fungi and protists).

Through the production of organic sheath material, cyanobacteria trap and bind clastic sediments and form a tough, cohesive scaffold within which the community lives. Contained in the sediments are evaporite salts whose dissolution chemistry may be altered through the formation of organic films (Zutic and Legovic 1987). A wealth of micropaleontological evidence shows that these mats and their analogues have been growing and subsequently buried on Earth for at least 3,500 million years (Awramik 1984). The presence of microbial mats through the aeons is consistent with the equally long-term maintenance of ocean salinity. By studying the effect of salt on those communities of organisms intimately associated with the formation of evaporites and, in turn, the effect these microbial communities have on the salt dynamics within the evaporite community, we hope to elucidate a small portion of the global salt cycle.

We are now growing these same bacterial communities (*Microcoleus*-dominated cyanobacterial mats) in the laboratory in small-scale evaporite basins. Since all the nutrients cycle within the boundaries of the basin, each set-up is in effect a miniature salina ecosystem. With these miniature ecosystems we can make direct measurements under controlled conditions of the salt dynamics within a salina. By comparing the salt dynamics in the ecosystem containing the microbial communities with the salt dynamics in an identical experimental set-up from which all life has been removed (by gamma irradiation) we hope to assess the extent of biological modulation of what are necessarily chemical phenomena. In particular we expect the presence of these microbial communities to retard the re-dissolution of salts and possibly to act as nuclei in the formation of salt crystals. The deposition of salts within the microbial mats and their subsequent burial provides a plausible mechanism for a biological role in the removal of marine salt.

Experiments incorporating abiological controls are an admittedly crude method for determining the gross effects of life on the sediments, but should provide useful, if putative, tests of the Gaia hypothesis. And since our laboratory-bound microbial mats are wholly functional ecosystems we believe they are ideal models for studying Gaian phenomena. Long before the evolution of eukaryotes, microbial mats were the dominant form of life on Earth (Margulis 1982: Margulis, *et al.* 1986). As analogues of those pre-Cambrian communities, modern microbial mats have the potential to reveal pre-Cambrian Gaian processes. Unlike the mathematical model systems generally employed to study the fluxes of elements and energy, a model system based on a living, breathing microbial community will contain the one component distinguishing Earth from its barren neighbours Venus and Mars — the biota.

Although the mechanisms controlling the composition and total salinity in the oceans are not known, the Gaia hypothesis provides an alternative to the strictly chemical and physical models which have been proposed to date. In denying the mechanistic view while acknowledging the reciprocal effects between the environment and the biota, the Gaia hypothesis recognizes the potential for life to act as a geological force on the face of the Earth.

References

Awramik, S.M. 1984. Ancient Stromatolites and Microbial Mats. In Y. Cohen, R.W. Castenholz, H.O. Halvorson (eds). *Microbial Mats: Stromatolites.* Alan R. Liss, Co. New York:

Azam, Farooq. Personal Communication.

Brown, S.. Margulis, L. Ibarra, S. and Siqueiros. D. 1985. Desiccation Resistance and contamination as mechanisms of Gaia. *BioSystems.* 17:337–60.

Garrels, R.T. and Mackenzie. F.T. 1971. *Evolution of Sedimentary Rocks.* New York: W.W. Norton. p.400.

Holland, H.D. 1978. *The Chemistry of the Atmosphere and Oceans.* New York: J. Wiley. p.351.

—— 1984. *Chemical Evolution of the Atmosphere and Oceans.* Princeton University Press. p.582.

Khlebovich, V.V. 1969. *Marine Biology.* 2:338–45.

Lovelock, J.E. 1979. *Gaia: A New Look at Life on Earth.* Oxford University Press.

Margulis, L. 1982. *Early Life.* Boston: Science Books International. p.160.

Margulis, L., L. Lopez Baluja, S.M. Awramik, D. Sagan. 1986. Community living long before man. *Science of the Total Environment.* 56:379–97.

Whitfield, M. 1981. The world ocean: mechanism or machination? *Interdisciplinary Science Reviews.* 6(1):12–35.

—— 1982. The salt sea — accident or design? *New Scientist* 94(1299):14–17.

Whitfield, M. and A.J. Watson. 1983. The influence of biomineralisation on the composition of seawater. In P. Westbroek, E.W. de Jong (eds). *Biomineralization and Biological Metal Accumulation.* Dordrecht: Reidel. p.523.

Wilson, T.H. and P.C. Maloney. 1976. Speculations on the evolution of ion transport mechanisms. *Federation Proceeding.* 35(10):2174–79.

Zutic, V. and T. Legovic. 1987. Organic matter at the fresh-water/sea-water interface of an estuary. *Nature.* 328:612–14.

Acknowledgements

The author would like to thank Jenny Stricker, Lorraine Olendzenski and Lynn Margulis for their help in the preparation and review of this contribution.

– 8 –
The Geological Impact of Life

Peter Westbroek and Gerrit-Jan de Bruyn

In recent decades a unitary view of global dynamics has emerged. The theory of plate tectonics provides a frame of reference at a physical level. Geochemical models describe the history of the earth in terms of material fluxes between chemical reservoirs. The art of rock dating is now refined to the point that global events can be distinguished from local perturbations. However, a major stumbling block for the development of a comprehensive theory of Earth dynamics is the traditional concept of life in the geological sciences. Physical and chemical forces are thought to be primarily responsible for the development of our planet, whereas the biosphere is thought of as a decoration, but of trivial importance from a geodynamical point of view.

Yet in contrast to this traditional view, leading scientists over the ages, including Hutton, Darwin, Spencer, Vernadsky and Hutchinson have been among those who underscored the importance of the biota in transforming geology. Indeed only now are we coming to realize that without insight into the nature of the active role of life we cannot gain a proper understanding of the dynamics of our planet.

The Gaia hypothesis of Jim Lovelock and Lynn Margulis is an important outcome of the integration between the sciences of life and Earth. In addition to the concept of 'life as a geological force' it conveys the notion of global homeostasis and the maintenance of optimum conditions by and for the biota. Is Gaia to become the leading theory of Earth dynamics, the ultimate frame of reference for research into global change? Many scientists gratefully welcome the new look that this hypothesis provides of life on Earth, but others remain uneasy.

In the Gaian perspective the geological forces of life must be enormous. Life is thought to be in charge on this planet, providing salutary homeostasis with regard to climate as well as the chemical and physical constitution of the atmosphere, the oceans and the outer crust. A curious contradiction springs to the mind: the masses of the atmosphere, the hydrosphere, and the Earth's crust are, respectively, two and a half thousand, one million and ten million times the total mass of all living organisms on Earth together. The biosphere is a flimsy film with many holes, vanishingly small in comparison with its environment. How can this insignificant structure influence the huge mills of Earth dynamics?

Nevertheless, the biota can deploy gigantic forces, despite their trivial mass. In the first place, life is a typical surface phenomenon. The biosphere occupies a strategic position at the interface of rocks, water and air, and is ideally located to influence the chemical traffic between these three phases. In addition, solar radiation has no problem reaching the biosphere, so that the biota can be kept in a strongly energized condition. Another important factor is that living systems can act as catalysts in many reactions — they can hasten the course of geological processes, often by a factor of more than a million.

The long time span of life is yet another reason why the biota can have influenced the history of our planet in important ways: life has been around for over 3.5 billion years. Even a minor influence can have a gigantic cumulative effect if sustained for such a period.

The Earth as a dynamical planet — the rock cycle

If we were in a position to overview the entire Earth from space, and if in addition our perspective of time were to be highly contracted, we would see that our planet is a very dynamic one. Continents would move about in all directions over its surface; sometimes they would cluster together and then they would shatter apart again. We would see how new ocean crust was generated along mid-ocean ridges, how it would shift away on either side, and how, in less than 200 million years, it would be pushed down again into the underlying mantle.

Along these zones of ocean crust consumption (or of 'subduction'), and also where continents collide, mountain chains are formed. The rock masses are pushed up, and as soon as they rise above the surface they are attacked by weather and wind, fragmented and reduced to clay, sand and dissolved materials (weathering). The débris is washed away (erosion), is transported downslope and deposited as sediment. Locally, it may hang on for some time, but eventually it will be pushed back to the surface, crushed or dissolved and deposited further down. Steadily, the mass travels from the continents into the shelf seas, and finally it will be dumped on the deep-sea floor. Now it will be carried along with the shifting ocean crust to a deep sea trough to be plastered onto the continent, or subducted into the deep earth. It will be compressed, heated, maybe even melted and allowed to re-solidify, and in a subsequent phase

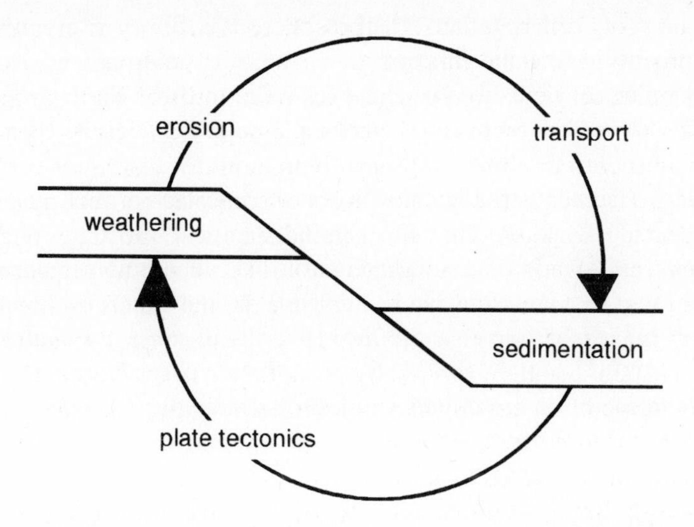

Figure 8.1. The rock cycle from a physico-chemical point of view.

of mountain formation it will be pushed up again towards the surface. The whole process will now begin all over again.

The materials at the outside of the Earth are involved in a continuous cyclic motion which may last for hundreds of millions of years — the rock cycle. The principle is shown in Figure 8.1.

Biosphere and rock cycle

Through their strategic position at the interface of rocks, water and air, and in the light of the Sun, living systems can play an active role in particular in those processes of the rock cycle taking place on the outside of the planet: weathering, erosion, transport and sedimentation. The nature of this biological intervention is best revealed by considering the contrast between the slow motion of plate tectonics and mountain formation in comparison with the frantic activity of life. Essential nutrients, such as phosphate, iron, copper or molybdenum are supplied in minute concentrations to the biota from the depths of the Earth. Hence, biological activity is maintained through the evolution of a huge variety of mechanisms whereby organisms can exploit to their own advantage the very limited nutrient supplies.

Nutrient supplies are increased in the first place by a dramatic speeding up of weathering by the activity of biological systems. Fungi, bacteria, and plant roots penetrate into small cracks in the rocks and create micro-environments where the minerals can readily disintegrate. From a biological point of view, weathering may be compared with mining: raw materials are extracted from the rocks and supplied to living systems.

The nutrients are then kept in circulation by extensive biological recycling. The weathered surface layers or soils play an important role in this repeated utilization. They form an indispensable substrate for vegetation: here, the débris of dead plants are broken down by organisms and the liberated nutrients are made available to the plants again. Excess nutrients are washed out or withdrawn from the biologically catalyzed circulation by storage in the tissues, by precipitation or evaporation, whereas limiting nutrients are usually recycled very efficiently. The nutrient fluxes tend to be diverted by the living communities in such a way that their concentration is adapted to local needs.

Although living systems promote the breakdown of rocks in the weathering process, the resulting débris is kept in place as soils through multiple mechanisms. Overgrowth, roots and slime production are among the stabilizing factors. Nevertheless, the re-utilization of the nutrients is never exhaustive. The biologically catalyzed cycles are leaky and over the longer term the nutrients are diluted. Living communities are undermined and disappear; the soil cover is washed away and fresh rocks are brought to the surface. Now, the process can start all over. Meanwhile, the washed-out nutrients may stimulate biological activity downstream. In this way, life in the oceans is maintained by these nutrient fluxes.

Ultimately, the used end-products of the biota are dumped on the deep-sea floor and enclosed in the slowly accumulating sediments. Sea-floor spreading will bring the refuse to a deep-sea trough where it is subducted. The sedimentary mass is subjected to high temperatures and pressures and pushed up during the formation of a mountain ridge. Thus, it is made available as raw material for a new cycle. Not only does plate tectonics serve as a sewage system for life, it also is responsible for the regeneration of fresh nutrients from the fluxes of refuse. It is doubtful whether life would persist for long in the absence of plate tectonics. While Figure 8.1 shows the classical, physical view of the rock cycle, Figure 8.2 shows the same process from a biological point of view.

The behaviour of living systems with respect to toxic materials is totally different. Like the nutrients, these substances may be liberated through the weathering of rocks. In addition, toxic compounds occur in air and in water, and they may even be generated as by-products of biologically catalyzed reactions. A huge variety of mechanisms has been described whereby poisonous materials are actively removed from biological

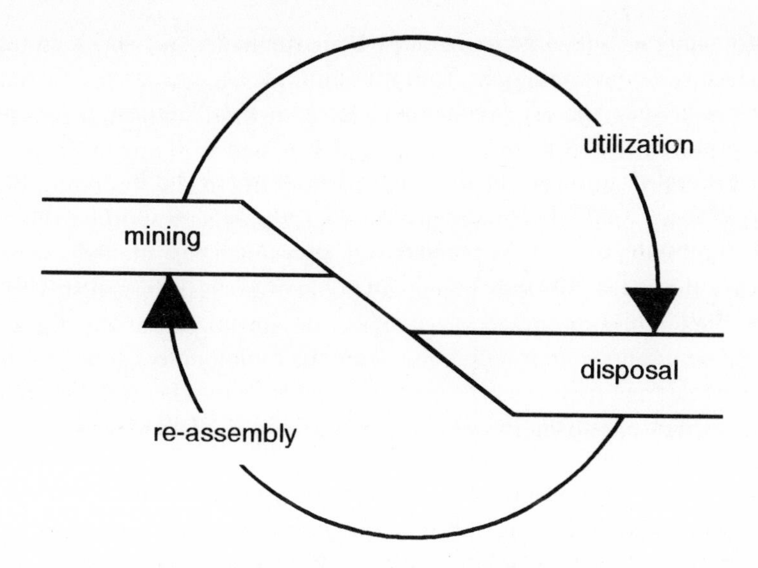

Figure 8.2. The rock cycle from a biological point of view.

systems. For instance, heavy metals may accumulate in the cell walls of many bacteria, to be kept away from cellular machinery.

Dead or living organisms, loaded with heavy metals, are often taken up in sediments, so that the overlying waters are cleansed. In the ocean, poisonous materials are withdrawn from the upper water layers where planktonic organisms may bloom. Toxic nitrogen and sulphur compounds as well as, for instance, mercury, may be volatilized and released into the atmosphere. Thus, in contrast to the nutrients, toxic materials tend to be withdrawn from the biological circulation, or are even removed altogether from the biosphere. Some can be converted into useful or harmless materials and then be further channelled through the nutrient cycles. Ultimately, most toxic materials will end up in the deep sea sediment, together with the final remains of the biota. After a very long time they may be brought back into circulation by the internal dynamics of the Earth.

One aspect needs further clarification. The interaction of the biota with the rock cycle is an energy consuming process. Without solar radiation the process would soon come to an end. The light is captured by the biota and transformed into chemical energy. This energy is conducted through a fine network through the biosphere and sets the entire machinery in operation. Finally, it escapes in a low-grade form into space.

The biosphere is a flimsy, but exceedingly complex and highly energized shell around the Earth. The geochemical fluxes wind together here into elaborate self-organizing and self-perpetuating networks. In the remote past they have emerged from non-biological geochemical fluxes. This is life: a very special geochemical process. Biochemistry is a constituent part of geochemistry.

This general description of the interaction between the biota and the rock cycle sums up the behaviour within the biosphere of the substances that are important for life. In practice, the processes will be more complex, in particular because non-biological processes continually disturb the activity of the biota.

Crystal spheres — the biosphere as a household

The most telling illustration of the simple principles described above is found in the sealed spheres of glass of about 20 cm. diameter put on the market by *EcoSphere Associates* in Tucson, Arizona. The spheres are filled three-quarters with sea water and one quarter with air. Algae and small red shrimps are enclosed, and no doubt there is also a rich bacterial community. Some fine gravel is on the floor. Only light and heat can be exchanged with the surroundings. The producer claims that the shrimps can survive for 10 years, until they die of old age. Twenty chemical nutrient elements must be recycled most efficiently throughout that period in order to keep this exceedingly complex and fragile system going. Many toxic compounds are continuously kept away from the biochemical circulation. Such sealed-off biological communities may be considered as separate biospheres. Similar systems on a much larger scale are now used in biospheric experiments and for supporting the crews of prolonged journeys in space.

Biospheres, large and small, may be compared with a household. We conduct the fluxes of food and energy through our homes, remove the waste and take care that everything is in place, so that we can live as conveniently as possible. Also in the biosphere the fluxes of nutrients and energy are efficiently utilized, and harmful materials are kept out of the way. Why not conclude that the chemical constitution of the biosphere is optimized by and for the biota?

The similarity between biospheres and a household is no more than an analogy, however, and the comparison should not be pushed too far. It is evident, for instance, that the biospheric order is not the result of intentional judgement of an intelligent being. The only steering factor is natural selection and the organization that we perceive has emerged by itself. Spontaneously the food chains interweave so that a discrimination is made between nutrients and toxic materials. The nutrients are sucked into the biosphere and their availability is enhanced by recycling; toxic materials are expelled. This picture of a self-reproducing biosphere, actively maintaining optimal conditions for its own survival is maybe the most telling and best documented illustration of the Gaia principle.

Gaia undermined

However attractive the Gaia concept may be, it does not fully reflect the real development of our planet. All one may say is that there is a tendency in the biosphere towards biologically regulated optimization and stability. But also countless examples are known where a biologically stabilized condition is undermined, not necessarily by external influences, but also resulting from the operation of the stabilizing system itself.

Oxygen

One example is the accumulation of oxygen in the atmosphere, a dramatic event that took place some two billion years ago. It is generally assumed that before this time, the atmosphere contained little or no oxygen. As a result of its strongly oxidizing properties this gas is extremely toxic and it readily converts organic matter into carbon dioxide and water. Organisms, like ourselves, that now live in close contact with oxygen can survive only because they have a rich repertoire of detoxifying mechanisms at their disposal.

Figure 8.3 represents the mechanism responsible for the accumulation of oxygen. The gas is a by-product of photosynthesis, the process whereby certain microorganisms, algae and plants convert solar radiation into the chemical energy on which all further life depends. The relatively inert carbon dioxide and water are converted into a reactive mixture — organic matter (CH_2O) and oxygen. Respiratory processes reverse the reaction, so that carbon dioxide and water are regenerated. This biologically catalyzed cycle of carbon must have had its beginnings shortly after the origin of life. The cycle is leaky, however: a small portion of the organic carbon is enclosed in the accumulating sediments and may remain there for a very long time. Thus, a gigantic reservoir of organic matter could be formed in the Earth's crust. For each molecule of organic carbon withdrawn in this way from the biological circulation, one molecule of oxygen was liberated. Originally, however, the gas could not accumulate in the atmosphere. It reacted immediately with reduced iron and sulphur

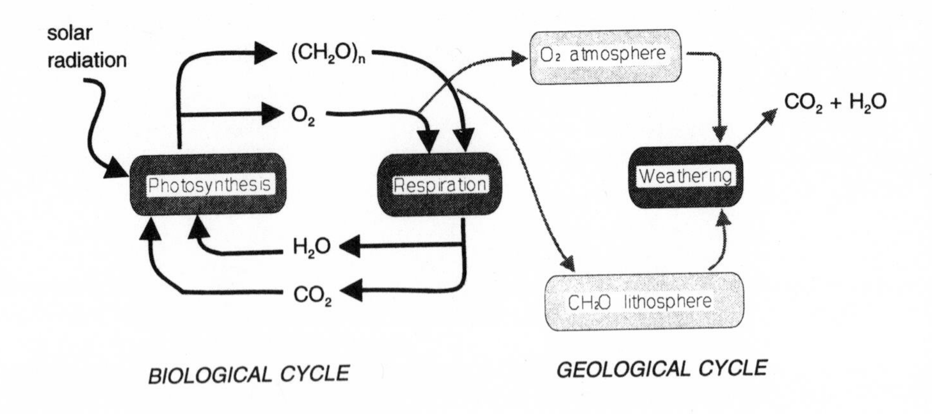

Figure 8.3. The origin of atmospheric oxygen.

and as a result huge reservoirs of oxidized iron and sulphur (rust and gypsum) were stored in the crust together with the organic carbon. Thus, a steady geochemical trend, whereby ever larger amounts of iron and sulphur were transferred from the reduced to the oxidized state, was characteristic for the early development of the Earth. Finally, the iron and sulphur appearing at the surface were reduced to a point where oxygen could freely accumulate in the atmosphere.

The original biosphere, adapted as it was to an oxygen-free atmosphere was suddenly exposed to a ubiquitous, poisonous gas. The offspring of this early life still occurs in peatbogs, in marine sediments and in our intestine. Only a fraction of the biota could adapt to the new and hostile environment, and even learned to utilize it. This was the beginning of an impressive new deployment of the biosphere. We ourselves are totally dependent on oxygen for our own survival. The transition of an oxygen-free to an oxygen-rich atmosphere shows how a global environmental crisis may be brought about by biological evolution, and how a stabilizing biological regulatory system was destroyed and replaced.

It is worth noticing at this point that the presence of oxygen in our atmosphere is not only the result of photosynthesis, but also of the operation of plate tectonics: the relief of the Earth's surface is maintained by the internal movements of the planet. Fresh sedimentary basins are produced continually, and it is here that the organic carbon accumulates so that oxygen can be liberated. Hundreds of millions of years later the occluded organic material returns to the surface where it undergoes a delayed reaction with oxygen.

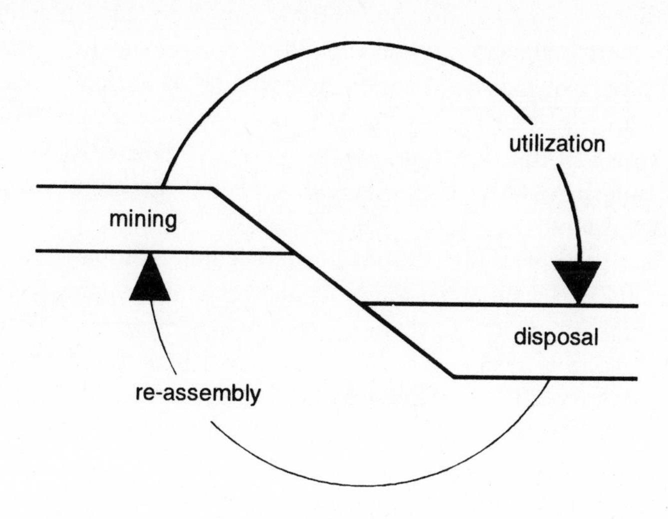

Figure 8.4. The rock cycle from a cultural point of view.

Culture

Human society is a second example of a living system of which the emergence has upset the natural equilibrium. Evolution could be extended outside the constraints of strictly biological organization by a unique combination of tool production, abstract thinking and language, and thus the Earth was subjected to the growing demands of human culture. New geochemical fluxes, comparable in size to the natural ones were set into operation. The heart of the problem is shown in Figure 8.4.

The extraction of raw materials from the environment, their utilization and also the removal of the refuse are strongly intensified compared with the pristine situation (Figure 8.2). New and non-natural chemicals are brought into circulation at a huge scale, and the societal needs for raw materials are qualitatively different from the natural ones. Culture has not yet developed a counterpart of the subtle recycling and detoxification network in operation in nature. Culture overgrows the Earth with an explosive force and with constant changes in character through the development of technology.

Presently, there is a general awareness that this rampant growth exerts a deep influence upon the global ecosystem. However, in contrast to common wisdom, this influence is also very old. Very early in its existence, far more than a million years ago, humanity deforested vast terrains by burning. Erosion rates must have increased dramatically, the nutrient fluxes from the continents to the oceans were amplified and algal blooms were stimulated. Carbon dioxide was removed from the atmosphere and deposited as dead organic material on the ocean floor. Carbon dioxide is a major greenhouse gas, and its removal may have hastened a cooling trend of the Earth's climate, already underway since early Tertiary times. Possibly the ice age was the first global environmental catastrophe, literally ignited by our ancestors.

The development of the cultural forces is gaining momentum, and we are tragically uncertain about the outcome. Some draw courage from the Gaia hypothesis, believing that the natural tendency towards salutary homeostasis will protect us from a catastrophe. But are we not destroying the Gaian household from which we have emerged? Geological history demonstrates that the Earth is subjected to continual change. Periods of stasis alternate with episodes of rapid change. The Gaia hypothesis relates to only one aspect of this shifting scene: the tendency of the biosphere towards stabilization and optimization of the conditions for life. On the one hand, environmental fluctuations are counteracted, but on the other the system is kept out of equilibrium by the very operation of biological regulation, so that sudden and dramatic changes may ensue.

It is possible that many of the global regulatory mechanisms maintaining suitable conditions for life in the past are currently being eradicated by the development of culture. A catastrophe could well mark the beginning of a new and flourishing era in the history of life. But it is questionable whether our progeny would be included. Research programmes may help us to understand the extent of the problem. But that will not be enough. Ultimately, a drastic societal reorganization will be required. If somehow the change can be kept under control, new and unprecedented opportunities may emerge for humanity and nature alike!

– 9 –
Vernadsky's Biosphere as a Basis of Geophysiology

W.E. Krumbein and A.V. Lapo

Geophysiology is the science of the phenomena and processes of Earth as a living system. Earth can be regarded as 'super-organism' *sensu* Hutton (1788) or bioid (bioplanet) *sensu* Krumbein (1986). Earth acts as an organism that is fed externally and internally with 'life energy' and 'nutrients.' It controls its environments and in turn is shaped by its environments. It is a dynamic system in a fluctuating equilibrium. Excursions from ideal equilibrium have occurred in the life history of Earth in the form of events and catastrophes. Deviations or excursions may be innate to the system as through biological and internal events or externally derived as through Milankovitch cycles, or the effects of meteorites and comets. It is at present not possible to decide whether the lower mantle and the core of the Earth are parts of the living entity or separate systems. In response to Milankovitch-cycle type fluctuations or to increasing solar luminosity through geological time the bioplanet has increased the amount and speed of the biocycling of matter and energy. Increased capturing of solar energy into reduced energy-rich organic and inorganic compounds as well as changes in the back-coupling to bygone biospheres (Lapo 1987) are consequences of such changes.

According to Vernadsky, the energy and matter turnover rates of the bioplanet accelerate or slow down depending on the equilibrium between external and internal parameters of the living matter system. The status change of elements from reduced to oxidized and their cycle through the individual sub-systems, including the atmosphere, hydrosphere, biosphere, crust, mantle, last between one year and up to hundreds of millions of years. The multitude of expressions of the genetic diversity pool by dint of Darwinian evolution and the individual environmental conditions created by the activities of living matter are intimately coupled (Krumbein and Dyer 1985). The amounts and rates of (bio-)sedimentation, (bio-)erosion, and (bio-)transport with and against gravity belong to this dynamic living matter system.

Main concepts of geophysiology

Earth exhibits special equilibrium conditions far from thermodynamical, astrophysical and geochemical equilibria because the planet is alive (Krumbein and Dyer 1985, Krumbein 1986, Krumbein and Schellnhuber 1990). Therefore the methods by which Earth is studied should be geophysiological ones (Lovelock 1984). Geophysiology is defined as the science of the normal functions of Earth as a living natural body (Krumbein 1983, Krumbein and Schellnhuber 1990).

The reactions of Earth can and must be compared with the interplay of organs or organelles of one and the same organism with their mutual physical, chemical, biochemical, sensory and motor functions as controlled by memory and memory storage in the widest sense. Thus organisms create their environment and in response to their environment they create themselves (Krumbein and Dyer 1985).

In geophysiological terms living matter — that is the sum of living organisms — organizes and constantly re-organizes itself according to the energy and matter flows from outside the system. The interior parts of the Earth, where direct biochemical life processes cannot go on, do not directly share the cycle, but are increasingly used as storage and buffering material for the energy and material cycles through the self-organized system of thermodynamical equilibrium. Oscillations and excursions, including events as well as directional changes outside and inside the system, are balanced by changes in the mode of operation or in the quality and quantity of operation including both increases or decreases of complexity. The evolutionary trends can be described as progressive or temporal asymmetry. Intergenerational and intragenerational memory are qualities of life that are difficult to conceive for the totality of Earth. The noosphere concept of the Paris group (Bergson 1907, Le Roy 1927, Teilhard de Chardin 1925, and Vernadsky 1924; 1945; 1972) seems, however, to imply such capacities for Earth.

The concepts of Pliny the Elder (*Gaia*) and of James Hutton (*super-organism*) therefore encompass the total genetic diversity as well as the total amount of matter and energy cycled through the system. Earth as a living body or as the species *Terra sempervirens* can be regarded as a 'bioplanet' or a 'bioid' in contrast to the non-living 'geoid' (Krumbein 1986). Krumbein (1983; 1984) reminds us of Giordano Bruno's concept of 'cyclic developments' around intermediate states of chaos that was in dangerous conflict with the orthodox Christian concept of 'creation and destiny' of his time. If cyclic interactions exist then the mass of life is constant to the same degree and underlies the same physical principles as matter, energy and space. The causality of this system may perhaps be derived or imagined, but it is non-deterministic by definition and thus has the potential of evolution or emergence.

Evolutionary patterns on Earth may be regarded as increasing or decreasing organization that results in counteracting changes in external energy flows. When external energy increases, more information will be stored and more energy and matter will be used in the process: when external energy decreases, life stores less energy and information in biological cycles (Krumbein 1983).

The biosphere and noosphere concepts of Vernadsky

Vernadsky was the first to introduce the notion of living matter into the Earth sciences and determined it as follows: 'The living matter of the biosphere is the sum of its living organisms' (Vernadsky 1944, 487). Vernadsky (1926; 1929) states that in simple terms the biosphere is our environment, the 'nature' in which we live. In his various works Vernadsky gave several definitions of the biosphere, always emphasizing two distinctive features: First, that 'the biosphere is the envelope of life, hence, the area of existence of living matter' (Vernadsky 1954, 178); Secondly, that 'the biosphere may, by reason of its essential nature, be regarded as a part of the Earth's crust that is provided with the power to transform the radiations from the cosmos into active terrestrial energy: electrical, chemical, mechanical and thermal' (Vernadsky 1986, 11).

In his works Vernadsky emphasized the ubiquity of life:

> The pressure of living matter is shown in the ubiquity of life over the Earth's surface. There is no part of it that has always been absolutely lifeless. We find vestiges of life on the most arid rocks and sandy deserts. There is always a shifting, temporary form of vegetable life. Such relatively *dead* areas, however, constitute a strictly limited part of the whole surface of the planet. (pp.37f).

And indeed, the most unfavorable localities prove to be inhabited: thermal springs, in which the temperature of water reaches the boiling point and, in some cases, even exceeds it; perennial snow in the Himalayas, where at a height of 8,300 metres at least nine species of bacteria and algae can be found; arid deserts (African deserts, famed for their aridity, are, for example, populated by more than 500 species of insects); and hypersaline lakes where cyanobacteria, archaebacteria, green algae and one species of shrimp flourish, while flagellates and diatoms drag out a miserable existence, but, nevertheless, exist! Strange as it may seem, even the Dead Sea is populated by archaebacteria and algae.

In the geological time-scale an incomplete biogeochemical cycle usually leads to differentiation of the elements and to their accumulation in the atmosphere, hydrosphere, or in the sedimentary envelope of the Earth (Vernadsky 1945a). Vernadsky defined 'the area of former or bygone biospheres' as an envelope of the Earth, that had at some time in the geological past been subject to the influence of life. Today there is general agreement that most, if not all, granites are nothing but re-organized and anatectic sedimentites with their biological history. Vernadsky (1965, 35) wrote that the Earth's crust 'encompasses within the range of several dozen kilometres a number of geological envelopes which some time in the past were biospheres' cycling in multiple cycles at the surface of Earth before being buried for several or hundreds of millions of years. Thus, on viewing Earth as if a snapshot from Space we encounter the biosphere, the stratosphere (sedimentary envelope), the upper and lower metamorphic envelope, and the granitic envelope or fingering system.

Vernadsky's understanding of the Earth's crust as 'an area of bygone biospheres' was based on the following 'empirical generalizations,' formulated in a posthumous publication in the third issue of *Problems of Biogeochemistry* in which he said that 'Never in the course of geological time, were there really azoic periods, i.e. geological periods deprived of life.' Hence, any sedimentary rock traceable on this planet reaching as far back as 3.7 GA (billion years ago) has also the imprint of life or life processes.

> From this it follows that in the first place present-day living matter is genetically related to the living matter of all bygone geological epochs. And, in the second place, it follows that during all this time, the Earth's environments in the biosphere were suitable for the existence of life, i.e. the physico-chemical conditions of the planet's surface were close to those of present day *cum granum salis.* (Vernadsky 1980, 122).

According to Vernadsky, the work of living matter in the biosphere is manifested in two main forms: (a) chemical (biochemical) and (b) mechanical. Geological activity of the first type — construction of the body of an organism and digestion of food — is, naturally, more important in Vernadsky's view:

> There is a continuous stream of atoms passing to and from living organisms from and into the biosphere. Within the organisms a vast and changing number of molecules are produced by processes not otherwise known in the biosphere. (1945, 3).

In fact, continuous metabolic interchange between the living organism and the external environmental conditions is the manifestation of the majority of functions of living matter in the biosphere. According to the calculations of a biologist, during the lifetime of a human 75 tons of water, 17 tons of carbohydrates, 2.5 tons of proteins and 1.3 tons of fats pass through his body. However, in terms of the geochemical effect of his physiological activity, humans are far from being an important kind of living matter in the biosphere. The geochemical effect of the physiological activity of organisms is in inverse proportion to their sizes, and the activity of prokaryotes — bacteria and cyanobacteria — proves to be most significant.

The second type of work of living matter, the mechanical, is manifested in land ecosystems with a well developed soil cover which allows animals to make deep shelters. The Soviet zoologist A.N. Formosov was one of the first to point out that owing to the mounds made by burrowing animals, unweathered minerals get into the upper layers of the soil and, upon decomposition, are involved in the biotic cycle. The American geologist M. Chaffrey noted that termites and ants may become good assistants for geologists in generating waste dumps around their 'mines,' which sometimes reach heights of 70 metres!

Mechanical biogenic migration of atoms is widespread not only on land, but also in the marine ecosystems, and its role in the latter may prove to be even more significant as witnessed by marine snow, faecal pellet sinking and many other biological activities in the oceanic system that act much faster than molecular diffusion or chemical precipitation.

Although living matter accounts for only a few tenths of a percent of the total mass of the biosphere, Vernadsky believed that:

> There is no force on the face of the Earth more powerful in its results than the totality of living organisms. The more one studies the biosphere the more is one convinced that in no case are its phenomena separated from life and its cycles. (1986, 16).

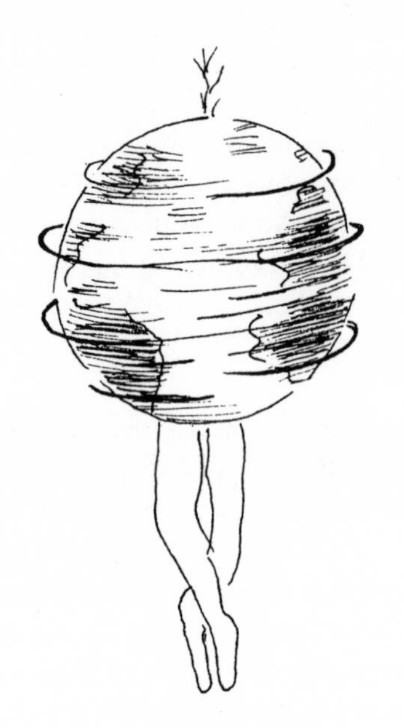

Figure 9.1. In the autumn the Earth rotates marginally faster because deciduous trees have shed their leaves and because of the decline in transpiration.

Figure 9.2. With the coming of spring, trees begin to lift their water to their leaves and the Earth spins a little slower.

Thus, when we calculate how high are the chances that any oxygen or carbon dioxide molecule exhaled 2,000 years ago by the dying Caesar in his *'et tu Brute,'* might be inhaled today by a reader of this article we get the astonishing answer. The chances are almost 99 per cent. Moreover, the sum of living matter has been found to be capable of changing the rotational speed of Earth merely by the trees sending an enormous amount of water into their leaves in Spring (10–20 metres high) compared to the Autumn when trees shed their leaves. This marked effect is greater with the land mass rich northern hemisphere compared with the oceanic southern one and is comparable to the pirouette of a Prima ballerina, according to whether her arms are close to the body or spread out (Figures 9.1 and 9.2).

Vernadsky realized that the most active geological and geochemical 'functions' among the representatives of the organic world would be found in microorganisms. It is they that are responsible for the majority of those biogeochemical reactions within the Earth's crust that result in the formation of exogenic deposits of many chemical elements. Thus, many reactions in the Earth's crust that were previously considered to be abiogenic are, in fact, biogeochemical (Lapo 1987). Vernadsky introduced the concept of organogenic parageneses of chemical elements. He phrased it as follows:

> Living matter is far from being indifferent to the surrounding chemical bodies; it chooses certain chemical elements from the environment and makes them a part of its body. Its life capacities consist substantially in extracting certain chemical elements from the environment, taking them through the organismic compounds and fluids, and returning them to the environment, often as new compounds. Thanks to this, the organism always contains a combination of certain chemical elements. Such simultaneous presence of chemical elements in the Earth crust we shall call their *organogenic paragenesis,* since it is caused not by the chemical properties of elements, but by the properties of organisms. (1984, 147).

As early as the beginning of this century, Vernadsky drew attention to the decomposition of clays by diatoms, which had been first discovered by the famous English oceanographer John Murray jointly with R. Irvine. Their experiments were partly repeated by Vernadsky in 1918–21 and served as a basis for the following conclusions:

> It seems that the weathering of alumosilicates in nature, in soils, is connected with unicellular vegetable organisms (bacteria, fungi, algae) and constitutes a part of a process which is of a paramount importance for the vegetable cover of the Earth and for the geochemistry of the sea (Vernadsky 1939, 15f. See also the review of older literature on biocorrosion and biological rock decomposition by Krumbein 1966; 1972).

The activity of living matter also controls the energy balance of the biosphere and Vernadsky suggested that 'the principal, if not the sole, transformer of solar energy into chemical energy in the biosphere is living matter, which distributes that energy all over the planet' (Vernadsky 1940, 88). Hence, living matter is the only factor on the Earth's surface (in addition to surface tension) which effects the reverse movement of matter, upwards, from the ocean to the continents.

> Terrestrial organisms feed on marine food on such a large scale that this may compensate for — or at any rate return to the land — a commensurable portion of those chemical elements that rivers take from the land to the sea in solution. Since the Mesozoic era mainly birds have fulfilled this function. (Vernadsky 1959, 93).

In recent years Vernadsky's biotransport concept has been developed and further expanded to plate tectonics by Krumbein, Dyer (1985), and Schellnhuber (1990). Shoals of sea fish going up rivers for spawning also contribute. A considerable portion of matter is transferred from freshwater bodies to land by countless hordes of winged insects. Regarding horizontal shifts, only tornadoes and hurricanes can compete with accumulations of homogeneous living matter in the mass of the substance transferred and in the distances over which it is transported, as for in stance in the mass transfer of organic material through the savanna of Africa, the pampas of South America and the Great Plains of North America as well as through the tundra and deserts of Asia. There are no other competitors to these huge biotransport mechanisms which probably also play and played an important role in recent and bygone oceans.

And, finally, considering the functions of living matter in the biosphere, Vernadsky for the first time put forth a fundamental idea of its medium-forming activity. According to this concept, living matter not only adapts itself to the environment (this problem has been discussed by biologists since Lamarck's time), but also controls and shapes the environment, thus ensuring the most favourable conditions for maximum utilization of its geochemical potentials. Krumbein with Dyer (1985), and with Schellnhuber (1990) recently revived and elaborated this concept.

Summing up Vernadsky's ideas of the leading role of life in the generation of the Earth's crust, the geochemist A.I. Perelman has formulated the following statement as 'Vernadsky's Law':

> The migration of chemical elements in the biosphere is realized either with the direct participation of living matter (biogenic migration), or it proceeds in a medium, the specific geochemical features of which (O_2, CO_2, H_2S, etc.) are

> conditioned by living matter, both that part inhabiting the given system at present, and the part that has been acting in the biosphere throughout geological history' (1979, 215).

Krumbein and Schellnhuber (1990) expanded this concept into theories of energy storage at global dimensions whereby organic matter is deposited and then oxidized through sulphate being reduced to sulphide (pyrites). Thus, huge energy reservoirs are created through input of solar energy into the geochemical system by recent and bygone biospheres.

Summarizing, Vernadsky formulated a version of his three 'biogeochemical principles':

Principle 1: The biogenic migration of chemical elements in the biosphere tends towards a maximum of its manifestation (1986, 77);

Principle 2: The evolution of species, in tending towards the creation of new life, must always move in the direction of increasing biogenic migration of the atoms in the biosphere (1986, 80);

Principle 3: During all geological periods, since the Cryptozoic, the population of the planet had to be the maximum possible for all of the living matter then in existence (1965, 286).

Vernadsky (1945, 10) illustrated these principles with the following:

> The course of this evolution only begins to become clear to us through a study of the biosphere's geological past. ... Five hundred million years ago, in the Cambrian geological area, skeletal formation of animals, rich in calcium, appeared for the first time in the biosphere, those of plants appeared over two billion years ago. That calcium function of living matter, now powerfully developed, was one of the most important evolutionary factors in the geological change of the biosphere. No less important changes in the biosphere occurred from seventy to one hundred and ten million years ago, at the time of the Cretaceous system, and especially during the Tertiary. It was in this epoch that our green forests, which we cherish so much as well as the cover of the world with grasses were formed for the first time. This is another great evolutionary stadium, analogous to the noosphere. It was probably in these forests that man appeared around fifteen or twenty million years ago.

These principles are fundamental for understanding the function of the Earth as a living planet. In his scientific testament — a paper on the noosphere — Vernadsky wrote:

> While the quantity of living matter is negligible in relation to the inert and bio-inert mass of the biosphere, the biogenic rocks constitute a large part of its mass, and go far beyond the boundaries of the biosphere. Subject to the phenomena of metamorphism, they are converted, losing most traces of life, change into the granitic envelope, and are no longer part of the biosphere in the sense of living matter. The granitic envelope of the Earth is the area of former biospheres. (pp.6f).

Contemporary scientists of the lifetime of Vernadsky found his concept of the granitic envelope as a product of former biospheres paradoxical. But it is known that 'truth lies at the bottom of a well,' and Vernadsky's views gradually began to be assimilated by geological science. In the sixties, based on Vernadsky's ideas, the geographer and geochemist Thomas F.W. Barth concluded that:

> all rocks we see today were once sediments ... The rocks may have been altered by plutonism, metamorphism, metasomatism, they may have been, at least partly, remelted and existed in the form of magmas and lavas, but at some time in the past they formed from sediments.

Sediments, on the other hand, as we have established, formed under the active participation of living matter under the conditions of a biosphere throughout the entire geological history of the Earth. Captured sunlight and the amount of sedimentation and sedimentation rates ruled the redox state, the concentration of elements and the energy content of the final sedimentary rocks produced in the control of the biosphere.

The concept of the new global tectonics that has taken shape during the last few decades has revealed a possible mechanism for the formation of the granite layer of the Earth's crust from sedimentary rocks. According to the concepts, the oceanic Earth crust moves like a conveyor belt from the ocean ridges to the continents. It is exactly on this belt that sediments are deposited; they gradually move forward under the continents, where they undergo metamorphic transformations. As a result of these processes, most traces of the activity of living matter in the metamorphic rocks are erased. We thus need to 'eliminate the metamorphism' to decipher the sedimental nature of ancient metamorphic rocks. The following remarkable words we owe to Vernadsky:

> Life appears as a great, permanent and continuous infringer on

> the chemical 'dead-hardness' of our planet's surface ... Life therefore is not an external and accidental development on the terrestrial surface. Rather, it is intimately related to the constitution of the Earth's crust, forms part of its mechanism, and performs in this mechanism functions of paramount importance, without which it would not be able to exist. (1929, 30).

Thus Vernadsky was the first person to give a logical answer to Immanuel Kant's enigmatic statement about the special shape and continuous reshaping of the Earth. Kant said in quoting from Burnet's philosophy of the Earth:

> Burnet thought the high and bare mountains and oceanic abysses of the Earth to be useless and a part of divine punishment of the sinful mankind. A thought in which he was, doubtless, wrong ... Whether the spherical shape of Earth or its deviations from the ideal geoid shape are more important, needs, however, further consideration and elaboration (1763, 1770, 1783).

Field theory of life and evolutionary field

The assumptions and notions made on the geophysiology of Earth as an integrated living system with a long life history imply a field theory of life (Krumbein 1983) or an evolutionary field (Cramer 1989). If Hutton was right also in the light of 'modern' science with his super-organism statement then the possibility exists to treat the bioplanet ordinarily as an organism, a species with one representative individuum which constantly and permanently reorganizes itself or keeps itself organized by means of biotransfer of energy and material reaching the system from outside or inside. The single individuum concept thus allows a monist approach to the mind-body dilemma or mind-body aporia, which itself is as old as the philosophy of science. Similar to Laplace, Monod had the concept of a materialistic, deterministic universe, while Jantsch and many others were more inclined to that of a constantly self-organizing and fluctuating universe with astonishingly indeterministic aspects. Our experiences over the past decades with biogeochemical cycles of the dimensions not of millennia but of millions of years against the background of the theories of Heisenberg and Prigogine brought us to the following ideas.

The substance of life or 'living matter' can be regarded as constant and underlies the same regularities as the field concepts of space and matter, gravity and other field theories. Evolution thus could be regarded as increasing or decreasing levels of organization with reciprocally increasing or decreasing entropies. Evolution with increasing energy pressure from outside the system thus can be matched by increasing levels of organization and complexity with decreasing levels of entropy. The genetic diversity (life) will be constant but the level of information stored will increase with increasing energy pressure and decrease with decreasing energy pressure. Life thus would participate in the basic laws of the universe. Here a field theory or evolution field theory is implied (see Table 9.1).

Four different comments about the theory of bioplanets made by different scientists may be interesting in this context:

(1) In his article about the Earth's crust and mantle Anderson (1984) stated: 'It has often been suggested, that life originated on Earth because of a coincidence between the narrow temperature interval over which water is liquid and the narrow temperature extremes that actually occur on Earth. The Earth apparently is also exceptional in having plate tectonics. If the carbon in the atmosphere of Venus could turn into limestone, the surface temperatures and those of the upper mantle would drop. The basalt eclogite phase change would migrate to shallow depths causing the lower part of the crust to become unstable. Thus there is the interesting possibility that plate tectonics may only exist on Earth because limestone-generating life evolved here.' He also designated Earth as 'a geoid with memory.'

(2) In 1989 R. de Wit contended that: 'The Gaia (of Lovelock and Margulis) only describes phenomena of the ways through which a self-regulatory mechanism of Earth is manifested. It does not give an explanation of the driving force(s) behind the mechanism.'

(3) In their textbook on geology Press and Siever (1986) state: 'Most believe the Earth's lithosphere is broken into some dozen plates, which for reasons not fully understood move over the interior.'

(4) An argument put forward by zoologists against the bioplanet theory (Krumbein 1986) was: 'An organism is defined as a complex of organized matter that is kept alive through constant flow of energy and matter into and out of the system which may fluctuate according to its

Table 9.1. Comparative juxtaposition of natural laws and theories in the gravity field (left) and life field (right). After Cramer (1989), Krumbein (1983, 1989); Krumbein and Dyer (1985) and Krumbein and Schellnhuber (1990).

General experience	
Matter is heavy, sluggish, inert.	Living matter reorganizes itself and its environment, constantly creating new patterns
Early attempts at description	
Aristotle: weight is number of democritic atoms.	*Aristotle:* Enteleche.
	Zedler: natural economy is organisation, internal constitution and functional relation of a complex whole; namely, the holy trinity and its expressions in nature.
Lucretius: atoms are invisible and dead.	*Lucretius:* atoms are invisible and alive
Empirically derived natural laws	
Galileo: laws of falling bodies	Laws of entropy; evolution of stars
Kepler: planetary motion	Genetic code
Newton: laws of motion/gravity	*Verhulst:* laws of growth
Einstein: laws of relativity	Radioactivity decreases
Theories	
Newton: gravitational field	*Krumbein* (1983) field theory of life
Heisenberg: relation of uncertainty	*Cramer* (1989) theory of the evolutionary field
Summaries	
A gravitational field does exist in which matter is heavy. Weight and gravitational field are inseparable from matter; the gravitational field exists in three-dimensional space. Space time relations can be defined.	Life is constant; in any evolutionary field living matter (matter with memory) organizes itself. Physical time and mental durance are comparable but inexchangeable; there is competition between morphologies rather than between stationary processes. The life field (genetic diversity) creates, depending on available energies, material environments which in turn reorganize the informational level. Bacteria are evolutionarily sluggish. Their genetic stability and biochemical adaptations form the basic patterns, literally unchanged for billions of years, into which changes of the mode of operation and evolutionary arabesques are embedded (slaving principle in dynamic physics). Evolutionary loops of macroorganisms keep the life field in equilibrium, whereas excursions through quasi-chaos conditions seem to be necessary to guarantee the stability limits of the evolutionary field.

interaction with the physical environment. I see energy coming from outside but no matter.'

As an answer and conclusion to these four statements Krumbein has forwarded the following model for Earth as a living organism representing one single species of life form (1990):

(1) Earth or *Terra sempervirens* can be regarded as an organism or an emergently organized living system that uses an external energy source (Sun) for the maintenance of its informational, structural and processional organization.

(2) Earth constantly and selectively uses increasing or decreasing amounts of energy and matter from outside (Sun, dust, meteorites) and inside (geothermal flux, deeper buried elements of the crust, internal biogenically produced and abiogenic matter and energy reservoirs; see Jannasch 1989).

(3) It stores and organizes them in internal reservoirs which by its own energetic and matter organization are cycled faster or slower through biotransfer (creation of deposits), biotransport (accumulation and destruction of deposits and biogenically controlled plate tectonics) and constant informational re-arrangement of genetic informations and environmental conditions.

(4) Its microorganisms are used as a flexible and stable biotransfer and biotransformation platform (figured bass realization). Its macroorganisms may be figured as 'arabesques' or 'melodies' to enable regulation, back-coupling and triggering effects upon its different morphologies or stationary states (metamorphoses or emerging phase portraits).

(5) Its dynamical system is not 'evolutionary' in the Darwinian sense. The course of dynamic equilibria through space and time is no proof of qualitative evolution. Modern mathematical theories (Thom 1975, Mandelbrot 1982) imply rather back-coupled dynamic systems oscillating around chaos-and-order-limits (Krumbein and Schellnhuber 1990).

(6) Its major crises, events or catastrophes evidenced through its ontogenesis seem to be (a) extraterrestrial, e.g. meteorites, bolides, major Sun fluctuations; (b) home-made deviations immanent to the self-stabilizing system or short phases of quasi-chaos, which can be regarded as internal necessities of a system built of chaotic and organized islands, which occur even at constant external and internal fluxes of energy and matter, hence as exercises for the case of real external events and disequilibria such as Milankovich-cycles or bolide impacts (Milankovich 1920).

Figure 9.3. In an allusion to Joseph Beuys and his famous vest, we have designed the bioid as a self-supporting energy system. We see geophysiological warming by oxidation and release of heat: cooling by reduction and storage of energy.

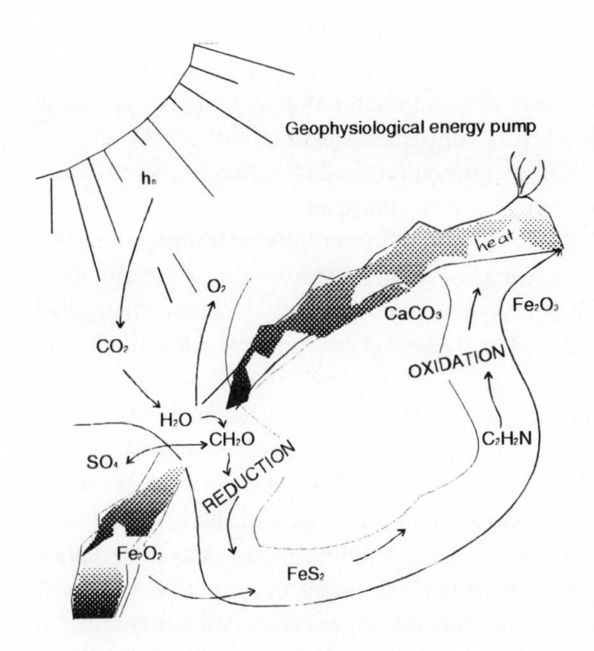

Figure 9.4. A geochemical explanation of Beuys' pump.

(7) Bioplanets must behave elastically. External and internal disturbances are buffered or shielded off or (in extreme cases) counteracted by changes in the operational mode. The operational modes of a bioplanet or Earth as an organism, however, are not arbitrary or randomly manifold. They are restricted to few well defined modi that can be

deduced from basical physical and chemical laws. Possibly they can be defined as various different modes of gaining, controlling and disseminating energy and matter at a global scale. We call this interplay geophysiology (Krumbein and Schellnhuber 1990).

Geophysiological reactions and processes

The concept of geophysiology put forward here embraces in its reactions and biological and bio- (geo-) chemical pathways a multitude of interacting and interrelated processes and components.

Table 9.2 is an integrated version of the main lines of thinking in the American (Margulis, Dyer), English (Lovelock), German (Krumbein) and Russian (Vernadsky, Lapo) approach to the functions of bioplanets. In order to further clarify the multitude of the functions of 'living matter' we give the following listing of factors, which may influence the overall reaction network on this planet:

(1) the biochemical or microbial processes which regulate the budget of materials and gases of the atmosphere, hydrosphere, pedosphere and lithosphere and hereby also the temperature budget of the planet at least in the near-surface layers (uppermost mantle and crust);

(2) the bioaccumulation, biotransfer and biodissemination of information, energy and mineral (matter) carriers and reservoirs;

(3) the biochemical, microbial or plant/animal-related biotransfer processes of biodeterioration, bioerosion and decay of rocks and minerals resulting in nutrient liberation for new life and in the formation of rocks, soils, solute content of the seas and gaseous and particulate content of the atmosphere;

(4) the biotransport of chemical species through microbe- and plant-fueled animals, which transport matter actively (living locomotion) or passively (falling of dead bodies or faecal pellets) that cannot be transported fast enough by diffusion-limited (chemical or eddy) processes;

(5) the organization and re-organization of living matter and information through an environment, which itself is under control of a life field. The maintenance of a life field depends on energy availability. Energy pressure, however, creates material environments and the latter re-organize the living matter and levels of information. Physical time and mental durability in the life field are comparable but not exchangeable (myths). There is no competition between morphologies but rather between stationary processes within the sometimes stable and sometimes apparently evolutionary life field.

Functions	*Characteristics of processes, organisms (organs) involved*
Energies	Adsorption of solar energy through photosynthesis and recycling of the captured energies from geological reservoirs through spontaneous or catalytic release. Catalytic release is exerted through chemolithoautrophic and chemo--organotrophic energy transformations in the bacterial and macroorganismic successive food chains. These processes can be achieved exclusively by *prokaryotes*. *Eukaryotes*, however, are involved.
Concentration (rock and reservoir formation)	Selective accumulation of organic materials (coal, petroleum, gas, kerogen) and inorganic nutrients and catalysator elements (sulphur, carbon, phosphates, iron, manganese, copper, molybdenum, zinc, cobalt and other elements) through the enriching activity of 'living matter.' Also these functions can be exclusively fulfilled via prokaryotes. The enrichment of phosphates, for example is, however stimulated by macroorganisms, although the final enrichment in phosphate beds is exerted by microorganisms. Bodies of organisms (living and fossil biota as well as biogenic ore bodies are examples.) Sedimentary rocks, granites, metamorphites.
Destruction (weathering, destruction, dissemination)	Mineralization of organic matter in the neobiogenic cycle; biogenically accelerated erosion, and degradation of minerals, rocks, mountains, ore bodies etc. (Krumbein and Dyer, 1985). These processes of decomposition of recent and fossil accumulations are mainly achieved by *prokaryotes* but can be influenced and improved by *eukaryotes*.
Organization (complexity, information, medium formation)	Transformation of the physicochemical parameters of the terrestrial environment through neobiogenic matter and its interaction with fossil biogenic materials that are continuously recycled biologically. The biota shape the environment and the environment in turn reorganises the biota. This process is organized through both *prokaryotes* and *eukaryotes*, i. e. the total genetic diversity of the bioplanet.
Transportation	Transport of organized matter against or with the force of gravity under continuous organization of molecules into structured, heavy and highly motile units. Faecal pellets reach the ocean bottom faster than by molecular diffusion; horizontal transport through fish, terrestrial animals, birds; this process is almost exclusively organized by *eukaryotes*. Essentially an explanation of the evolutionary sense of macroorganisms may be the need for fast transportation.

Table 9.2. The main phenomena and functions of 'living matter' in the bioplanetary system.

(6) the balancing of decreasing internal energy supply (decrease of radioactivity and initial energy of planetary aggregation) by increased energy storage in organic matter and reduced metal salt production and storage. For instance, CH_2O and FeS_2 are Sun energy and photosynthesis derived respiratory products of the Earth's microbes which can release enormous amounts of energy.

(7) the shielding and equilibration of increasing or decreasing heat pressure from outside. This is achieved by constant creation and maintenance of an atmosphere with high albedo effects. In order to achieve this the organs and organelles need to expand, more matter needs to be cycled faster through biochemical channels. Therefore deeper parts of the crust will probably be recycled faster.

(8) the maintenance of a matter cycle mainly aided by elimination of calcium from signal organisms through the creation of more and more limestones which in turn will facilitate faster movement of plates and deeper burials at the same time through changes in the eclogite-basalt borders.

(9) the organization and maintenance of the driving forces of the plate tectonic system are mainly delivered by this organization of matter in different reservoirs and pools and by faster bioerosion and biosedimentation processes as well as by increasing input of captured Sun energy into the crust.

(10) the geophysiological organizational level may have even reached the borderline of a noosphere (Vernadsky 1945; 1972) i.e. the step from intuitive, mythological or unconscious life processes to the attributes of life usually referred to for humans, one of the bioplanets most complex and fragile organs.

Noosphere development might entail:

(a) environmental engineering (i.e. creation, modification, adaptation, control, maintenance, repair, evolution, monitoring, spatial differentiation, temporal differentiation, coordination, improvement, industrialization etc. of the living matter-environment field);

(b) problem solving and transcendence;

(c) synergistic and contemplated coordination of biological with non-biological (atmospheric, geological, physical, cosmic etc.) phenomena and processes;

(d) laws and progressive nomogenesis;

(e) discovery, creation and use of newer and subtler, more complex and more diverse natural phenomena;

(f) progressive temporal asymmetry;

(g) development of refined natural economy or 'natural history';

(h) waste management, systems development, quality control and self-repair;

(i) self reflection?

Modern geophysiology derived from Hutton (1788), Lovelock (1984; 1987) and Krumbein (1983; 1986) leans on Vernadsky's pioneer ideas on the biosphere and on the role of living matter in its functioning. Whether man and his mindful (?) and purposeful (?) activities contribute to this huge living matter system and its geophysiology or whether man serves as the initial point of the noospheric development hoped for by Vernadsky is a consideration for the future. Geophysiological theories about the energy content of organic carbon and sulphide reservoirs, for example, and its release back into the living system after millions of years, about the complex biotic control on the atmospheric conditions and temperature at the Earth surface, about the speed of bio-weathering and bio-sedimentation on global geophysiological scales can be analyzed and shown to be right or wrong. The answer to the question of the existence of a noosphere and of man as a mindful geophysiological factor lies, as does the truth, fortunately or unfortunately in the metaphysical realm.

References

Anderson D.L. 1984. The Earth as a planet: paradigms and paradoxes. *Science* 223:347–54.

Bergson H. 1907. *L'Evolution créatrice.* Paris: Felix Alcan.

Büchner L. 1883. *Kraft und Stoff.* Leipzig: Theodor Thomas.

Buffon G.L. 1749–76 (44 volumes). *Histoire Naturelle générale et particulière.* Imprimerie Royale.

Bunyard P. and Goldsmith, E. (eds). 1989. *Gaia, the thesis, the Mechanisms and the implications.* WEC. 251.

Cramer, F 1989. *Chaos und Ordnung. Die komplexe Struktur des Lebendigen.* DVA Stuttgart.

Dumas J.B. and Boussingault J.B. 1841. *Essai de statique chimique des êtres organisés.* Masson. Paris (reprint: 1972. Paris: Editions Culture et Civilisation).

DeWit, R. 1989. *Interactions between phototrophic bacteria in marine sediments, thesis.* Groningen.

Hutton J. 1788. *Theory of the Earth.* Transactions of the Royal Society of Edinburgh. (Book version 1795 Vols. 1 & 2. Edinburgh).

Jannasch, H.W. 1989. The Microbial Basis of Life at Deep-sea Hydrothermal Vents. *News of the American Soc. Microbiol.* 55(8):413–16

Krumbein, W.E. 1983. Introduction. pp.1–4 in Krumbein (ed). *Microbial Geochemistry.* London: Blackwell.

—— 1984. Auf den Schultern des Riesen — Vom Zeitgeist in der Erforschung geomikrobiologischer Zusammenhänge. pp.435–60 in E.T. Degens, W.E. Krumbein and A.A. Prashnowsky (eds). *Ein Nord-Süd-Profil Zentraleuropa-Mittelmeerraum-Afrika.* Festschrift Knetsch. Mtt. Geol. Staatsinstitut Hamburg 54.

—— 1986. Biotransfer of minerals by microbes and microbial mats. pp.55–72 in B.S.C. Leadbeater and R. Riding (eds). *Biomineralization in Lower Plants and Animals.* Oxford: Clarendon.

—— 1990. Der Atem Caesars. Versuch einer Antwort auf die Frage ob die Geophysiologie eine Methode sei, die Erscheinungen und Vorgänge des Bioplaneten Erde in Bilder zu fassen. *Mitt. Geologisches Staatsinstitut.* Denkschrift Egon T. Degens. 69:267–301.

Krumbein, W.E. and B.D. Dyer. 1985. This planet is alive. Weathering and biology, a multi-faceted problem. pp.143–60 in J.I. Drever (ed). *The chemistry of weathering.* Dordrecht: Reidel.

Krumbein, W.E. and H.-J. Schellnhuber. 1990. Geophysiology of carbonates as a function of bioplanets. pp.5–22. in Ittekott, V.S. Kempe, W. Michaelis, A. Spitzy (eds). *Facets of modern biogeochemistry.* Berlin/Heidelberg: Springer.

—— 1992. Geophysiology of mineral deposits — a model for a biological driving force of global changes through Earth history. *Terra Nova.*

Lapo, A.V. 1987. *Traces of bygone biospheres.* Moscow: Mir.

—— 1989. Role of living organisms in processes of lithogenesis. pp.13–24 in T.N. Bogdanova, I. Khozatsky (eds). *Theoretical and Applied Aspects of Modern Paleontology* Leningrad: Manka. (In Russian).

Lovelock, J. 1979. *Gaia. A new look at life on Earth.* Oxford University Press.

Perelman, A.I. 1979. *Geochemistry.* Moscow: Vysshaja Shkola. (In Russian).

Press, F. and R. Siever. 1986. *Planet Earth.* San Francisco: Freeman.

Suess, E. 1875. *Die Entstehung der Alpen.* Wien: Braunmüller. See also: Suess, E. 1909. *Das Antlitz der Erde.* Wien (English: 1904–24. *The face of the Earth.* Oxford: Clarendon).

Teilhard de Chardin, P. 1925. L'histoire naturelle du monde. In 1957–59. *Oeuvres.* Paris: Seuil.

Vernadsky, V.I. 1924. *La géochimie.* Paris: Felix Alcan.

—— 1929. *La biosphère.* Paris: Felix Alcan.

—— 1939. On some fundamental problems of biogeochemistry (in connection with the work of the laboratory of biogeochemistry of the Academy of Sciences of the USSR–ASSSR). pp.5–17 in *Travaux du Laboratoire biogéochimique de l'Académie des sciences de l'URSS.*

—— 1940. *Biogeochemical studies.* Moscow/Leningrad: Izd. ASSSR. (In Russian).

—— 1944. Problems of biogeochemistry. *Trans. Connecticut Acad. Art and Sciences* 35:483–517.

—— 1945. The biosphere and the noosphere. *American Scientist.* 33:1–12.

—— 1945a. La biogéochemie. *Scientia.* 39(Oct–Dec):77–84.

—— 1954. *Selected works.* Izd. ASSSR Publ. 1. (In Russian).

—— 1959. *Selected works.* Izd. ASSSR Publ. 4. (In Russian).

—— 1965. *The chemical structure of the Earth's biosphere and its surroundings.* Moscow: Nauka. (In Russian).

—— 1972. Einige Worte über die Noosphäre. *Biologie in der Schule.* 21(6):222–31.

—— 1980. *Problems of biogeochemistry.* Trudy Biogeochim. ab. GEOKHI ASSSR. 16. (In Russian).

—— 1984. On the living substance participation in the soil formation. pp.130–51 in Vernadsky. 1988. *Life and Activity in the Ukraine.* Kiev: Naukova dumka.

—— 1986. *The Biosphere.* Oracle, Ariz./London: Synergetic.

– 10 –
The Evolution of Cooperative Systems

Brian C. Goodwin

The Gaia thesis, with its global orientation and its recognition of mutualist strategies as the robust basis of evolutionary change, provokes a re-evaluation of the role of cooperative interactions in living systems, which now include the planet as a whole. Out of this comes a programme of constructive praxis-science in the service of planetary well-being. Whatever our specialities may be, our concerns must now be with health and the environment, in the broadest sense of these terms. In this paper I present a case for the view that life is a cooperative enterprise, and its evolution involves an extension of collective action over larger and larger systems.

The origin of life

I shall start, logically enough, with the origin of life itself. There are essentially three conceptual scenarios in this area of experimental and theoretical research.

1. The hypercycle concept of Eigen and Schuster.
2. The microsphere or protocell studied by Fox.
3. The closed catalytic network described by Kauffman.

Each of these contributes significant insights into the origin and nature of the living process. And each is founded upon a particular notion of cooperative interaction.

The hypercycle is a construction that grows out of experiments conducted many years ago by Spiegelman (1967). These showed that the RNA of a particular virus (Qβ) can replicate in a test tube provided it is supplied with an enzyme (a replicase), the necessary nucleotide bases, and an energy source (ATP). This suggested to some that life may have started with these 'naked genes,' though notice that protein (the enzyme) is also necessary. So to define an autonomous replicating system, the RNA must code for the replicase, which it does in the virus.

Eigen and Schuster (1979) developed the kinetics of such systems and showed that it has many interesting properties. For instance, the size of the RNA molecule is limited to a maximum of about 4,000 bases, since otherwise the error rate is so great that the whole system becomes unstable. So such a system is unable to develop complexity. This is precisely what Spiegelman found in his experiments: the original virus RNA actually became progressively simpler (shorter) until it reached the minimum size compatible with its own replication in the presence of the replicase. It was then only 17 per cent of its original size, and replicated fifteen times faster than the original Qβ RNA. What evolution occurred in this system was retrograde — towards simplicity rather than complexity.

To get greater complexity in their model, Eigen and Schuster invented the hypercycle. This is a coupled set of basic replicators, each coding for its own replication, but now linked together so that they assist each other. The product of one replicator acts as an input to the replication of another. The result is that the interacting units reproduce faster as a total system than any single one on its own — an example of cooperative behaviour, or mutualism. The units have escaped the 'Prisoners' Dilemma' through a cooperative strategy.

There are many deficiences in this view of the origin of life, particularly the absence of any boundary that demarcates the coupled elements as an individual — as a proto-organism or a protocell. And this is where Sidney Fox's perspective, presented in the second Gaia conference and proceedings (Fox 1989), provides a very interesting alternative. His scenario for the origin of life is a microsphere that is generated spontaneously by a solution of thermal proteins resulting from a natural polymerization of amino acids under conditions simulating a pre-life marine littoral environment. In an aqueous solution of salts and a small amount of lipid the thermal proteins assemble into small spheres bounded by a protein-lipid membrane. The remarkable feature of such microspheres is that they have many of the properties that we associate with living cells: selective permeability of the membrane, a membrane electrical potential, and even action potentials, with only light as an energy source. The complex mixtures of polypeptides generated by spontaneous thermal polymerization also have catalytic properties, so the microspheres have a primitive metabolism.

These microspheres reveal another type of cooperative or collective behaviour: one which generates a phase separation by the interaction of units. These aggregate and produce a structural boundary, as between the protocell and its aqueous environment. Thus, we get individual entities, which is what was missing from the hypercycle model of the origin of life. The individual microspheres are capable of growth and budding, so they have a primitive kind of reproductive capacity. However, there is not yet evidence that they have what we would recognize as reliable self-reproduction with inheritance.

A model that suggests how this could arise in a microsphere-type system is Kauffman's (1987) autocatalytic protein network. Assuming simply that peptides have catalytic properties, albeit broad spectrum and non-specific, he showed that as the complexity of the peptide set increases (complexity measured by the length of peptide chains and hence the diversity of the amino acid sequences), there is a level of complexity at which all the members of the set, starting from amino acids (plus energy), will be generated by catalyzed reactions. At this point the network achieves catalytic closure, the capacity to reproduce itself. Here we see another form of cooperative behaviour at work: the interaction of peptides in generating themselves by catalytic action. This network also has a rich metabolism: the set of reactions that give rise to the peptide set, as well as many others arising from the broad-spectrum catalytic properties of the peptides. So this model gives us an insight into a highly plausible source of self-reproduction in a system of the type produced experimentally by Fox. The system is inefficient but extremely robust, which is the property required for the origin of life on Earth. The robustness comes from the property that self-reproduction is distributed over the whole system, together with the existence of a very rich metabolism that can accommodate to many different chemical environments. Computer simulation studies of these networks have recently demonstrated that the model does indeed have the properties anticipated.

These ideas have now been developed and extended in extremely interesting ways. Computer simulations of complex catalytic networks by Bagley and Farmer (1992) and by Bagley *et al.* (1992) have revealed their potential to generate a diversity of metabolizing and self-reproducing systems that can propagate themselves and evolve. This approach to the origin of life has been used to develop a logical calculus by Fontana (1992), allowing him to explore systematically the emergence of catalytic closure in networks of polymers described as symbol strings that act on other strings, facilitating reactions that produce yet other strings. He calls his theory *AlChemy,* short for Algorithmic Chemistry. This approach allows one to describe the generic or typical properties of cooperative, self-reproducing chemical systems, and hence to explore what aspects of the origin of life would be repeated if evolution happened again (Fontana and Buss 1994).

Organisms as cooperative and cognitive systems

Each of the three models for the origin of life illustrates a different aspect of cooperative behaviour. Living organisms are cooperative systems that are capable of evolving — of increasing their complexity in appropriate and dynamically stable ways. The notion of catalytic closure also gives us an initial insight into another property of living organisms that is difficult to define, but is as basic as the property of self-reproduction. Notice that naked replicators are not candidates for the origin of life. They must be enclosed in a domain with a boundary that therefore results in an individual entity — the proto-organism. Within this system, catalytically closed in some sense (capable of self-reproduction and with an inheritance of some kind) there are metabolic transformations and other functions (e.g., selective membrane permeability) that are relevant to the maintenance of dynamic stability of the individual and its reproduction. We can then introduce the notion of relevance or significance, which is the biological concept of function: what is a particular process for, what function does it serve in relation to the dynamic stability of the system? This is a property of significance or meaning relative to the process in which the system is engaged. It implies also a distinction between the system as subject and the world it interacts with as object — as object of knowledge. The system can be said to know its world in the sense of interacting with it and causing transformations that contribute to the stability or persistence of the system. Thus, prospective organisms are cognitive as well as cooperative systems: they maintain themselves by virtue of knowledge of their environments; they have an *Umwelt,* a kind of culture (Goodwin 1976; 1978). This is a major theme in the work of Maturana and Varela (1980; 1987).

Furthermore, there is cognitive closure in the sense that the organism lives in a self-sufficient and coherent world. These notions of closure are logical, not physical, concepts. They define properties of completeness and coherence (see Ho and Popp, this volume) that give the organism its subjective, individual properties despite that it is engaged in a continuous exchange of matter, energy, and information with its environment, hence its culture. It is interesting to note that we actually use the term culture for microorganisms or cells growing in a defined environment, the culture medium. Culture is that which sustains and enables — in this case growth and reproduction. I suggest that a bacterium, for instance, knows its environment in that it engages in discriminating actions upon specific aspects of the environment that allows it to sustain its own process, which is a life cycle. The dynamics of this process includes the known environment in which organism and environment define a single dynamic process. Nowhere are the implications of this general perspective more cogently and clearly drawn than in the work of Margulis (this volume) and in the Gaia hypothesis (Lovelock, this volume).

Cooperativity and process

The logical closure or coherence of the living state is what underlies the property of self-reproduction, as previously described in relation to catalytic closure. However, evolved organisms have developed a specialized structure as the locus for the storage and retrieval of the information required to make the catalytic and other polymers required for their reproduction, which is DNA. Nevertheless the whole organism, whether unicellular or multicellular, is required for the fulfilment of self-replication, and accurate replication of the DNA occurs only in a cellular context. So the principles of cooperative interaction still apply, and there are no autonomous naked replicators, no selfish genes. Furthermore, organisms reproduce by a cyclic process, not by a self-replicating event. Neo-Darwinism, however, uses an event ontology to describe life cycles by singling out the DNA as the vehicle of inheritance and regarding the generation of a new organism as the production of a new genotype, a singular event producing a singular entity. Consider, for example, the life cycle shown in Figure 10.1, that of the unicellular marine alga *Acetabularia acetabulum.* The cycle can be regarded as beginning with the fusion of two gametes, involving the coming together of two complements of DNA to give the diploid chromosome number of the zygote. The zygote then undergoes a developmental process, resulting in the adult form in which haploid gametes are again produced and released, and the cycle recommences. From a neo-Darwinian perspective the significant event is the production of the diploid genotype, from which development follows as a revelation, as Monod (1971) put it. That is to say, the causes of development are to be found in the DNA.

However, this is simply wrong, since an understanding of development requires much more than a knowledge of the information coded in DNA, as I have argued elsewhere, including the second Gaia conference (Goodwin 1989; 1985; 1990). The process of morphogenesis involves a distributed causality that is expressed by the field concept, in this case a *morphogenetic field.* This involves the participation of many components whose cooperative interplay results in the systematic and repeatable

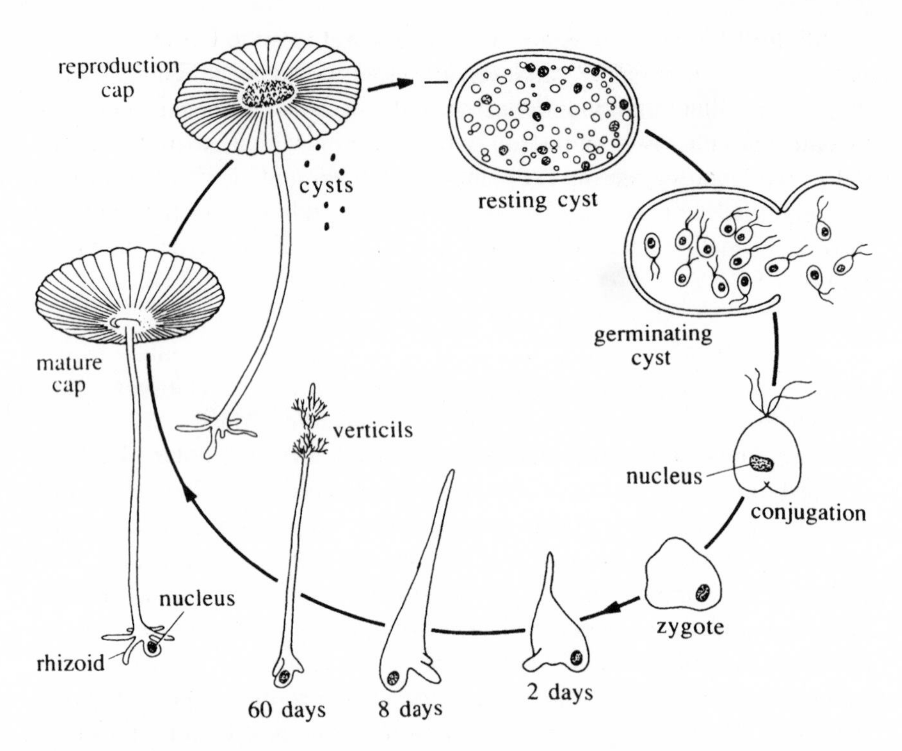

Figure 10.1. The life cycle of Acetabularia.

generation of a sequence of specific forms, resulting in the adult morphology. The detailed nature of this process as studied experimentally and by computer simulation in the case of *Acetabularia* was described in the previous conference proceedings, so I shall not repeat this here. What emerges from the analysis is an understanding of the nature of the morphogenetic process whereby the adult organism is generated. It is, technically, a moving boundary process in which geometry and dynamics are intimately linked in an unfolding of organismic form. The genotype is clearly involved in this but does not act as a 'central directing agency' (Webster and Goodwin 1982). Rather it is one of the components of the cooperative system, hence a memory storage and retrieval bank whose activity contributes to and stabilizes a particular morphogenetic trajectory that characterizes the species through specifying parameter values and initial conditions. The type of causality involved is immanent causation, in which the organism is both the cause and effect of itself. It undergoes change (process) in order to be itself, as Brady (1987) has vividly characterized these properties of organisms, elaborating on Goethe's dynamic vision of life. Organisms are not billiard balls knocked about by random mutation of the genome and shaped by natural selection. They are self-organizing processes of a particular type, engaged in characteristic patterns of transformation. This reinstates organisms as real entities in biology with the status of natural dynamic forms which are not reducible to a set of causes arising from their genomes and their environment. The latter define necessary but not sufficient conditions for the sequence of transformations that constitute a life cycle of the type shown in Figure 10.1.

Social dynamics

Moving up a scale from individual organisms to social order, the same contrast of description can be seen between a neo-Darwinian analysis and one based upon the cooperative interplay of elements that together constitute a higher-order system. Consider the case of social insects, such as ants. The predominant view as expressed by, for instance, E.O. Wilson (1968), is that colony structure and dynamics are determined by caste relations, each individual ant having its particular morphology and its role in the colony specified by a combination of its genotype and its environment (for example, the nutrient it receives during development). Colony organization is then reducible to these rigidly specified roles, which are in turn accounted for by genotype and environmental causes.

However, in the majority of ant species there is no rigid caste structure. Instead, individuals all have the same morphology and change roles both spontaneously and under perturbation. A very interesting example of experimental work that has painstakingly established the dynamic flexibility of colony organization is provided by Deborah Gordon's studies of harvester ants of the species *Pogonomyrmex barbatus.* She distinguished four categories of activity which she described as foraging, patrolling, nest maintenance, and midden work (Gordon 1983; 1986). By marking individuals in specific categories with a drop of paint, she could identify spontaneous changes of activity by individuals over the course of several days of observation (Gordon 1987). It also became apparent that there were preferred patterns of change, such as from midden work to foraging or nest maintenance, but rarely vice versa. Under perturbation, such as placing toothpicks near the nest entrance before the day's activities began, thus presenting nest maintenance workers with a major clean-up job, Gordon (1989a) observed more extensive patterns of role change that affected foragers and patrollers as well as the nest maintenance crew, numbers in different categories rising or falling in characteristic and repeatable ways. Evidently the colony is a dynamic unity rather than a mosaic of elements. Furthermore, old and young colonies display characteristically different stability to a given perturbation, older colonies being more stable (for instance, relaxing back towards normal numbers in the four categories more quickly after perturbation). Since an ant lives for a year whereas the colony can last up to ten years, we have here another high level property of the collective that cannot be accounted for by the properties of its components as separate entities. There is a cooperative emergence of behaviour that relates part to whole in an integrated mannner (Gordon 1989b). A model of the colony as a parallel distributed network of interacting units, similar to a neural network, describes how dynamic stability of the whole can arise from the interacting individuals (Gordon *et al.* 1992).

Another dramatic example of emergence of order in ant colonies is provided by the observations of Franks *et al.* (1990) and by Cole (1991) on the rhythmic activity patterns of ants of the genus *Leptothorax.* Cole showed that isolated ants, or groups at low density with few interactions, show chaotic patterns of activity-inactivity (i.e., they move on a strange attractor, characteristic of deterministic chaos). However, above a critical density this chaotic pattern undergoes a sudden transition to rhythmic order, a regular oscillation of activity-inactivity arising with a period of about 25 minutes. In the brood chamber, this results in a regular and reliable feeding and caring regime for the young.

A model of the ant colony as a network of interacting, individually chaotic individuals shows how this emergence of order occurs as a result of simple excitation between ants (Sole *et al.* 1993; Miramontes *et al.* 1993). Sociality and cooperative behaviour arise as a robust consequence of interactions whereby an active ant excites an inactive ant so that waves of activity propagate over the colony. At a critical density, characterized by maximum dynamic diversity (entropy), the colony develops coherent behaviour and becomes a superorganism, with its own level of autonomy. This provides another level in the hierarchy of emergent order that characterizes the cooperative, interactive dynamics of the living state. The organized properties of the emergent whole cannot be reduced to the dynamics of its parts (which in this case are chaotic), though it is possible to describe these as a result of a particular dynamic order in the system as a whole. The value of mathematical modelling and computer simulation is in revealing that the properties of the whole relate to, but cannot be dynamically decomposed into, the properties of the parts.

Biology and anthropology

I end with some thoughts on the implications for our understanding of the human condition deriving from a biology that recognizes the irreducible reality of levels of cooperative or collective behaviour in the evolution of life on earth. Recall that the organism, as previously described, is not reducible to the effects of its genes and environmental influences, regarded in neo-Darwinism as the sufficient causes of species and individual characteristics. The perspective developed here is that the organism is a dynamic form of a particular type, engaged in a process of transformation, its life-cycle. Genes and the environment contribute to this process in distinctive ways; but the organism is the locus of order and action that generates characteristic morphology during development from zygote to adult and characteristic patterns of behaviour in the adult, which are most evident in animals. Both morphogenesis and behaviour are examples of dynamic space-time forms that require the use of the field concept for their description and analysis. Fields are domains of relational order and distributed causality. A magnetic field, for example, is distributed in space with an intensity of field strength that varies according to a specific function of the intensity of neighbouring regions, defining a relational order. Morphogenetic fields embody physical, chemical and mechanical processes in distinctive ways that give rise to the characteristic forms of organisms (see for example, Goodwin 1990). Behavioural fields involve processes of perception, cognition, and action that generate characteristic patterns of activity in species, either at the level of the individual or the group, as described in the ant colonies.

The absence of any adequate concept of the organism from contemporary biology and its replacement by a set of genetic and environmental causes is what threatens the reality of the person in an anthropological context, and results in the sociobiological notion of the individual as a product of his or her genes and cultural influences (Wilson 1975). What this leaves out is the entire field of relations that intervene between an individual's inheritance and cultural influences on the one hand, and his or her behaviour on the other. This is equivalent to leaving out the morphogenetic field, the locus of relational order and transformational action that generates an organism of specific form. But what, for an individual, is this field of relations that generates individual behaviour? According to Ingold (1990), it is the nexus of social relations that the developing human organism has with other humans that defines the field from which the individual person emerges. This includes the processes of perception, cognition and action within the individual. Just as all aspects of the morphogenetic field need not be localized within the physical domain of the organism (for instance, electrical currents generated by *Acetabularia* in the sea-water in which it develops extend beyond the cell wall), so the behavioural field need not be localized within the individual. Language, for instance, has a distributed relational order that is only partially localized within individuals, existing as a structure among them in the social order. A biology centred on the reality of organisms as coherently transforming agents, both in development and in evolution, necessarily focusses on generative questions: how are we to understand the organisms we see about us as possible forms of life; thus, how are they generated, brought into existence? Neo-Darwinism with its focus on natural selection is, by contrast, preoccupied with persistence: how do the organisms we see about us survive? These are quite different questions, though the latter is in fact explained as part of any theory that answers the former, as I have argued elsewhere (Goodwin 1990).

Likewise, an anthropology based on persons requires a theory of sociality, that is, 'the generative properties of the relational field within which persons are situated' (Ingold 1990). This leads to a view of the connection between relationships and consciousness:

> ... sociality should be understood as the inherent, generative dynamic of a relational field. You will recall my earlier allusion to the concept of the morphogenetic field, defined as a domain in which each part of the living organism is given by its relations with neighbouring parts. To translate this concept into the terms of our current discussion, replace morphogenesis by the genesis of social form, and replace parts by persons. Then each person, developing in continuous contact with other persons in the social field, is constituted by his or her relations with those others. In organic life, every part enfolds every other person. A phrase that Strathern uses to describe a Melanesian conception captures perfectly what I have in mind: persons, she writes, 'contain a generalized sociality within.' The same analogy holds in the comparison of organic reproduction with the reproduction of social form. Just as in the organism, the whole can be reconstituted by a reverse unfolding from the part, so in social life the relational structures enfolded in the consciousness of the person may be reconstituted through their unfolding in purposive, social action. (Ingold 1990).

So we end up with a view of biology as the unfolding of generative potential, expressed in evolution as the emergence of progressively extended domains of relational order that embody cooperative interactions of components into coherent collectives. This clearly has strong resonances with the perspective on evolution described by Ho and Popp in this volume, though they proceed from a rather different starting point. As the evolutionary process unfolds, different levels of organization continue to express distinctive qualities of relational order so that emergent wholes do not dissolve parts into a new order; nor do the properties of parts exhaustively define the qualities of wholes. The interplay is cooperative and mutual. We are only beginning to learn the implications of these insights in relation to Gaia.

References

Bagley, R.J. and J.D. Farmer. 1992. Spontaneous emergence of metabolism. pp.93–140 in C.G. Langton, C. Taylor, J.D. Farmer and S. Rasmussen (eds). *Artificial Life II.* Reading. Mass: Addison-Wesley.

Bagley, R.J., J.D. Farmer and W. Fontana. 1992. Evolution of a metabolism. pp.141–58 in C.G. Langton, C. Taylor, J.D. Farmer, and S. Rasmussen (eds). *Artificial Life II.* Reading, Mass: Addison-Wesley.

Brady, R.H. 1987. Form and cause in Goethe's morphology. pp.257–300 in F. Amrine, F.T. Zucker, and H. Wheeler (eds). *Goethe and Science: Reappraisal.* Boston: Reidel.

Cole, B.J. 1991. Is animal behaviour chaotic? Evidence from the activity of ants. *Proc. Roy. Soc London* B 244:253–59.

Eigen, M. and P. Schuster. 1979. *The Hypercycle.* Berlin: Springer.

Emmet, D. 1984. *The Effectiveness of Causes.* London: Macmillan.

Fontana, W. 1992. Algorithmic Chemistry. pp 159–210 in C.G. Langton, C. Taylor, J.D. Farmer, and S. Rasmussen (eds). *Artificial Life II.* Reading, Mass: Addison-Wesley.

Fontana, W. and L. Buss. 1994. What would be conserved if 'The Tape Were Played Twice'? pp. 223–44 in *Complexity: Metaphors, Models, and Reality.* Reading, Mass: Addison-Wesley.

Fox, S. 1989. The changing face of natural selection. pp.41–52 in P. Bunyard and E. Goldsmith (eds). *Gaia and Evolution.* Wadebridge Ecological Centre.

Franks, N.R., S. Bryant, R. Griffith and L. Hemerik. 1990. Synchronisation of the behaviour within nests of the ant *Leptothorax acervorum. Bull. Math. Biol.* 52:597–612.

Goodwin, B.C. 1976. *Analytical Physiology of Cells and Developing Organisms.* London: Academic Press.

—— 1978. A cognitive view of biological process. *J. Social. Biol. Struct.* 1:117–25.

—— 1985. What are the causes of morphogenesis? *Bioessays* 3:32–36.

—— 1989. Gaia and Generation. *Proc. Second Camelford Conference.* pp.91–102.

—— 1990. Structuralism in biology. pp.227–44 in *Science Progress.* Oxford: Blackwell.

—— 1994. *How the Leopard Changed its Spots; the Evolution of Complexity.* London: Weidenfeld & Nicolson.

Gordon, D. 1983. Daily rhythms in social activities of the harvester ant. *Psycho* 90:413–23.

—— 1986. The dynamics of the daily round of the harvester ant colony *(Pogonomyrmex barbatus). Anim. Behav.* 34:1402–19.

—— 1987. Group-level dynamics in harvester ants: young colonies and the role of patrolling. *Anim. Behav.* 35:833–43.

—— 1989a. Dynamics of task switching in harvester ants. *Anim. Behav.* 38:194–204.

—— 1989b. Caste and change in social insects. *Oxford Surveys in Evolutionary Biology,* 6:55–72.

Gordon, D., L.E.H. Trainor, and B.C. Goodwin. 1992. A parallel distributed model of the behaviour of ant colonies. *J. Theoret. Biol.*

Ingold, T. 1990. An anthropologist looks at biology (Curl Lecture, 1989). *Man.* (NS) 25:208–29.

Kauffman, S.A. 1986. Autocatalytic sets of proteins. *J. Theoret. Biol.* 119:1–24.

Maturana, H. and F. Varela. 1987. *The Tree of Knowledge: the Biological Roots of Human Understanding.* Boston: New Science Library.

Miramontes, O., R.V. Sole and B.C. Goodwin. 1993. Collective behaviour of random-activated mobile cellular automata. *Physica.* D 63:145–60.

Monod, J. 1972. *Chance and Necessity.* London: Collins.

Scribner, N.Y., H. Maturana and F. Varela. 1980. *Autopoiesis and Cognition: The Realization of the Living.* Boston: Reidel.

Sheldrake, R. 1981. *A New Science of Life.* London: Blond & Briggs.

Sole, R.V., O. Miramontes and B.C. Goodwin. 1993. Oscillations and chaos in ant societies. *J. theoret. Biol.* 161:343–57.

Spiegelman, S. 1967. An *in vitro* analysis of a replicating molecule. *Am. Scient.* 55:221–64.

Webster, G.C., and B.C. Goodwin. 1982. The origin of species: a structuralist approach. *J. Soc. Biol. Struct.* 5:15–47.

Wilson, E.O. 1968. The ergonomics of caste in the social insects. *Amer. Natur.* 102:41–66.

—— 1975. *Sociobiology.* Harvard University Press.

– 11 –
Symbiosis and Individualism: Cooperation in Conflict

Jan Sapp

The contention that symbiosis was a primordial characteristic of life and a major source of evolutionary innovation was developed by various biologists during the early decades of the twentieth Century. These arguments found their ultimate expression in the frequent suggestion that all plant and animal cells are symbiotic complexes. Between 1905 and 1920 the Russian botanists, Konstanin Merezhkovsky developed the idea that chloroplasts, cell nuclei, and cytoplasm were symbiotic micro-organisms. Merezhkovsky (1920, 65) offered the term *symbiogenesis* for 'the origin of organisms by the combination or by the association of two or several beings which enter into symbiosis.' During the same period, the French biologist Paul Portier developed his theory that mitochondria were symbiotic bacteria. Portier's work culminated with his book, *Les Symbiotes* (1918) which was the cause of considerable controversy among leading biologists in France during the 1920s. The argument that mito-chondria were symbiotic bacteria was developed again by the American biologist, Ivan Wallin in his book, *Symbionticism and the Origin of Species* (1927). The symbiosis theories in each of these cases, were based on detailed comparative morphological and physiological studies of cell organelles, most prominently, chloroplasts and mitochondria. These views found few adherents. On the contrary, they were severely criticized, ridiculed or simply ignored as they fell between the cracks of the research programmes, theories and doctrines of the major biological disciplines. (Sapp 1991; 1994a; 1994b).

From the point of view of bacteriology and pathology, the idea that the energy-generating organelles of the cell mitochrondria and chloroplasts originated as symbiotic bacteria conflicted with the disease-causing attributes of these organisms. From the point of view of genetics, the idea that chloroplasts and mitochondria were symbionts relied on the assump-tion that these parts of the cell were bearers of hereditary properties comparable to the nucleus. Yet, this view conflicted with the predominant if not exclusive role assigned to nuclear genes in heredity. American geneticists claimed nuclear genes to be the 'governing elements,' largely immune from the rest of the cell and dictating its activities (see Sapp 1987). This view was solidified in the 'evolutionary synthesis' of the 1930s and 40s which was based on gene mutations and recombination as the sources of evolutionary innovation. It was not until the 1960s and 70s with the recognition that chloroplasts and mitochondria possess all the essential equipment for 'life' — DNA, transcription enzymes for making RNA, and a full protein synthesis apparatus — that the symbiotic theory re-emerged to occupy a prominent position in biological thought (Margulis 1981). In the twentieth century the principal evidence for the symbiotic origin of plant and animal cells shifted from physiological and morphological studies of cytoplasmic organelles to their genetics and detailed molecular structure.

Yet, symbiosis is an ecological concept. It is seldom recognized today, that the theory that symbiosis was a major source of evolutionary innovation was made as soon as the word symbiosis was coined in 1879 and the suggestion that plant and animal cells evolved from several symbiotic associations was discussed soon after. These theories were first raised when biologists attempted to systematize the functional relationships among organisms based on studies of what was often called the social life of lower plants and animals. The idea that such relations could lead to evolutionary change and the construction of new individuals emerged from detailed physiological studies of the association of algae and fungi in the formation of lichens, the presence of photosynthetic algae in animals, nitrogen-fixing bacteria in the root nodules of legumes, and studies of the fungus-root mycorrhizal associations. Some biologists saw in these associations evidence of cooperative relations which conflicted with the generally held beliefs about the parasitic role of such organisms. However, the scope and significance of such relationships became the subject of heated debate.

The theoretical limits of this dispute were framed by two widely divergent positions. At one extreme was the view that the above cases were illustrative of evolution in action: a means by which higher more specialized organisms could have evolved from lower less specialized ones. According to this view, relations in which organisms mutually furthered and supported one another was a phenomenon of wide occurrence. Such mutualistic symbiosis often led to permanent interdependence whereby the association was better enabled than any of the individual partners alone to enter into the struggle for existence. At the other extreme, many biologists continued to see in these relations, only the action of self-interested parasites and interpreted all organismic interactions in terms of conflict and competition. According to this view, stable associations involving reciprocal benefits rarely, if ever, occurred and interpretations of such phenomena in terms of mutual assistance could be dismissed as sentimentalism. It was in the context of this dominant belief in the exclusive parasitic role of microorganisms and in evolution by individual struggle that biologists discussed the meaning of symbiosis.

Evolution by association

When, in 1867 the Swiss botanist Simon Schwendener published his short paper putting forth his 'dual hypothesis' that all lichens were actually an association of a fungus and an alga, his suggestion was met with bitter opposition. Part of the reason for this resistance resulted from the kind of social imagery Schwendener employed. Lichens, he argued, represented a master-slave relationship. The fungus was the master; the green algae were the slaves. He went on to describe how the fungus envelopes its prey with a close network of threads which is gradually transformed into an impenetrable sheath. But whereas the spider sucks the blood out of its victim and only abandons it when it is dead, the fungus excites the algae taken in its web to greater activity and even more intense reproduction. It thus makes more vigorous growth possible and the whole colony develops well. The algae kept in slavery are transformed in a few generations to such a point that they are no longer recognizable. Schwendener's interpretation of lichens was an abomination to lichenologists. Lichenology had always been an esoteric pursuit, and the then leading lichenologists bitterly rejected a view which as the Reverend J.M. Crombie put it: 'pitilessly robbed their favourite Lichens of their independent existence and turned them by the stroke of a magician's wand into a spider-like tyrant Fungus and a captured and enslaved Alga.' (de Bary 1887, 418, Ainsworth 1976, 97).

Although the lichens lost their independent integrity forever, the portrayal of the association as a master-slave relationship was soon challenged. To many botanists, this interpretation seemed to be belied by Schwendener's own physiological studies of the fungus and alga in isolation. According to Schwendener, the alga brought about synthesis starting from the carbon dioxide of the air, the fungus brings to the alga water and the mineral salts of the soil. The relationship seemed to be much more equitable than Schwedener was prepared to admit. Moreover, parasitism implied some harm to the host organism. Yet, as the German botanist, Johannes Reinke (1873) pointed out, describing the relationship in terms of 'parasitism' was inconsistent with the long-continued healthy life of the associated organism. To Reinke, the relationship of the alga to the fungus was that of the leaves and roots of a green plant. He suggested the use of the term 'consortium' as a term to express the relationship.

Many botanists came to see in the lichen relationship the possibility of a more general phenomenon: associations between phylogenetically distinct organisms that ranged from the loosest to the most intimate and essential, and from the most antagonistic and one-sided to the most beneficial for the well-being of both associates. A neutral term was required that did not prejudge such relationships as parasitic. Therefore, in 1877, the botanist Albert Bernhard Frank (1839–1900) at Leipzig coined the word *symbiotismus*.

Frank carried out detailed studies of various kinds of symbiosis and became one of the chief advocates of the view that many associations involving microorganisms could not be labelled as parasitism. Though the word symbiosis began to be used extensively in the 1880s, the origin of the term was never attributed to Frank. It was attributed to the botanist Anton de Bary (1831–88), professor of botany, at the University of Strasbourg. De Bary was the editor of one of Germany's leading botanical journals: *Botanische Zeitung* and was well-known for his classic book, *Morphology and Physiology of the Fungi, Lichens and Myxomycetes* first published in 1866. De Bary introduced the term *symbiose* in an address entitled *The Phenomena of Symbiosis* delivered at a general meeting of the Association of German Naturalists and Physicians at Cassel in 1878.

De Bary included under this rubric various kinds of complex associations which ranged along a continuum from parasitic relations, to those in which the associates helped and supported each other. The latter he referred to as 'mutualism.' The term mutualism had been introduced into biology by the Belgian zoologist Pierre-Joseph van Beneden a few years earlier in a communication to the Royal Academy of Belgium. Van Beneden's lecture, 'A word on the Social Life of Lower Animals' (1873) was later elaborated in his popular book, *Les Commensaux et les Parasites* which was translated into German, and English, as *Animal Parasites and Messmates* (1876). In this text, van Beneden argued against the view, common in his day, that all intimate relations involving 'lower animals' living in or on 'higher animals' were parasitic. On the contrary, he argued that the kinds of social relations in animal societies were as varied as those found in human societies. Drawing on analogies from human societies, he classified the various social relations of lower animals in terms of 'parasitism,' 'commensalism' and 'mutualism.' 'The parasite,' van Beneden argued, 'is he whose profession it is to live at the expense of his neighbour, and whose only employment consists in taking advantage of him, but prudently, so as not to endanger his life.' (p.85). The commensal, on the other hand, 'is he who is received at the table of his neighbour to partake with him of the produce of his day's fishing ... The messmate does not live at the expense of his host; all that he desires is a home or his friend's superfluities.' (p.1). In referring to commensals (or messmates), van Beneden was thinking of various species of fish which swim alongside larger individuals from which they receive aid and protection, and crabs lodging among mussels which exchanged food for lodging. The mutualists, he added:

> are animals which live on each other, without being either parasites or messmates; many of them are towed along by others; some render each other mutual services, others again take advantage of some assistance which their companions can give them; some afford each other an asylum, and some are found which have sympathetic bonds which always draw them together. They are usually confounded with parasites or messmates (commensals). (p.68).

De Bary looked for analogous associations among plants. He described the case of blue-green algae, *Anabaena* living in symbiosis with a genus of small aquatic ferns, called *Azolla,* that float on the surface of freshwater ponds and marshes. Each leaf of *Azolla* is divided into a dorsal and ventral lobe. The ventral lobe floats on the water, and the blue-green algae live inside special sealed cavities of the leaves. De Bary noted that no stage of the life cycle of the fern was free of the algae and yet it was clear to him that the algae did no harm to the *Azolla.*

De Bary then referred to lichens that were: a form of vegetation comprising thousands of species, in which all the individuals present not only the association of two or three different species, but which are constituted only by this association.

In fact, de Bary offered mutualistic symbiosis as a mechanism of evolutionary innovation in addition to evolution by natural selection based on the accumulation of individual variations within populations of species. By the 1870s the presence of chlorophyll bodies had been recognized in about fifty different species of invertebrates, from protozoa to planarian worms and sea anemones. The main interest in these chlorophyll-containing animals lay in their bearing on the long-disputed relations between plants and animals; for neither locomotion nor irritability was particular to animals, and many insectivorous plants habitually digest solid food. This problem in turn led to the question of whether these green bodies were organisms of plant origin (algae) or originated as differentiated parts of the cytoplasm of the animals. It had long been usually assumed that this chlorophyll was an animal specific product endogenous in its nature: 'animal chlorophyll.' However, during the early 1880s it was shown that these chlorophyll granules could be forcibly removed from the animal and yet continue to live. As a result a number of biologists came to reject the hypothesis of 'animal chlorophyll' and assert that all these inclusions were examples of cooperative living of plant symbionts.

In November 1881, K. Brandt read a paper giving the results of a series of observations on the *Zusammenleben* of algae and animals before the Physiological Society of Berlin. For the algae found in the bodies of *hydra, spongilla, stentor,* he created the generic name *Zoochlorella.* For those in the 'yellow cells' which occur in the Radiolarians and sea anemones, he created the generic name *Zooxanthella.* Brandt experimentally demonstrated that these algae were capable of carrying on an independent existence after removal from the animal in which they were found, and were able to produce starch-grains. He examined the physiological function of the algae and found them to be of service to the host in supplying food. So long as the animal contained few or no green or yellow algae they were nourished, like true animals, by the absorption of solid organic substances; but as soon as they contained a sufficient quantity of these algae, they were nourished, like true plants, by assimilation of inorganic substances. In the latter case the algae living in the animals performed all the functions of the chlorophyll-bodies of plants. Finally, he compared the modes of life of these *phytozoa* (as he termed the animal which subsisted on the algae contained within them) with that of lichens. With the *phytozoa,* he remarked there was, however, this remarkable peculiarity, that while the alga might be morphologically the parasite, physiologically it was the animal that had the characteristics of a parasite.

This theory of 'reciprocal accommodation' was developed independently the same year by the British botanist Patrick Geddes, under the heading 'Symbiosis of alga and animals' read before the Medical Faculty of the University of Edinburgh in October 1881. Geddes published his paper in *Nature* in 1882 and called for further experimental investigation.

It was clear to Geddes that the incorporation of algae in animals was an evolutionary adaptation that would favour those animals which possessed them:

> And if there be any parasitism in the matter, it is by no means of the algae upon the animal, but of the animal, like the fungus, upon the alga. Such an association is far more complex than that of the fungus and alga in the lichens, and indeed stands unique in physiology as the highest development, not of parasitism, but of reciprocity between the animal and vegetable kingdom. (Geddes 1882, 304f).

These examples of cooperative living were soon allied with another striking example of mutualism: microorganisms living in the root tubercles of *Leguminosae*. The benefit which the leguminosae exerted on the soil had been known since ancient times, and Justus von Liebig showed that it was based on an increase of nitrogen. By the end of the 1880s tubercules containing nitrogen-fixing bacteria had been found on nearly all the leguminosae.

The root tubercles of legumes were regarded as functionally analogous to the mycorrhizae, an association between fungi at the roots of high plants. The presence of fungi on the roots of trees had been known since the middle of the century, but they had commonly been supposed to be of a parasitic nature. However, during the middle of the 1880s the hypothesis was put forward that this relationship like the others mentioned above was of mutual assistance. This theory was developed principally by A.B. Frank who in 1885 coined the word 'mycorrhiza' for the fungus roots. Frank began these studies at the instigation of the German State Forestry Department in connection with a scheme for the development of truffle culture in Prussia. Truffles were known to be associated with certain broad-leaved trees and this association was commonly supposed to be parasitic in nature. Frank investigated the relationship of the fungi which he found regularly infecting and frequently distorting the roots of forest trees including oaks, beech and conifers. He suggested that the fungus was a functional substitute for the root hairs through bringing to the plant both mineral salts and organic nitrogenous food from the humus. The plant, for its part, would yield carbohydrates, while the endotrophic fungus would make a final contribution to the nutrition of the plant by being digested by it and thus providing it with nitrogenous matter.

By the end of the 1880s, it was clear to many of those who studied these intimate associations that one could detect as de Bary put it:

> every conceivable gradation ... between the parasitism which quickly destroys its victim and that in which parasite and host

> mutually and permanently further and support one another — the relation which is most conspicuous in the formation of Lichens and which van Beneden has termed *mutualism.* (1887, 369).

However, not all biologists agreed that these organisms were 'mutually and permanently furthering and supporting one another.' Many believed that there were few if any cases in which plants living in or on another could do other than pay-back advantages they gained by an ill-turn. For them permanent mutualistic symbiosis, if it ever occurred in the 'Vegetable Kingdom' was rare, and the notion of *mutual support* was better understood in terms of *mutual exploitation.*

The politics of mutualism

> Don't compete! Competition is always injurious to the species, and you have plenty of resources to avoid it! That is the *tendency* of nature, not always realized in full, but always present. That is the watchword which comes to us from the bush, the forest, the river, the ocean. Therefore combine — practise mutual aid! That is the surest means of giving to each and to all the greatest safety, the best guarantee of existence and progress, bodily, intellectual, and moral. (Kropotkin 1902, 62).

Although de Bary and other biologists borrowed the term mutualism from van Beneden, the term had its roots in social theory and political movements of the 1860s. It emerged in direct opposition to *laissez-faire* economic theory and individual struggle and competition leading to natural and social progress. Historians of biology have argued forcefully that natural history during the second half of the nineteenth century was often characterized by attempts to embed socio-political theory securely in the 'objectivity' of nature. The use of natural law as the basis for a given view of society became commonplace in social, political and economic theory, and the Darwinian theory of evolution was often employed as a new, powerful justification for industrial capitalism.

In *The Origin of Species,* Darwin devoted considerable time to studying such mutualisms as insects pollinating flowers and he mentioned the dispersal of mistletoe seeds by birds, yet his fundamental ecological and evolutionary thinking was that adaptation and speciation could be explained by individual competition. In effect the notion of progress through struggle found its biological basis in *The Origin,* and for nineteenth century intellectuals, struggle and competition as basic elements of the universe were elaborated in both the natural and social realms, and indeed, most (including Darwin) saw no fundamental difference between them. Leading intellectuals such as Herbert Spencer in England championed *laissez-faire* and individualism, believing that the final result of competition is an increasing integration of all members of society into a differentiated, more integrated, and efficient social organism. This differentiation, like the development of an individual organism, led inevitably to a higher state of society, in which violent competition (for example, war) was replaced by the peaceful competition of the free-market. Thus competition was ultimately the source of human progress, and as such was the main characteristic of what is usually called 'Social Darwinism.'

While competition and progress-through-struggle were dominant themes of both natural and social science in the nineteenth century an undercurrent of political and intellectual opposition developed in concert. In Britain, various associations such as trade unions, Chartism and the 'Friendly Societies' were formed to allow workers to deal with catastrophes such as illness or funerals. The analogous organizations in France were the mutual aid associations. Beginning in the period of the Revolution, the different *Mutualité* societies were a hot bed of socialist ideas, and provided the inspiration for the development of revolutionary socialism. French *mutuellisme's* most famous exponent was Pierre-Joseph Proudhon, a young working-class student who became famous for his book *What is Property?* which he answered simply 'property is theft.' Proudhon is recognized today as a founder of socialist and anarchist movements.

Proudhon denounced political revolution as unnecessary and even dangerous to liberty. Instead, he believed that the path to socialism could be blazed through the development of a system of mutual credit, through which workers could borrow the funds to amass capital and create cooperatives which would eventually replace capitalism. In short, Proudhon's idea of socialism was one of just and equal exchange, made possible by eliminating unfair advantage of the capitalists which came from their inheritance of property. Mutual credit would allow workers to produce on equal terms with capitalists, since the accumulated wealth would disappear, credit would be freely available to all.

In this context van Beneden introduced the term mutualism to the Royal Academy of Belgium in 1873 (Boucher 1985). Van Beneden drew on analogies of industry, human social relations and morality from human society to describe the social relations, he saw in nature. For example, when making analogies between the 'lower animals' and human societies, he compared the high living of certain industrialists to the life of parasites (van Beneden 1876, xvii).

Yet, van Beneden was a Catholic with deep religious convictions. His mutualisms were tinged equally with ideas from natural theology; they were examples of perfect adaptations created by the divine wisdom of God (p.xxvi). Natural theology had a long history and developed in direct opposition to the views of the seventeenth century political theorist Thomas Hobbes who in his famous political treatise, *The Leviathan* of 1651, represented the state of nature as a war of each against all. Hobbes argued that without a powerful government, an almighty Leviathan to restrain human life, men would live as animals without virtue and morality, without agriculture, arts and letters. However, as Worster (1977, 45) has argued, natural theology led by Linnaeus implicitly accepted the assumptions underlying the Hobbesian view, but argued that Nature did in fact have laws which prevented such disorder and disharmony. The Creator, they argued, had established a vast system of subordination to assure peace in the natural world. Each species had been assigned a fixed place in a social hierarchy or scale of being. The infinitude of species ranged in an ascending ladder of nobility, therefore, was more than a taxonomic system; it was also a description of ecological relatedness. The chain of being was a system of economic interdependence and mutual assistance. Even the most exalted creatures must depend upon those lower on the scale for their existence, man and worms alike live to preserve each other's life. All these views have been made explicit in van Beneden's *Animal Parasites and messmates.*

Among evolutionists, mutualism was posited either explicitly or implicitly in direct opposition to a belief in evolutionary progress resulting from a pitiless struggle for individual advantage. This view was prominent in the writings of the Russian anarchist, Prince Peter Kropotkin which culminated in his book *Mutual Aid.*

Kropotkin's book was based on a series of articles he published, beginning in 1880, in the widely read magazine, *The Nineteenth Century.* They were written in response to an article published by one of England's leading evolutionary authorities, Thomas Huxley. In 1888, Huxley issued what Kropotkin called his 'Struggle for Life' manifesto: 'Struggle for Existence and its bearing upon Man.' From the point of view of the moralist Huxley wrote:

> the animal world is on about the same level as the gladiators show. The creatures are fairly well-treated, and set to fight;

> whereby the strongest, the swiftest, and the cunningest live to fight another day.

Huxley continued, that as among animals so among men,

> the weakest and stupidest went to the wall, while the toughest and shrewdest, those who were best fitted to cope with their circumstances survived. Life was a free fight, and beyond the limited and temporary relations of the family, the Hobbesian war of each against all was the normal state of existence. (quoted in Kropotkin 1902, 13).

Kropotkin strongly opposed the central assumptions underlying this Hobbesian view, and argued that evolutionary progress in both animal and human societies could never emerge by a bitter competitive struggle between organisms. For him, the basis of human social relations and behaviours resulted from evolution. If humans were inherently co-operative as he believed them to be, then cooperative behaviour itself was an important progressive element in organic evolution. Kropotkin argued that both the meaning and extent of the struggle for existence in evolution had been exaggerated, while the importance of sociability and social instincts in animals for the well-being of the species and community had been underrated.

In *The Origin of Species,* Darwin had insisted that the term 'struggle for existence' be used in its 'large and metaphorical sense including dependence of one being on another, and including (which is more important) not only the life of the individual, but success in leaving progeny' (Darwin 1859, 62). Yet, as Kropotkin recognized, Darwin himself chiefly used the term in its narrow sense. Following publication of *The Origin,* a mass of facts were gathered for the purpose of illustrating a real competition for life. The concept of struggle became narrower still when Herbert Spencer and his followers 'raised the 'pitiless' struggle for personal advantage to the height of a biological principle which man must submit to as well' (Kropotkin 1902, 13). Yet, sociability, Kropotkin argued, was as much a law of nature as mutual struggle, and it would be difficult to estimate the relative numerical importance of both.

However, Kropotkin's discussions of mutualism were primarily concerned with cooperation within species rather than between species as discussed by botanists: herding instincts of deer against a common foe, the colonies built by termites and ants. As he put it, 'The ants and the termites have renounced the "Hobbesian war" and they are the better for it.' (p.20) Nonetheless, his opposition to Darwinists' claims illustrates well the general context in which cases of symbiosis were discussed and understood by biologists of the late nineteenth century. Indeed, one cannot exaggerate the extent to which exponents of Darwin's views maintained the notion of a pitiless struggle for individual profit.

The Hobbesian plant community

The examples of mutualistic symbiosis as represented by lichens, mycorrhizal fungus, bacteria in the root nodules of leguminosae, and algae in invertebrates were posited either implicitly or explicitly in virtual conflict with evolution in terms of organisms competing and dominating each other in a ruthless struggle for existence. The idea that the above cases of symbioses were mutualistic faced severe criticism. Instead all apparent examples of mutualism had to be brought into line with parasite-host relations. The views of American botanist Roscoe Pound (1893) were representative of this attitude:

> Ethically, there is nothing in the phenomena of symbiosis to justify the sentimentalism they have excited in certain writers. Practically, in some instances, symbiosis seems to result in mutual advantage. In all cases it results advantageously to one of the parties, and we can never be sure that the other would not have been nearly as well off, if left to itself. (Roscoe Pound 1893, 521).

In the late nineteenth century, Pound and his co-workers, including Charles Bessey and Frederick Clements were engaged in an effort to introduce experimental methods and quantification into botany. After collaborating with Clements on the phytogeography of Nebraska, Pound gave up science and went into law. Eventually, he became Dean of the Harvard Law School and a founder of the sociological school of jurisprudence (Glueck 1965). Pound was a Quaker, he opposed the Welfare state but welcomed the co-operation of churches and fraternal organizations with the courts, saying:

> This cooperation of organized religion and organized morality with the law is the more gratifying, because if individual, self-reliant, free enterprise has been an American characteristic *cooperation* has not.

Cooperation was not a characteristic of nature either, or at least, not of plant communities. Pound dismissed interpretations which suggested that symbiotic associations involved cooperation. Symbiosis, he argued, was simply a name for the living together of parasite and host. All apparent examples of cooperation in plants were only that: apparent — they were the result of individual self-interested parasites. One of the associates always dominated, and if the other associate benefited, it did so at a price. It was crucial therefore, to understand the cost as well as the benefits accruing to the associates:

> There is a sort of mutualism between man and wheat, for example. Wheat is cultivated by man and enabled to grow in quantities, and in localities which, under ordinary conditions, would be impossible. It gains this partial exemption from the struggle for existence only at the expense of an immense number of individuals sacrificed, but it is, nevertheless, a great advantage which it gains. This may be called mutualism. (p.509).

Pound made similar arguments for the relationship between alga and fungus represented by lichens. If the colony of algae benefited by protection, as he assumed they did, it was at a cost of many lives of algae that were attacked by the fungus. In the vegetable kingdom there were no exemptions from the struggle for existence between organisms. Pound was especially critical of the interpretations and claims of Frank. As mentioned earlier, during the 1880s Frank devoted his work to the study of lichens, mycorrhiza, and nitrogen-fixing bacteria. In each of these cases, he saw more examples of cooperation and began to offer interpretations other than in terms of conflict and instability. In some cases, Frank argued, one organism benefited another without receiving anything in return, and without it being harmed in any way. For example, in the case of mycorrhiza, Frank argued that the fungus attached itself to roots of the trees 'without the former being parasitically affected or its vital phenomena disturbed.' In the case of nitrogen-fixing bacteria, Frank again offered an interpretation other than parasitism. He postulated that the *Leguminosae* possessed the power of attracting the bacteria owing to a response to some secretion. Finally, in the case of some species of lichens, Frank argued that some species of algae had become so adapted to life in lichens and so accustomed to it, that they have partially or wholly lost the power of independent growth.

Frank's 'claims' and 'assertions,' in Pound's view were simply bogus, and he ridiculed Frank's interpretations regarding mutualistic symbiosis as 'decidedly fishy' (p.514). Pound rejected any suggestions that such cases could result in perfect reciprocity leading to the formation of complete inseparable interdependence. For example, regarding lichens, it was well-known that the algae could be separated from the lichen, and that they would then vegetate in the ordinary way independently. That was one of the arguments that the fungus was parasitic and not the algae. He denied that any examples of dependent algal species were known (p.513). He also denounced Frank's claim that mycorrhiza benefited trees without gaining anything in return. The idea of such an organism giving without receiving was too much to take. This, he wrote, was merely one of 'Frank's statements calculated to try our patience and credulity' (p.515). Instead, Pound supported the claims of other more 'sober' writers who argued that mycorrhizal fungi did no benefit to the trees and orchids they infected: on the contrary, he argued, they were 'probably injurious by taking nourishment properly belonging to the tree' (p.516).

Finally, Pound dismissed Frank's suggestion that the roots of the *Leguminosae* possess the power of attracting the bacteria through some secretion. Instead, he argued that the bacteria were parasites: 'They are there for their own purposes, and are incidentally beneficial to the plant' (p.519). Bacteria, algae and fungi were thieves; if their hosts gained any advantage from them, it did so only at a price.

Similar views were expressed in the writings of other leaders of the new science of ecology including the Danish botanist, Eugenius Warming:

> The plant-community is the lowest form; it is merely a congregation of units in which there is no cooperation for the common weal but rather a ceaseless struggle of all against all. (Eugenius Warming, *Oecology of Plants,* 1909, 349).

In the history of ecology, Warming is recognized for producing one of the key syntheses that forced the scientific world to take note of this new field. His classic work, *Plantesamfund* was first published in 1895 and then in 1909 was revised and translated into English as *Oecology of Plants: An Introduction to the Study of Plant Communities.* Although Warming's book was devoted to an understanding of plant communities, discussions of 'symbiosis' occupied nine pages of the 373 pages of the main body of the text. Even then, he used the term to embrace the various kinds of bonds of various strengths — from the intimate to the loosest and most casual — that can hold individuals and species together to form communities. Thus in a section entitled 'The Communal Life of Organisms,' Warming discussed the relations of parasite with host, master with slave, mutualists, epiphytes and saprophytes. In his view these various types of symbiosis were 'not sharply delimited from one another' (p.84). Like Pound, he understood most intimate associations in terms of parasite-host interactions, and doubted that mutualism characterized by complete reciprocity of benefit between plants ever existed. However, his interpretations of the various well-known cases differed. For example, Warming viewed lichens as representing the exact opposite to mutualism. Following Schwedener, he viewed it as case of slavery and he classified it as 'Helotism.'

In the few paragraphs devoted to 'mutualism,' Warming mentioned mycorrhiza, the symbiosis of leguminosae and bacteria, and blue-green algae living in special cavities in the underside of the leaves of *Azolla,* as well as *cyanophycae* which enter the roots of *Cycads.* However, like Pound, Warming found it difficult to believe that one organism could benefit another without profiting in return. If fungi aided forest trees, if bacteria aided *Leguminosae,* they also had to profit from this association. Why else would they enter the roots? For Warming such apparently stable and cooperative relations were exceptions to the normal behaviour in plant communities.

Warming attributed the principles for understanding the complex relations between species to Darwin:

> Organisms were never at peace with one another ... This struggle is caused by endeavour on the part of species to extend their area of distribution by the aid of such means of migration as they possess. (1909, 83, 349).

He recognized that this struggle would be less intense between species which differ widely in the demands they make for light, heat, nutrients and so on. Thus he argued:

> the case is quite conceivable in which the *one species should require exactly what the other would avoid;* the two species would then be complementary to one another in their occupation and utilization of the same soil (p.94).

The best plants could do for one another was to protect others from the elements, as for example when a larger shrub serves to shelter a smaller one from the wind. 'In the plant-community,' Warming asserted, 'egoism reigns supreme' (p.95).

Making new individuals

Warming could not see symbiosis as an importance source of evolutionary innovation, nor see how it could lead to the emergence of new adaptations, new structures nor to wholly new organisms. However, for the few botanists who investigated mutualistic symbiosis among lower plants and believed that such cooperation was of wide occurrence, it was clear that mutualistic symbiosis could lead to highly specialized morphological and physiological changes and result in new and 'higher' organic forms that were better able to survive in a struggle for existence than any of their component symbionts. Indeed, it was possible that this process had led to the evolution of all plants and animals. The argument, that symbiosis had led to evolution, was highly developed in the nineteenth century by botanist, Albert Schneider at the University of Illinois:

> The morphological changes accompanying the functional relationships may be very marked or scarcely perceptible, nor is the adaptation quantitatively and qualitatively equal for all the symbionts. The adaptation is rather complementary, one organism supplies a deficiency (morphological or physiological) of the others. Theoretically there is no limit to the degree of specialization and perfection that this form of symbiosis may attain. In fact, mutualistic symbiosis implies that there is a higher specialization and greater fitness to enter into the struggle for existence. (Schneider 1897, 940).

In his view, equating symbiosis and societies or communities as Warming did, only confused the nature of the phenomena of symbiosis as biologists had come to understand them. Although both societies and symbiosis were evident of biological interdependence, the general difference was that in the former the interdependence was remote whereas in the latter it involved a physiological relationship. Through limiting the phenomena to prolonged contiguous associations, Schneider saw in symbiosis a branching series of relationships from various kinds of symmetrical and asymmetrical antagonism, to various kinds of mutualism and ultimately leading — in a phylogenetic sense — to complete dependence of both associates into the construction of new complete individuals. In antagonistic symbiosis or parasitism, the morphological and physiological specializations and adaptations were limited. While one of the symbionts may benefit, the other will be injuriously affected.

> Antagonist symbiosis is therefore a destructive association. The morphological and physiological changes tend toward dissolution rather than evolution. It is a change from the higher to the lower, hence a katabolic change. (1897, 936).

However, antagonistic symbiosis could be converted to mutualistic symbiosis. This, he believed occurred early in the phylogeny of the relationship. In terms of evolutionary innovation, mutualistic symbiosis was a phenomenon of wide occurrence and in many instances it reached a high degree of morphological and physiological specialization resulting in organisms that were more fit for a struggle for existence. This was most beautifully illustrated for him in the case of lichens. These plants, he argued, were of wider distribution and possessed greater vitality and physiological activity than either of the symbionts. Schneider also accepted the idea that one organism could benefit another without reciprocity. He designated this 'one-sided mutualism,' 'nutricism': 'a form of symbiosis in which one symbiont nourishes the second symbiont without receiving any benefit in return' (p.940). The case of mycorrhiza was a classic example:

> The function of the fungus is to supply the tree with food-substances and moisture taken from the soil. It also supplants the function of the hair-cells which are wanting in the mycorrhiza. It has been proved, experimentally, that the tree is greatly benefited, while no evidence could be found to indicate that the fungus is benefited (p.941).

The root-tubercles of the *Leguminosae* provided Schneider with a further example of an evolutionary morphological change resulting from what he considered to be a mutualistic symbiosis. The tubercles he argued were 'neoformations' induced by the bacteria which grow and multiply in the parenchyma cells. The bacteria take their food supply directly from the cell contents of the host. In return, the latter receives nitrogen compounds formed by the bacteria in the process of binding the free nitrogen of the air. Schneider distinguished these cases of mutualistic symbiosis in which both associates could lead independent existences, from those in which one or all the symbionts were permanently dependent. The latter, he designated as 'individualism.'

Semi-individualism was represented in the 'lower lichens' in which the algal symbiont was capable of leading an independent existence, while the fungus could not. It was possible that the root-tubercles of *Leguminosae* was another example.

Nonetheless, referring to Frank's work he argued:

> Some recent experiments would however, lead me to believe that the algae likewise have lost the power to continue independent existence. ... Lichens would therefore form complete individualism. (p.944).

He further suggested that some of the cases of algae living in lower animals such as *hydra* may also represent complete individualism. Based on this reasoning Schneider speculated that:

> Future studies may demonstrate that the cell, and hence the individual, is neither more nor less than complete individualism. The plasmic bodies, as chlorophyll granules, leucoplastids, chromoplastics, chromosomes, centrosomes, nucleoli, etc. are perhaps simply the symbionts comparable to those in the less highly specialized symbiosis (1897, 944).

The suggestion that cellular bodies such as chromosomes, centrosomes and plastids were symbionts was not the unique insight of Schneider. On the contrary, such ideas peppered discussions of the nature of plant and animal cells during the 1880s and 1890s. As cytologists brought forward evidence of various self-reproducing bodies in the cell, they merged these results with those of lichens and algae living in 'lower animals.' The idea that chloroplasts were symbiotic microorganisms was first suggested by Johannes Reinke and A.F.W. Schimper (1882). The idea that mitochondria were microorganisms was suggested first by Richard Altmann in 1890. The contention that the nucleus, the cytoplasm of the cell were symbiotic microorganisms was put forward first by Shôsaburô Watasé (1892) and by Theodor Boveri (1904). We thus have important precedents to modern theories of symbiosis' role in evolution, not least to the serial endosymbiosis theory of cell evolution.

References

Altmann, R. 1890. *Die Elementarorganismen und ihre Beziehungen zu den Zellen.* Leipzig.

Ainsworth, G.C. 1976. *Introduction to the History of Mycology.* Cambridge University Press.

Boucher, Douglas. 1985. The Idea of Mutualism, Past and Future. In D.H. Boucher (ed). *The Biology of Mutualism.* London: Croom Helm.

Boveri, Th. 1904. *Ergennisse uber die Konstitution der chromatischen Kernsubstance.* Jena. p.90.

Brandt, K. 1881. Über das Zusammenleben von Algen und Tieren. *Biologisches Centralblatt* 1.

Bary, Anton de. 1879a. Die Erscheinung der Symbiose. Vortrag auf der *Versammlung der Naturforsher und Ärzte zu Cassel.* Strassburg.

—— 1879b. De la Symbiose. *Revue Internationale des Sciences.* 3:301–9

—— 1887. *Comparative Morphology and Biology of the Fungi Mycetozoa and Bacteria.* Oxford: The Clarendon Press.

Beneden, Pierre-Joseph van. 1873. Un Mot sur la Vie Sociale des Animaux Inférieurs. *Bulletin de l'Académie Royale de Belgique.* Serie 2. 36:779–96.

—— 1876. *Animal Parasites and Messmates.* London: Henry King.

Famintsin, A. 1907. Die Symbiosis als Mittel der Synthese von Organismen. *Biologische Centralblatt.* 27:23–364.

Frank, A.B. 1877. Über die biologischen Verhältnisse des Thallus einiger Krustenflechten. *Beitrage zur Biologie der Pflanzen.* 2:123–200. p.195

—— 1886a. Über die auf Wurzelsymbiose beruhende Ernährung gewisser Bäume durch unterirdische Pilze. *Berichte der deutschen botanischen Gesselschaft.* 6:128–45.

—— 1886b. Neue Mitteilungen über die Mycorrhize der Bäume und der *Monotropa hypopitys. Berichte der deutschen botanischen Gesellschaft.* 6:27–37.

—— 1887. Über neue Mykorriza-formen. *Berichte der deutchen botanischen Gesellschaft* 5:395–409.

Geddes, P. 1882. Researches on animals containing chlorophyll. *Nature.* 25:363.

Green, J. Reynolds. 1909. *A History of Botany 1860–1900.* Oxford: Clarendon.

Kropotkin, Peter. 1902. *Mutual Aid. A factor of Evolution.* Reprinted 1914. Boston: Extending Horizons.

Margulis, Lynn. 1981. *Symbiosis in Cell Evolution.* San Francisco: Freeman.

Merezhkovsky, K. 1920. La plante considérée comme un complexe symbiotique. *Bulletin de la Societe des Sciences Naturelles.* 6:17–98.

Portier, Paul. 1918. *Les Symbiotes.* Paris: Masson.

Pound, Roscoe. 1893. Symbiosis and Mutualism. *The American Naturalist.* 27:509–20.

Reed, Howard S. 1942. *A Short History of the Plant Sciences.* Chronica Botanica.

Reinke, J. 1873. Zur Kenntniss des Rhizoms von *Corallorhiza* und *Epipogon. Flora.* 31:145, 161, 177, 209.

Sapp, Jan. 1987. *Beyond the Gene: Cytoplasmic Inheritance and the Struggle for Authority in Genetics.* New York: Oxford University Press.

—— 1991. Symbiosis in Evolution: An Origin Story. *Endocytobiosis and Cell Research.* 7:5–36

—— 1994a. Symbiosis and Disciplinary Demarcations: The Boundaries of the Organism. *Symbiosis.* 17:91–115.

—— 1994b. *Evolution by Association: A History of Symbiosis.* New York: Oxford University Press.

Schimper, A.F.W. 1833. Über die Entwicklung der Chlorophyllkorner und Farbkorper. *Botanische Zeitung.* 41:105–14.

Schneider, A. 1897. The Phenomena of Symbiosis. *Minn. Botanical Studies* 1:923–48.

Schwendener, S. 1867. Über den Bau des Flechtenthallus. *Verhandlung Schweizerischen Naturforschung Gesellschaft Aarau.* 88–90.

Wallin, I.E. 1927. *Symbionticism and the Origin of Species.* Baltimore: William & Wilins.

Watasé, S. 1893. *On the Nature of Cell Organization.* Woods Hole Biological Lectures.

Warming, E. 1909. *Oecology of Plants. An Introduction to the Study of Plant-Communities.* Oxford: Clarendon.

Worster, D. 1977. *Nature's Economy. A History of Ecological Ideas.* Cambridge University Press.

– 12 –
We are all Symbionts

Lynn Margulis, Ricardo Guerrero and Peter Bunyard

Symbiosis has been the spur to evolution by bringing about novel combinations that enable organisms to pioneer and generate new habitats. We see similar breakthroughs in science. The combination of phase contrast microscopy and image-enhancing techniques from remote scanning space satellite research enable the scientist of today to look at living images from within the cell at the very limits of light microscope resolution. The highly dynamic, ever-changing but highly structured interior of the cell is now revealing the importance of the symbiotic theory as the foundation of the eukaryotic, hence nucleated, cell.

Bacteria apart, all organisms, absolutely all, are the result of an association of several individual organisms, which came together in the distant past, are united by physical proximity, have pooled their genes and have given rise to complex organisms with increasing powers. Thus, eukaryotic cells, almost without exception, contain organelles such as mitochondria, that we now know were derived from free-living bacteria. Indeed, mitochondria have their own DNA, their own time for division and in mammals like us are passed on during human reproduction through the female line, since none accompany the sperm. If eukaryotes evolved as fused beings in what sense are they 'individuals'? Add on the countless bacteria in the gut and other passageways that serve to maintain a healthy organism and you have a composite individual, made up of ancestral symbiotic associations that have become permanently interwoven, with the fate of both or more symbionts contingent one on the other. Some symbiotic associations are looser whereby the boundaries of each organism and its cell(s) remain well defined and distinguishable.

Without question symbiotic associations of the past aeons, and in particular of the bacteria-dominated Archaean have been prime motors of evolution, supplemented by random mutations, as all symbionts, whether in combination or unassociated, are acted upon by natural selection. Symbiosis, defined as the living together of member organisms of different species, thus puts at the disposition of the new-combined organism a quantity of strange genes, which characterize distinct and occasionally even advantageous properties. Such a symbiotic combination favours the composite organism's survival relative to its uncombined 'parents' in a changing environment.

Today we have come to recognize that symbiosis is not just a curiosity, exemplified by the bizarre associations between fungi and algae or bacteria that spawn such strange excrescrences as the British soldier lichen, *Cladonia cristatella,* with its upright knobbly form compared to the fuzzy, slimy nature of its contituent bionts, the *Cladonia* fungus and the alga *Trebouxia.* Rather symbiosis is centre stage in the evolution of nucleated organisms and without it no animal or plant would exist.

Symbioses are continuous interactions, with actual physical contact between two or more organisms. They may become obligatory such that a new more complex being forms by 'symbiogenesis.' *Symbiogenesis* (or *symbionticism)* are names given to the evolutionary process that entails permanent physical contact between two or more symbionts such that a new individual emerges.

Nearly a century ago, in the early 1900s, various Russian biologists began to emphasize the role of symbiosis in evolution. Andrei Sergeivich Famintzin (1835–1918) experimented with the isolation and growth of chloroplasts from plant cells. Konstantin Sergeivich Merezhkovsky (1855–1921) followed such work by developing his 'two-plasm' (cell-within-a-cell) theory whereby he claimed that chloroplasts originated from what were then called 'blue-green algae,' but which today are known as cyanobacteria. He observed that chloroplasts, standard organelles inside plant cells, simply split in the manner of bacteria to reproduce independently of the nucleus and therefore of 'mitotic' cell division. It was Merezhkovsky who invented the term *symbiogenesis* meaning the origin of new beings through symbiosis. In the United States I.E. Wallin — independent of Merezhkovsky — stated his principle of *symbionticism* in 1927, in which he stressed the importance of obligate bacterial symbioses in the origin of species. Far ahead of his time, he proposed that mitochondria, like chloroplasts, had an exogenous origin. His ideas were ignored.

The idea of symbiosis as source of evolutionary novelty, banished from mainstream neo-Darwinist dogma on the origin of species, has in recent years received a great fillip in discoveries that chloroplasts have their own DNA which resembles that found in living cyanobacteria far more than it does that of the eukaryote nucleus. In 1966, mitochondria were found to possess bacteria-like DNA, similar to that in certain purple non-sulphur bacteria capable of aerobic respiration.

What kind of organism first sheltered these various bacterial intruders?

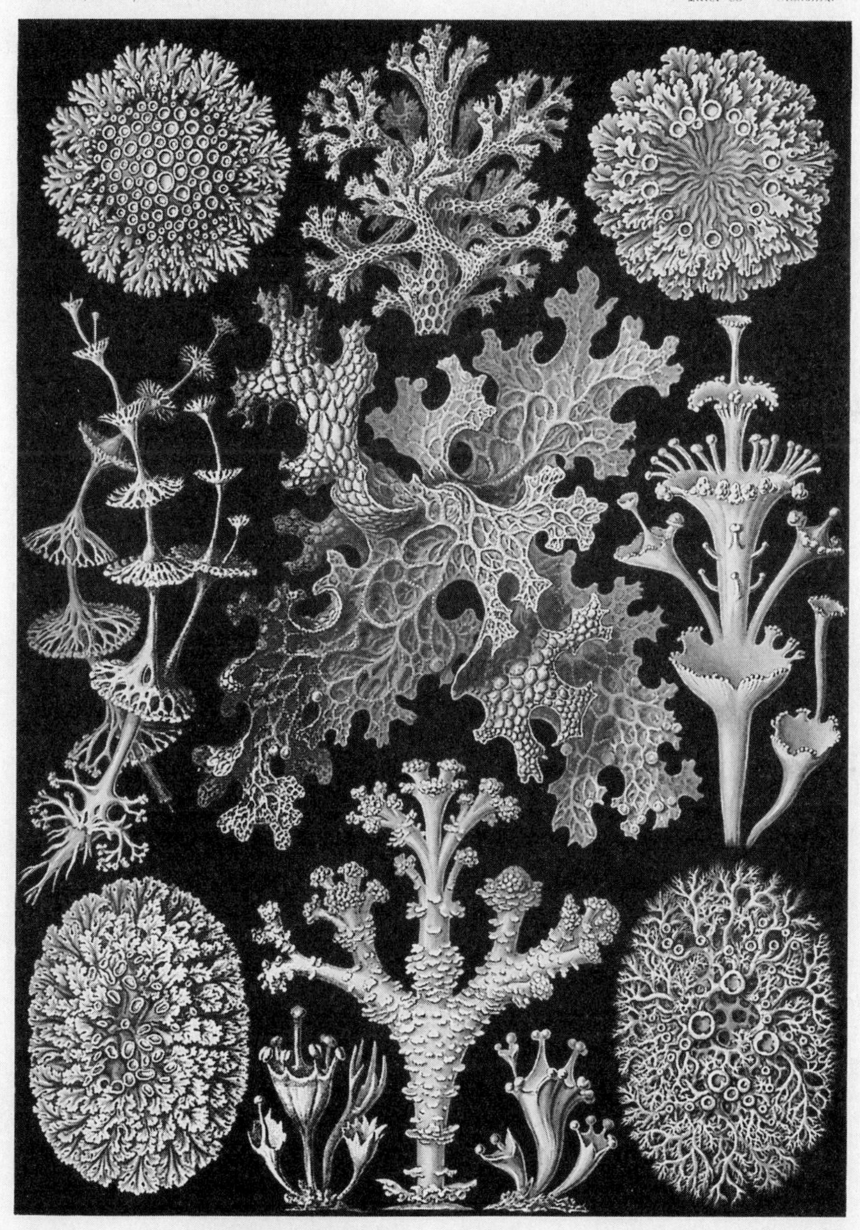

Figure 12.1. Various species of lichens from a work by Ernst Haeckel originally published in 1904. Lichens exemplify the generation of new forms from the close symbiotic relationship between species of different kingdoms.

The most likely, from current research, is an organism akin to *Thermoplasma,* a tough microorganism that lives in acidic hot springs. Like other bacteria, *Thermoplasma* has DNA that is loose in the cell. (The DNA of eukaryotes is bundled into rod-shaped chromosomes and enclosed in a nucleus.) Yet, *Thermoplasma* differs from other bacteria in that *Thermoplasma* DNA is coated with a histone-like protein similar to that found making up chromosomes of eukaryotes. The suggestion is that the bacterial ancestors of *Thermoplasma* came into being early, prior to some two billion years ago when oxygen began to build up in the atmosphere during the banded-iron era of the early Proterozoic aeon. This symbiotic merger led to the first eukaryotes; the protoctists, a group to which algae, seaweeds, ciliates, amœbae and malarial parasites belong. Initially the larger *Thermoplasma* may have been invaded and even destroyed by other small, compact bacteria that had the metabolic equipment to use up oxygen in respiratory processes. However, the advantage to the respiring bacteria of having their food supplied on tap turned their aggression into tolerance. Meanwhile *Thermoplasma* not only had a means through its new-found smaller partners of mopping up toxic oxygen, but also of benefiting from the far more efficient Krebs-cycle breakdown of carbohydrates into their constituent carbon dioxide and water. The eukaryotes therefore emerged from the consortium formed by *Thermoplasma* and its would-be-predators. All ancestral eukaryotes initially obtained their food by absorbing the excess, the environmental waste of photosynthesizing bacteria. But in some descendants that relationship too turned into a symbiosis as the photosynthesizer itself was ingested. Indeed, as digestion was resisted, some now intracellular would-be food was retained — and became chloroplasts. Through symbiogenesis green algal cells and hence the ancestors of the green plant lineage were now in the process of evolving.

Confirmation that predatory bacteria exist and that they do on occasions form obligatory associations has been forthcoming. At least three kinds of bacteria, namely *Bdellovibrio, Vampirococcus* and *Daptobacter,* have been found to prey on other bacteria or indeed on protists. These predators are just as essential to the microecological community as are the birds of prey and big cats in the macroecological world of the African savannah. Furthermore, bacteria and protoctists are just as specific to particular habitats and communities as are the fauna and flora of a blackwater river in western Amazonia. The curious naturalist is therefore no more likely to find a termite hindgut protist *Trichonympha* in a sulphurous Spanish lake or a laminated microbial mat than one is likely to find a flamingo in the Gobi Desert.

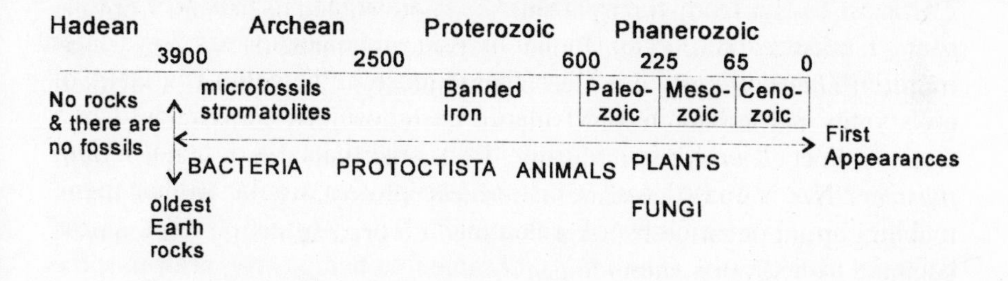

Figure 12.2. An evolutionary time-scale.

An ecosystem invariably has a productive component, either photosynthetic or chemoautotrophic. Brightly coloured bacteria, algae or plants are the photosynthetic producers in the light, whereas in energy-rich dark environments supplied with the appropriate chemicals, chemoautotrophs, for instance sulphur-, iron-, ammonia- or methane-oxidizing bacteria, are the producers. In addition, an aquatic ecosystem must have its bacteriovores, algivores and predators in the sense that they prey on the live bodies of others, as well as degradative species that transform dead bodies and other complex organic matter to assimilable fragments. These may include myxobacteria, labyrinthulids, ciliates, acrasiads, chytrids, carrion-eating birds, scavenging mammals and many others. But even in today's ecosystems decomposition must always include osmotrophs (usually bacteria, protoctists and fungi) that feed on the others and recycle the biochemicals into the bodies of the producers and consumers, and eventually into the air, water and soil.

A sulphurous community

Ricardo Guerrero, in particular, has studied the gamut of microbial interactions in an anaerobic sulphurous lake in northeast Spain, close to Girona. Lake Cisó is a small body of water some 300 metres west of Lake Banyoles. Covering just 498 m^2 and seven metres deep at its deepest, the lake is unusual in that anoxygenic phototrophs can be found throughout the water column all year long.

The surface waters undergo striking colour changes from bright red to brown that reflect the photosynthetic pigments of the changing bacterial population. Other than ciliates and mastigotes that feed on bacteria and occasional blooms of green algae that colonize the surface when the winds blow in some oxygen, Lake Cisó is devoid of eukaryotes.

Chromatium is a reddish purple sulphur phototrophic bacterium from the same family as *Thiocapsa* found in bacterial mats. However, it has motile, flagellated cells that live planktonically. *Chlorobium,* a smaller, green, non-motile phototrophic sulphur bacterium, lives suspended in the water below *Chromatium.* Meanwhile, below both types of photosynthesizers live various colourless desulphovibrios, which are sulphate-reducing gram negative bacteria that feed on organic matter and convert sulphate to hydrogen sulphide gas.

The sulphate leaches into the lake from rich layers of gypsum and the desulphovibrios are able to generate continual supplies of hydrogen sulphide to the oxygen-poor surface waters. Both *Chromatium* and *Chlorobium*

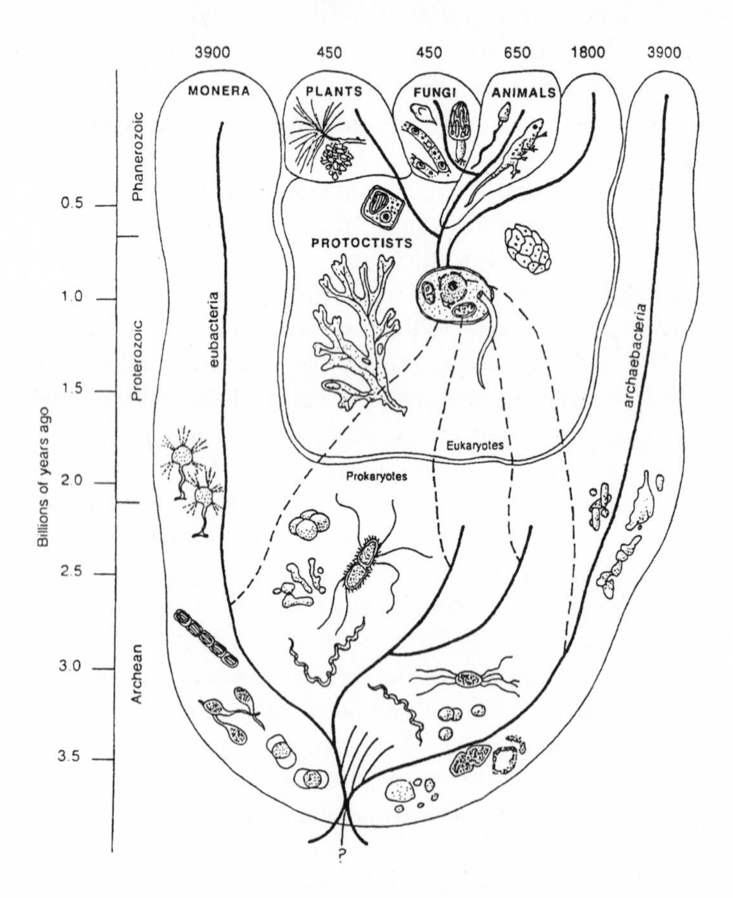

Figure 12.3. This diagram shows the evolutionary relationships between the five kingdoms of organisms., We see organisms of the 'macrocosm' with our unaided eyes whereas the rest are subvisible inhabitants of the microcosm. (Drawing by Laszlo Meszoly).

require hydrogen sulphide for growth, splitting it through photosynthesis and leaving behind a residue of sulphur. While *Chlorobium* cells extrude the sulphur, *Chromatium* deposits it as globules inside the cell.

Being flagellated, *Chromatium* swims upwards to the light and therefore gives the upper surface its deep red colour. It is more tolerant of oxygen than *Chlorobium* and less tolerant of high hydrogen sulphide levels. The lower layer of *Chromatium* cells tends to be light deprived and the cells die and sink. *Chlorobium,* on the other hand, through its pigmentation absorbing light that penetrates through the upper layers of *Chromatium,* can just about derive sufficient energy for photosynthesis. Nonetheless, it does better when the population of *Chromatium* is less dense. Members of these genera of photosynthetic microbes together prevent any light reaching the lower depths.

The lake shows the typical boom and bust cycle of planktonic blooms. Part of the bust-side of the cycle is related to nutrient levels, part to poisoning through high sulphide levels, but part is now known to be related to predation on *Chromatium* by two newly discovered bacteria, *Vampirococcus* and *Daptobacter.* These bacteria attack debilitated photosynthesizers in the layers below the main bloom. Finally, dying cells or fragments of cells sink to the bottom where they provide the bottom-dwelling desulphovibrios with organic matter. Through microbial metabolism — actually 'sulphate breathing' rather than oxygen breathing — such organisms reduce the sulphate to hydrogen sulphide, comparable therefore to oxygen being reduced by hydrogen to form water, and the cycle continues.

Lake Cisó provides an interesting lesson in community ecology in that pure cultures free of extraneous pressures do not survive in the wild, but require qualitatively different populations to provide the nutrients and to metabolize their waste products. *Chlorobium,* for instance, provides *Chromatium* with an essential service of reducing hydrogen sulphide concentrations to levels that are below its threshold of toxicity. On the other hand, when *Chromatium* is in full bloom it is laying the seeds of its own bust cycle by holding back *Chlorobium.* The lake, therefore, is like an extended, differentiated tissue and the organisms interact with each other as if they were a being larger than themselves.

New kinds of individuality

That destructive relations, even obligate predation could turn into a close-knit symbiotic dependency, was an essential prerequisite for serial endosymbiosis as a hypothesis of evolutionary change. But where was the evidence for such transformation from aggressor to integrated partner? Kwang Jeon, a researcher at the University of Knoxville in Tennessee, had been studying the amœba, *Amœba proteus,* a strain of which had accidentally become infected by approximately 150,000 bacteria that had resisted digestion. Instead they had turned on the protist and had devastated it. However, Jeon carefully cared for some of the amœbae that had survived the bacterial onslaught. These had incorporated some tens of thousands of bacteria into their cytoplasm. Furthermore, these amœbae could no longer survive without the bacteria and vice versa. Strangely too, the number of bacteria that were tolerated amounted to some 40,000 — any in excess are digested.

Termites have come to be known as one of the best examples in the repertoire of symbiosis. These insects, numbering close to 2,000 species,

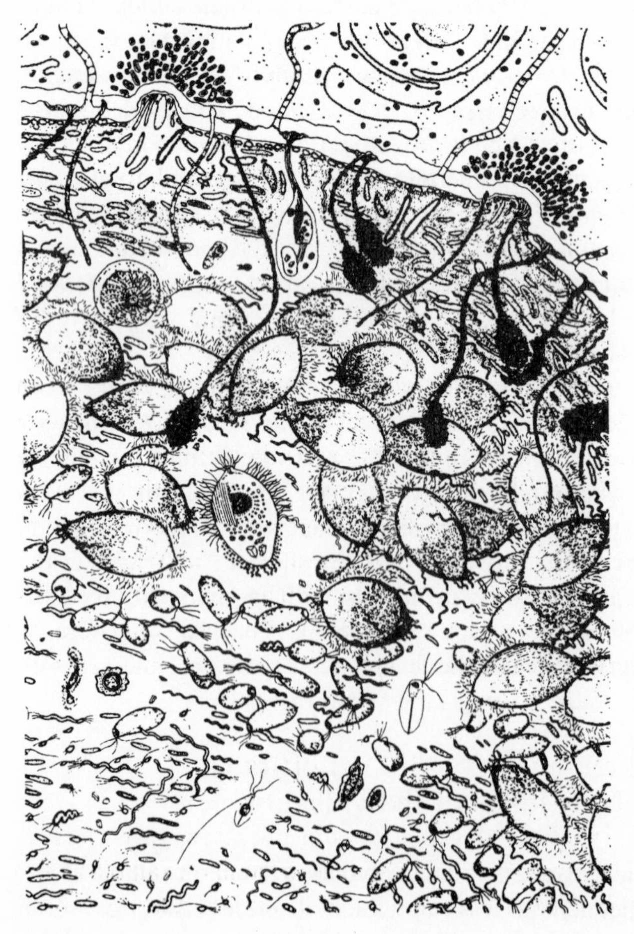

Figure 12.4. A representation of the community of micro-organisms living inside the desert termite hindgut. Without these microscopic partners the termite would not be able to digest cellulose. (Drawing by Christie Lyons).

contain in their intestine numerous prokaryotic and eukaryotic organisms. One of the better known is the protoctist, *Mixotricha paradoxa,* a unicellular eukaryote, which in the Australian termite, *Mastotermes darwiniensis,* plays an important role in the digestion of cellulose. Indeed, the termite would be unable to metabolize the cellulose were it not for wood-ingesting protists like *Mixotricha. Mixotricha* carries three kinds of bacteria permanently lodged on its surface, two of which are spirochætes. The small surface spirochætes attach themselves to protuberances on *Mixotricha's* membrance. Related to the treponemes that cause syphilis, these helically-shaped bacteria, through waves of rhythmic beating, propel the large bulk of *Mixotricha* through the termite intestine. Furthermore, *Mixotricha* lacks mitochondria, but makes up by possessing internal symbiotic bacteria that carry out vital metabolic functions.

The termite essentially feeds on the 'waste products' of the combined forces of such symbionts, and therefore provides the right milieu for such processes to occur. Approximately half the weight of these dry-wood eating termites is made up of its intestinal symbionts, thereby certainly adding to the confusion as to what is an individual. Thus, the Sonoran desert termite, *Pterotermes occidentis,* contains some hundred to one thousand million prokaryotes and up to one million eukaryotes per millilitre of hindgut fluid. When the termite moults it sheds the entire contents of its hindgut as a package. Newly moulted individuals gain a new gut microbiota by proctodial feeding whereby an infected termite presents its rear end to the mouth of an uninfected individual. Newly hatched eggs also obtain their gut microbiota in the same way. In general, the microbe community cannot survive longer than a few hours when exposed to the oxygen of air. The microbial community of wood-eating cockroaches, presumed to be the ancestors of termites, through engaging in a form of sex, can form hard-walled cysts by which they survive desiccation and starvation until introduced into another insect.

Cattle perhaps are not so different from termites in that respect; their rumens being home to countless bacteria and ciliates that help digest the cellulose of grass. Humans too require the effort of bacteria to ensure the breakdown and digestion of organic matter.

Symbiotic transmission of traits

In recent years, as a result of developments in microscopy, in genetics and in biochemical analysis, including that of proteins, examples have come to light of symbioses between bacteria and larger organisms, whether fungi, plants or animals. Whereas classical biology viewed the world as primarily divided between animals and plants, such a division becomes entirely blurred at the borders of the microcosm and within. Hence, a plant photosynthesizes because it possesses former bacteria, now entirely dependent, in the form of chloroplasts.

Animals, on the other hand, are not expected to photosynthesize. However, Robert Trench from the University of Santa Barbara in California has observed that *Tridachia crispata,* a kind of sea slug, pierces the cytoplasm of green algae and extracts out the chloroplasts. 'Then,' says Trench, 'the *Tridachia* introduces the chloroplasts into its own gut cells and continues on its way while pretending to be a plant.'

Such horizontal transmission of characteristics, rather than the vertical transmission that is implicit in eukaryotic meiosis and sex, offers all sorts of advantages. For one, as Professor Lynda Goff, of the University of Santa Cruz in California points out, whereas meiotically-driven sex needs be between organisms of the same species that therefore share close compatibility, symbiotic relationships involve passing on of genes from different species and even different families or classes of organisms. Hence symbiotic transmission transcends the barriers that normally separate species.

Lynda Goff has discovered a remarkable type of association among certain large red algae. One variety invades another by forming filament connections. She has observed through using microscopes including the electron microscope that the invading algae send intact nuclei from their cells into the victims' cells. Thus, through an act of nuclear transfer very much like sex, one type of alga completely takes over the metabolism of another.

Microtubules and undulipodia

Eukaryotic cells in general have a dynamic quality — their insides are incessantly moving. Many enjoy rapid alterations of shape and form that bacterial cells cannot match. Eukaryotes, such as amœbae, extend and withdraw amorphous, ever-changing pseudopodia; others, like *Euglena,* use a single long undulipodium to sense friend, foe and food in a watery medium, or some, like *Paramecium,* use hundreds of short undulipodia (cilia) on their surface to swim. Others use them to sweep material across their surfaces. Eukaryotic cells engulf food by enclosing it in membranous sacs, by which means they transport it around. Furthermore, they can rearrange their organelles individually and their cytoplasm in bulk, as for instance, during mitotic cell division when the chromosomes move along microtubule tracks to the centre of the cell preparing to divide. The respective halves of each chromosome then move apart as the nucleus reproduces by division. Many of these features, denied to bacteria, may paradoxically derive from characteristics of incorporated, formerly-independent, bacteria.

The centriole, found in nucleated cells, such as animal tissue cells and in many protoctists, is a curious structure that underlies organelles of motility. In cross-section under the electron microscope the centriole is seen to be exactly the same structure as the kinetosome at the base of the sperm tail, the cilium and all other undulipodia. The kinetosome or centriole has nine bundles of triplet microtubules arrayed in a cylinder. The shaft of all undulipodia has nine bundles of doublet microtubules in which each bundle contains two rather than three microtubular sticks.

The centriole is best known for its behaviour during animal cell mitosis. In fact it divides into two before the chromosomes become visible, with each of the two progeny migrating to opposite ends of the cell. A mitotic spindle then appears, itself made of the same microtubules as the centriole and kinetosome. The spindle now radiates out from each polar centriole as a few of its tubules connect to the chromosomes. Then, the spindle tubules act as cables, providing tracks for the chromosomes to travel on to their respective poles within the dividing cell. The centriole, with its triplet microtubules, nine sets in a circle, and the same structure as the kinetosome, probably evolved from it. In many protoctists and animal cells the two organelles are manifestly the same in so far as the centrioles migrate to the cell surface where, as they spawn the growth of new undulipodia shafts, they become kinetosomes.

Microtubules play many different roles in the eukaryotic cell. They provide the scaffolding which gives the cell its internal structure, and like scaffolding, they withdraw and reshape. As revealed in phase contrast microscopy, combined with video and electron microscopic images, the microtubules also act as freeways for traffic within the cell, with encapsulated food and particles passing hither and thither in seemingly endless streams. This 'organized' movement within eukaryotic cells is in marked contrast to the stasis perceived in the cells of bacteria.

That centrioles and kinetosomes reproduce at times distinct from nuclear reproduction strongly suggests they may be under autonomous control from their own genetic material. In 1924 the Russian biologist, Boris Kozo-Polyansky, mentioned that undulipodia might have come from 'flagellated cytodes' by which he meant swimming bacteria. I.E. Wallin, in a single sentence, essentially said the same in 1927, picturing

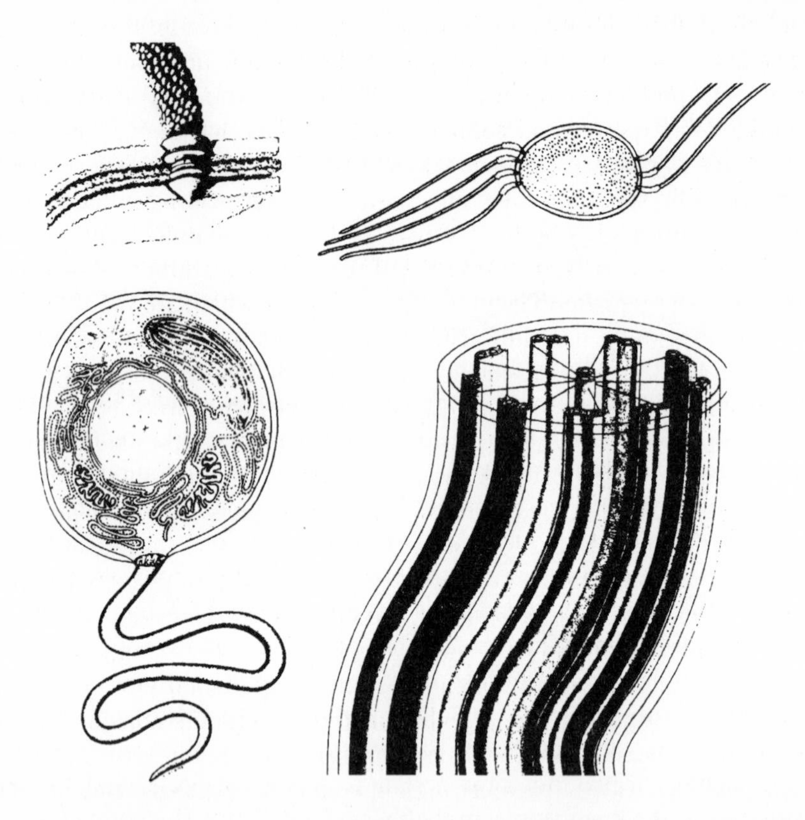

Figure 12.5. Prokaryotic cells (top right) move by flagella (top left). The flagella spin on a rotary motor. Eukaryotic cells (bottom left) move by means of undulipodia (bottom right) — waving feet — composed of tubulin microtubules arranged in a characteristic [9(2)+2] pattern. (Drawing Christie Lyons).

them as outboard motors in propelling ancient protocells. Although this work has only recently come to light, it is clear that both these biologists had the prescience to see that motile bacteria could be permanently 'borrowed' for use as activating appendages. Once wholly incorporated into another cell former squirming bacteria could influence its internal processes. Margulis independently proposed spirochæte symbioses, giving testable details to the old idea of motility symbioses.

Spirochætes have been found associated with many different protists, such as with *Mixotricha paradoxa* in the termite gut. Perhaps one of the more outlandish and controversial suggestions with regard to the serial endosymbiosis theory (SET) is that symbiosis between *Thermoplasma* and corkscrew shaped ancestors of the spirochæte gave rise to the cell architecture of eukaryotes including the machinery for internal motility and mitotic division. It follows from this bizarre suggestion that the axonic structure of nervous tissue, comprised of tubulin neurotubules and hence the same protein as microtubules, is derived from the same bacterial source. Brain power and complex animal behaviour would therefore be an emergent property of ancient symbioses between organisms related to the syphilitic spirochæte and an acid-resistant fermenting prokaryote like *Thermoplasma.*

Again where is the evidence? Undulipodia are common elements in eukaryotic organisms. They include cilia, all of which are motile hairlike structures with an internal architecture in cross-section that reveals nine pairs of microtubules arranged in a circle with two central pairs. Overall this pattern is described as a [9(2)+2] structure. No spirochæte has so far been found with a [9(2)+2] internal structure. However, some spirochætes have single or even pairs of tubules similar to the underlying structural elements of undulipodia. Proof of any ancient symbiotic link would have to be forthcoming in the form of a discovery that kinetosomes underlying cilia and all other organelles with the [9(2)+2] pattern possess their own DNA. Such DNA, should it exist, would have to share sequence homology with that found in the genome of the tubule-containing spirochætes.

Two lines of research indicate the strong likelihood that undulipodia have their own autonomous genetic material. Certain strains of *Paramecium* have been found with an unusual swimming trait caused by abnormalities in the fringe of undulipodia that propel the protist along. Thus, instead of swimming in a straight line, the abnormal paramecia twist and gyrate. The abnormality is passed on from generation to generation but not in ways that conform to a normal sexual exchange. Indeed, if the genetic abnormality lay in the nucleus, then, when nuclei were exchanged, the abnormality should be passed on to some of the offspring of the previously normal swimmer. In fact, only those descendants that inherit the outer layers of cytoplasm (the cortex) of the abnormal swimmer inherit the abnormality. This phenomenon indicates inheritance outside the nuclear genome and therefore 'cortical inheritance.'

Possibly the clinching discovery comes from research at the Rockefeller University in New York. David Luck and John Hall, in 1989 claimed to have discovered DNA associated with the kinetosomes of the undulipodium of *Chlamydomonas,* a green algal protoctist. Each *Chlamydomonas* cell has one large chloroplast and two undulipodia. Hall and Luck selected *Chlamydomonas* cells that failed to swim properly and thereby reach light. The crippling of the organism's ability to swim most often was due to a problem in at least one of the pair of undulipodia. Sexually active *Chlamydomonas* regularly fuse as mating partners to produce cells with twice the usual amount of genetic material. These 'diploid' cells then divide by meiosis, parcelling out half their DNA to each offspring, to form normal cells.

When a *Chlamydomonas* cell suffering from several swimming abnormalities fuses with a normal swimmer and the resultant diploid cell divides, then contrary to conventional genetics in which the abnormalities would distribute themselves, the abnormalities all stay together from one generation to the next. In searching for the mass of 'culpable' DNA, Luck and his team used a fluorescent tracer which showed up as two distinct spots, not in the nucleus, but one each at the base of the undulipodium, associated with each tiny kinetosome. This dramatic discovery provides substantial support for the contention that undulipodia and their kinetosomes had an autonomous bacterial origin. Other *Chlamydomonas* workers have not been able to confirm the findings of Luck and Hall. The next step will be to ascertain if the kinetosome-centriole DNA does exist and to look for patterns of similarity between undulipodia and tubule-containing spirochætes of the same size. The search for similarities in the proteins of undulipodia and their microtubules with the tubules of spirochætes will need to be pursued in parallel with genetic research.

Bacteria that swim derive their motility from a rotating flagellum. The rotary motor involved in this kind of motion relies on a flow of hydrogen ions at the base where the motor is embedded in cell membrane. Undulipodia, on the other hand are powered all throughout their length by an ATP-driven process. Spirochætes derive their motility from the writhing motions of their entire body as their bacterial flagella rotate. Microbiologists doubt any energy for their motion derives from ATP, rather they believe it all comes from hydrogen ions. Unresolved, these differences in mechanism argue against the theory of the 'spirochæte origin of undulipodia.'

The proposition is that the first autopoetic systems had the structure and metabolism of simple fermentative, obligatory anaerobic bacterial cells, which according to the Russian biologist Oparin originated from chemical mixtures on the early Earth. Anything less than a full-fledged membrane-bounded cell in terms of structure would not have the necessary attributes for self-sustaining reproduction while maintaining a dynamically stable *milieu intérieur.* Cells as organisms exist in structured communities. Comprised of organisms with different abilities and potentialities, communities appeared at the very beginning of life on Earth and persisted from hence on. Modern examples include the bacterial community found in Lake Cisó in Spain and the walking community we call the termite.

Symbiosis in the first ecosystems

While Eskimos have at least twenty different words to describe snow, Spaniards have at least forty different names to describe bulls and small calves. Moreover Spaniards can name all the different shapes of the horns and with single words can describe an animal's age to within six months. Thus we use language to express what we know well. In that context, when J.B. Haldane, as one of the disciples of Darwin, and a famous evolutionist, was asked for his opinion on the role of God in nature he answered that God must have an 'inordinate fondness of beetles' since he had created more than one million species of these coleopterans.

Scientists, whether of the last century or of this century, describe what they can see. Thus, whether a Darwin, an Odum or whoever, most scientists see life in terms of animals and plants, while tending to overlook microbes, as if they were relatively unimportant. But, if Darwin had seen our videos of microbial interactions, his view of the natural world would undoubtedly have been very different and his observations would have coloured his conclusions.

Here it is worthwhile making three points: first, scientists use examples that are available in their time; and when the examples change so change their views and quite likely too the paradigms of science itself. Second, we need to account for the importance of bacteria, including their versatility and powers of recombination, in the history of life on Earth. Third, we need to apply our new concept of bacterial ecology, with its special features of interactions within communities, as in bacterial mats, to our views of life on Earth and indeed even to morality.

A misguided focus on individualism

Our concepts tend to be based on a mammalian view of individuality. We talk of individual bacteria and how they die and whether or not they selfishly transmit genes. But these concepts are misguided in so far as truly individual organisms did not appear on Earth until the origin of the eukaryotic cell. Bacteria may indeed die, but normally they continue to divide, always therefore passing on something of themselves to their offspring even if in the end nothing is left of the original cell. As Paul Weiss has pointed out, differentiation in eukaryotic organisms oscillates between the body (soma) that normally dies out and the germ line (germen) that reproduces. The first time 'programmed' death appeared in the life history of an organism was in eukaryotes, not bacteria. An example is yeast. When you study a yeast cell that is budding under the electron microscope you will notice a scar left in the place where the bud has appeared and further scarring as more and more buds are generated and break off on different sites on the cell surface. Finally, when the original parent cell has generated some thirty buds it finishes reproducing and dies. Bacteria, on the other hand, are potentially immortal in that they can reproduce forever. An organism becomes an individual as it is comprised of different component organisms living together symbiotically in a mode requiring adjustment and integration. Individuality requires incessant reiteration. Familiar individuality therefore seems to come into being with the earliest eukaryotes. The wood-eating termite, for instance, depends wholly on its gut microbiota to digest cellulose. Under such circumstances it would appear that individuality arises only when the symbiotic organisms become so closely integrated that a new, more complex organism emerges. Such a paradoxical situation of individuality is well exemplified by the mitochondria when their free-living progenitors became wholly incorporated into the eukaryotic cell.

Two bacterial community types were particularly important from 3.5 billion years ago until the Cambrian some 600 million years ago, hence for well over 85 per cent of life's sojourn on earth. Stromatolites are rocks; hardened communities made up of cyano- and other photosynthetic bacteria such as phototrophic sulphur bacteria. Still other bacteria, including ones that produce sulphide, form part of the community structure. Stromatolites are common in the ancient fossil record.

Today, we have a few examples of living stromatolites, as at Shark Bay in northwest Australia where they have generated calcium carbonate rocks, with the skin of living tissue on top. Stromatolites are found mostly in the subtidal region. Some in the intertidal zone are covered by the incoming sea for part of the day.

Heterotrophy, taking in of preformed organic compounds as food, undoubtedly preceded photosynthesis, but was far more limited in terms of the food and energy it could provide. Through chlorophyll-based photosynthesis cyanobacteria generate oxygen. However, photosynthesis is not exclusively associated with the splitting of water and the production of oxygen. Essentially photosynthesis involves removing electrons from different sources, the energy for this metabolic function coming from sunlight. Thus, for many years the only sub-product of photosynthesis was sulphur. Oxygen only appeared on the scene after some sulphur bacteria evolved to remove electrons from water. The atmospheric accumulation of free oxygen waste was one of the first ecological catastrophes on Earth in that the gas threatened life. But life changed its strategy and through evolution organisms began to live with and exploit oxygen.

Banded-iron formation

Although cyanobacteria were already present 3.5 billion years ago oxygen only appeared in the atmosphere one billion years later. Initially the oxygen was taken up by many processes: reactions with carbon and nitrogen and other oxygen-grabbing elements. Iron in a reduced state, ferrous iron, with a valency of two, for instance, was converted into ferric iron with a valency of three. Oxygen only accumulated in the atmosphere when the process of surface oxidation had gone to completion.

It is conceivable that compared with today the ecosystem of early life was reversed in that anaerobic organisms would have been found in the top layers and aerobic organisms, such as the cyanobacteria underneath, close to the rocky, iron-rich substrate, where indeed the oxygen was being produced. Once oxygen began building up in the atmosphere, the layers were reversed; anaerobic organisms were found in the muddy bottom.

As evolution continued we find all manner of symbiotic combinations. The wood-eating cockroach provides a rich example in which several different organisms come together to create a composite organism. The hypermastigote, *Barbulanympha,* for instance, is covered in myriads of undulipodia. In addition, it has hundreds of undulating spirochæte bacteria attached to its posterior, the bacteria feeding on waste from the protist while the undulipodia propel it through the termite gut to sources of cellulose. Although the spirochætes can live as free-living organisms within the roach gut, in attaching themselves to *Barbulanympha* their bodies begin beating in synchronized waves, like the wind rippling across a corn field. Protists also contain bacteria inside their bodies perhaps that enable them to digest lignin. While the cockroach provides the motility and jaws to bite off woody fragments, the complex community of organisms working inside the wood-eating cockroach gut breaks down that wood into digestible food for the rest of the 'community that is the individual.'

Bacteria, inferior or superior?

For most of the history of the Earth the only organisms present were the prokaryotes: microorganisms, including bacteria, without nuclei. Yet, we cannot call them inferior. Indeed, as judged by their metabolic capabilities, they are far more versatile than we. Biochemical evolution was tied inseparably tothe evolution of microorganisms. Hence, the success of bacteria can be put down to their ability to exchange genes. For instance, the phototrophic bacterium, *Chloroflexus,* possesses a complex photosynthesizing apparatus that is a combination of those found in other families of phototrophic bacteria. Thus, biochemically, the different components of the photosynthetic apparatus probably result from a combination of green sulphur bacteria and non-sulphur bacteria. This association may be an example of horizontal transmission of genetic characters in bacteria. Symbiogenesis and gene exchange seem to generate individuality. Only after symbiotic associations of different organisms make a new one does significant morphological evolution and the possibility of individuality appear.

Genetic differentiation is difficult to measure, but an analysis of the percentage of guanine to cytosine can be used as an indication of the genetic distance between different organisms. Take the genus *Bacillus* where guanine to cytosine ratios in total DNA range over more than 50 per cent.Yet, the G+C variation encompassing all vertebrates, including fish, birds and man, is far less. The reason is that we instantly perceive differences in morphology but our eyes are not equipped to notice biochemical diversity. Microbial ecology forms the basis of the ecological principles adduced in this century. Thus bacterial ecology came first. We must appreciate that general ecology of plants and animals forms only the last chapter in the recent history of the Earth.

The sharing of the genome, as practised among bacteria, and the intrusion of one bacteria-type into another, thus transporting entire attributes all within the same generation, made new composite organisms, hastening on the process of evolution and taking us into the realm of Darwinian notions of how species evolved. We must dispense with extravagant anthropocentric labels to describe the driving forces behind evolution. 'Brute competition' is not the name of the evolution game, nor are co-operation and competition appropriate biological descriptors. We are all symbionts and where microbial community ecology has become so tightly integrated it is now cell physiology. Furthermore, bacteria and protoctists are not 'lower organisms' and we are not 'higher organisms;' they are smaller and we are only larger. We need our microorganisms as our microorganisms have come to need us.

References

Bermudes, D., G. Hinkle and L. Margulis. 1994. Do prokaryotes contain microtubules? *Microbiological Reviews.* Washington: Amer. Soc. for Microbiology.

Dorozynski, A. 1990. Nous sommes tous des symbiotes. *Science et Vie.* 875.

Hall, J. and Luck. D. 1989 (2 ed). *Symbiosis in cell evolution.* New York: Freeman.

Hinkle, G. and Margulis. L. 1990. Global ecology and the Gaia hypothesis. *Physiol. Ecol. Japan.* 27 (Special Number):53–62.

Khaklina, L.N. 1992. *Concepts of symbiogenesis: A historical and critical study of the research of Russian botanists.* New Haven: Yale University Press.

Kozo-Polyansky, B.M. 1924. *A new principle of biology. Essay on the theory of symbiogenesis.* Moscow (In Russian).

Margulis, L. 1990. Words as battle cries: symbiogenesis and the new field of endocytobiology. *Bioscience.* 40(9).

—— 1993 (2 ed). *Symbiosis in Cell Evolution.* New York: Freeman.

Margulis, L., D. Chase, and R. Guerrero. 1986. Microbial communities. *Bioscience.* 36:3.

Margulis, L. and R. Fester. 1991. *Symbiosis as a Source of Evolution.* MIT Press.

Margulis, L. and R. Guerrero. 1990. Origins of Life to Evolution of Microbial Communities: a Minimalist Approach. From C. Ponnamperuma and F.R. Eirich (eds). *Prebiological Self-Organization of Matter. Proceedings of the Eighth College Park Colloquium on Chemical Evolution.* Hampton, Va: Deepak.

Margulis, L. and G. Hinkle. 1993. The Biota and Gaia: 150 years of support for environmental sciences. In S. Schneider and P. Boston (eds). *Scientists on Gaia.* MIT Press.

Margulis, L. and McMenamin, M. 1990. Marriage of Convenience: The motility of the modern cell may reflect an ancient, symbiotic union. *The Sciences.* Sept/Oct.

– 13 –
Symbiosis and Sulphur-fuelled Animal Life in the Sea: Gaian Implications

A.J. Southward and E.C. Southward

The dictionary definition of symbiosis is 'the living together of organisms for their mutual advantage' and there is an implied understanding that the organisms may well be dissimilar in their structure and way of life. A good example of marine symbiosis and dissimilarity of the organisms involved is the association between microscopic unicellular plants (algae) and the reef-building, colonial corals (Muscatine and Porter 1977). The degree of mutualism in this association has only fully emerged in the past twenty five years. Basically, the plants supply organic compounds to the corals in return for nutrients such as nitrogen compounds which are scarce in the clear waters of the tropics where reefs flourish. The Gaian implications of this symbiosis are easily understood. The formation of extensive beds of precipitated calcium carbonate, mostly the skeletons of the corals, is probably an important component of the homeostatic mechanism for control of global carbon dioxide, and ultimately of the global temperature. Without symbiosis coral reefs would be far less developed.

There are, however, less obvious symbioses in the sea. One of these, recently discovered and the subject of this article, may have an important role in the cycling of sulphur in the sea, part of another global homeostatic mechanism connected with regulation of the Earth's water balance and temperature.

Discovery of sulphur symbiosis in the sea

The symbiosis between sulphur-oxidizing bacteria and marine invertebrates was recognized quite recently, and grew out of another recent important discovery in marine science, the existence of hydrothermal vents in the deep ocean floor and an associated rich fauna (review by Grassle 1986). It is only fourteen years since oceanographers first detected the hydrothermal vents at mid-ocean ridges in the deep Pacific.

	seawater (mmoles/kg)	**ventwater** (mmoles/kg)
hydrogen sulphide	nil	6,500
sulphate	28,600	nil
silica	160	21,000
barium	0.14	17 to 95
strontium	87	87 to 90
magnesium	52,700	nil
manganese	trace	300 to 1,100
iron	trace	1,800

Table 13.1. Some major chemical differences between seawater and hydrothermal vent water. (based on Edmond et al. 1982).

A year or two later they collected specimens of a surprising fauna clustered around the vents, comprising giant representatives of several kinds (phyla) of marine invertebrate animals which appeared to flourish where the heated sea water was issuing. The hot water was enriched in metal compounds and hydrogen sulphide (Table 13.1) but low in oxygen, having passed over hot lava beds inside the ocean crust. It was soon suspected that the abundant large animals were part of a food chain based on chemosynthetic bacteria that were using reduced inorganic compounds, principally the hydrogen sulphide dissolved in the issuing hot water, as energy sources to make organic matter from carbon dioxide (Table 13.2). This dependence of the vent communities upon geothermal sources has been confirmed since (Jannasch 1985, Jones 1985, Childress 1988). Normal deep sea communities depend on limited fall-out of particles from the sea surface where floating plants live and fix carbon dioxide into organic matter by means of energy gathered from the Sun's radiation (photosynthesis). Food based on geothermal sources at the hydrothermal vents is much more abundant and has allowed the development of richer communities than in surrounding deep sea areas.

The most surprising result of the researches that continued at the hydrothermal vents was the finding that several kinds of animal have

	free energy difference in kilojoules per mole
$H_2S + \frac{1}{2}O_2 = S^0 + H_2O$	–210
$HS^- + 2O_2 = SO_4^{2-} + H^+$	–716
$S^0 + 1\frac{1}{2}O_2 + H_2O = H_2SO_4$	–496
$S_2O_3^{2-} + 2O_2 + H_2O = 2SO_4^{2-} + 2H^-$	–936

Table 13.2. Oxidation chemistry of sulphur compounds involved in symbiosis.

done away with intermediate steps in the food chain (Grassle 1986, Childress 1988). They do not eat the sulphur-oxidizing bacteria that float in the vent water and encrust the rocks, nor do they eat intermediate forms of life that do so. Instead they live in symbiosis with internal colonies of bacteria. The symbiotic bacteria grow in cell 'factories,' for instance in the gills of clams and in the transformed digestive system (trophosome) of tubeworms, where they are provided with the sulphide, oxygen and carbon dioxide that are required to synthesize organic matter used by the host. These bacteria are technically termed *chemoautotrophs,* meaning that they use chemical energy to manufacture from inorganic materials the organic compounds that sustain life.

Symbioses between other unicellular organisms (microscopic plants) and marine invertebrate animals, including the corals mentioned above, with other coelenterates such as sea anemones and with clams (bivalve molluscs) have been known and studied since the last century. The microscopic plants in such symbioses are *photoautotrophs.* Like plants living on land they use energy from the Sun to make organic compounds from inorganic materials.

The association of some of the vent animals with internal chemoautotrophic bacteria, and the dependence of the whole community upon the geothermal energy that they tap, is a novel concept in biology that has transformed studies of life in the deep sea and now looks like transforming studies of shallow water life. The link to shallow water was suspected several years ago in clams living in coastal evironments such as salt marshes where there was a large amount of dissolved hydrogen sulphide in the sediments. These clams were discovered to have symbiotic chemoautotrophic bacteria in their gills, comparable to those in the deep sea animals that were living close to hydrothermal vents, and chemical evidence suggested that the bacteria were supplying most of the nutritional needs of the clams (Felbeck *et al.* 1981, Cavanaugh 1983, review by Southward 1987).

Since then symbiotic bacteria have also been shown to be present in many clams that live in sandy and muddy beaches, in the shallow seas around the coast, and in open fjords, places where there is little or no dissolved hydrogen sulphide (Dando *et al.* 1986). The bacteria in these clams gain access to the large amounts of sulphur that are bound up in the sediment as insoluble sulphides of iron, and it appears to be the task of the host to help undertake this extraction (Figure 13.1). Some small marine worms, notably oligochaetes and nematodes, that occur in sandy and muddy sediments also live in symbiosis with chemoautotrophic bacteria. Some of these undertake migrations in the sediment so that the

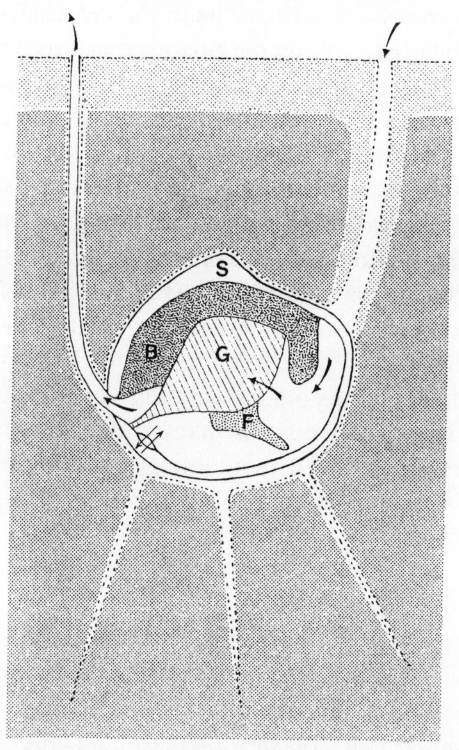

Figure 13.1. Diagram of a small clam (Lucinid bivalve) in the sediment. The oxidized upper layer of sediment is lightly stippled, the deeper anoxic sediment containing iron sulphide is darkly stippled. Arrows show the direction of water flow from the overlying water down the inlet canal, which is formed by the foot, across the gill and back to the surface through the outlet siphon. B = main body of bivalve; F = foot; G = gill; S = shell. The tunnels made by the foot below the shell in the anoxic sediment are also identical.

bacteria are alternately supplied with sulphide from the deeper layers and oxygen from nearer the surface, to allow chemoautotrophy to proceed.

Perhaps the most interesting finding was that all members of a whole major group (phylum) of marine invertebrates, the tubeworms known as Pogonophora, live in symbiosis with chemoautotrophic bacteria (Southward and Southward 1988). This phylum includes the giant tubeworms at hydrothermal vents and their widely distributed smaller relatives that live in sediments in some coastal seas, in fjords, down the ocean slope, and in deep sea trenches. They all contain symbiotic bacteria on which they depend for most of their nutrition. One exception from the general rule of dependence on sulphide in this group is a small pogonophoran that lives in the northern North Sea at the entrance to the Skagerrak. The symbiotic bacteria in this species are not chemoautotrophic sulphur oxidizers. Instead the bacteria utilize methane (North Sea Gas) from nearby seeps in the sea bed both as an energy source and as a source of carbon to make organic compounds (Schmaljohann and Flügel 1987).

Another recent finding is that communities similar to those at hydrothermal vents also occur away from mid-ocean ridges at what are known as cold seeps at subduction zones (places where parts of the Earth's crust are being forced under other parts of the crust) and at faulting along escarpments at the margins of the continents; comparable communities also occur at deep hydrocarbon seeps (Paull *et al.* 1985; Kulm *et al.* 1986; Brooks *et al.* 1987). These cold seeps are not like the mid-ocean ridge vents where the issuing water picks up both heat and reduced inorganic compounds during its passage through the outer layers of the Earth's mantle. Instead they have effluxes of cold water at local deep sea temperatures carrying reduced inorganic compounds and hydrocarbons squeezed out of sedimentary rocks.

Energy supply

The fundamental difference in energy supply is between the communities found at heated vents on the one hand and the animals on the shore, in the shallow sea and ocean slope sediments on the other hand. The former are using 'new' sources of energy derived from the Earth's crust, which may be termed geochemical. In contrast the reduced inorganic compounds, notably the iron sulphides that fuel most of the symbioses in the sediments unaffected by hydrothermal venting or cold seeps, are biogenic. The hydrogen sulphide is produced by bacteria, heterotrophs that live where there is no dissolved oxygen and are fuelled by organic matter in the sediment. These bacteria reduce sulphate to sulphide and produce methane from water and carbon dioxide as by-products of their removal of oxygen from these compounds.

The methane escapes to the sea and to the atmosphere where it is reoxidized and much of the sulphide is also reoxidized. But a not inconsiderable amount of the sulphide reacts with iron in the sediment to form insoluble (particulate) iron sulphide. The bacteria that produce the sulphide in the sediments take their energy from plant and animal remains derived from photosynthetic production at the sea surface, or in the case of coastal sands and muds, washed down from production on land. This is a secondary source of energy compared with the geochemical sources available to the special deep sea communities. However, without the activities of the symbiont-containing benthic animals much of the iron sulphide would remain buried in the sediment for millions of years (geological epochs). Thus the animals and their symbionts are using an energy source that would otherwise be unavailable to the cycle of biological production in the sea. They are also restoring to the sea the dissolved sulphate it contains, some of which eventually reaches the atmosphere in water droplets and contributes the natural component in 'acid rain.'

Thus the role of the sulphate-reducing bacteria in forming insoluble deposits of iron sulphide in marine sediments is balanced by the activity of the sulphide-oxidizing bacteria living in symbiosis. The association of the bacteria and the animals helps to reoxidize and redissolve the sulphur. The proportion of the two processes, formation of iron sulphides and their oxidation, constitutes a regulatory mechanism that helps maintain the present global balance of sulphur. The global cycling of sulphur is as much part of the Gaia mechanism as is the cycling of carbon; and the symbiotic bacteria and their hosts are playing an important part in it.

In spite of the difference in ultimate energy resources between the symbiotic associations at hydrothermal vents and those elsewhere that involve chemoautotrophic bacteria, the chemical reactions involved are similar, and energy is produced by oxidation of sulphur compounds (Table 13.2). Another common thread is that the bacteria apply the energy to the same enzyme, ribulosebisphosphate carboxylase, which catalyses the transformation of carbon dioxide to sugars as the first step in building the organic compounds required to sustain life. This is the same enzyme that is found in green plants which use solar energy to drive the conversion of carbon dioxide to sugars, underlining the common origin of the autotrophic process early in the history of life on Earth.

Bacterial participants in the symbiosis

Microbiologists study a limited number of sulphur-oxidizing bacteria that can be cultivated in the laboratory. From the growth and metabolism of these forms they can make deductions about the internal chemistry of the multitude of other forms of sulphur bacteria that exist in nature and make assumptions about their way of life (Kelly 1982; Kelly and Kuenen 1984). Similar deductions and assumptions have to be made about the symbiotic sulphur oxidizing bacteria, for although we can look at them with the electron microscope, they have proved reluctant to grow outside the bodies of their hosts, no matter the culture conditions supplied. From limited studies of some of the nucleic acids (5S RNA) it appears that the chemoautotrophic symbiotic bacteria so far analysed fall into different branches of the bacterial evolutionary tree (Olsen *et al.* 1986). Those from the vestimentiferan *Riftia* lie close to a primitive *Thiobacillus,* those from the vent clam *Calyptogena* are closer to a *Thiomicrospira,* while those from the shallower water bivalve *Solemya* appear closest to *Thiothrix.*

Physically the symbiotic sulphur-oxidizing bacteria show a great range of shape and size, from small rods (1 or 2 μm long and about 0.2 μm wide), rather typical of bacteria in general, to globular or ovoid bodies 2 to 5 or even 7 μm in diameter, or extremely long, thin rods (Southward 1987). The latter type are typically found in perviate pogonophores, while the largest spherical forms are in obturate pogonophores (vestimentiferans). Medium sized spheres and ovoids occur in clam gills, and oligochaetes, while small rods are typical of thyasirid bivalves. The larger ovoids occur in different sizes which are thought to represent changes during growth of the bacteria; the largest are regarded as 'bacteroids,' modified for storage of reserves, no longer capable of reproducing themselves. It is likely that each species of animal has a distinct species or strain of bacterium as a symbiont.

All the symbiotic bacteria have similar thin cell walls, but they have various sorts of inclusions in the cell, the commonest of which are sulphur globules. This sulphur acts as an energy store for the symbiosis. There can also be stores of inorganic phosphate, which is important for energy transfer, and in a few cases an organic polymer may be present in obvious storage granules.

There is some variation in the exact location of the symbiotic bacteria. In the pogonophorans, including the hydrothermal vent vestimentiferans, the bacteria occur several to a cell (bacteriocyte) and the cells are grouped in clusters, each well-supplied with blood vessels or sinuses that carry the raw material to the bacteria (sulphide, oxygen, carbon dioxide) and carry away the organic products for use by the host. The large vestimentiferans have distinct chemical transport mechanisms for all three raw materials (Childress 1988). In the clams and mussels the bacterial cells are placed in the gill filaments, behind the ciliated cells that produce a current of water through the gill. In some species (*Solemya, Calyptogena* and the lucinids) the bacteria occur in vacuoles in the cells, as in the pogonophorans. In other clams (thyasirids) the bacteria are placed in 'blisters' outside the main body of the cell, close to the water that bathes the gill (Southward 1987), and in some vent mussels the bacteria are entirely outside the host cells (personal observation). In the hydrothermal vent 'limpet' the elongated (filamentous) bacteria are also entirely on the outer surface of the gill (de Burgh and Singla 1985), while in the 'snail' from the western Pacific the bacteria are in vacuoles inside the cells (Hessler *et al.* 1988).

At the moment not much is known about how bacterial symbiosis is maintained, whether the invertebrate animals can pick up 'wild' bacteria from the environment or if the association is 'inherited.' Transfer of bacteria on the egg has been described for small oligochaete worms, and within the egg for vesicomyid clams (Giere and Langheld 1987, Endow and Ohta 1990). In some sea-anemones with algal (photoautotrophic) symbionts these are also carried in the egg, but in other photoautotrophic symbioses the symbionts may be acquired from the environment (Taylor and Harrison 1983). The difficulty of obtaining pure cultures of the symbiotic sulphur oxidizing bacteria suggests this type of symbiosis is an example of co-evolution, both host and bacterium being suitably modified, perhaps by exchange of genetic material. So far there is no evidence that the bacteria have transformed into cell organelles that are replicated by the genetic and reproductive organization of the host.

Hydrothermal vents occur at mid-ocean ridge spreading centres, zones of active volcanic activity and lava flows where new oceanic crust is formed (Grassle 1986). The crust moves slowly towards the continents on either side of the ridge and is ultimately buried (subducted) beneath the continental plates at the ocean margins. The vents constitute an extreme and local version of the global control mechanism for regulating the content of sulphur and other elements in sea water. Marine chemists regard the vents as the biggest source of input to the ocean of certain ions, particularly the heavy metals (Edmond *et al.* 1982). The vents are also biologically important since the efflux of sulphides nourishes large communities of sulphur-oxidizing bacteria, both free-living and symbiotic, that take part in the global sulphur cycle.

Oceanographers had been surveying the mid-ocean ridges for some time, but location of active vents required development of very accurate position fixing and sophisticated deep-tow instruments giving continuous photographic coverage, together with deployment of manned submersibles. The vents were first detected in 1976 and have been studied with submersibles since 1977. Crustal formation and sea-floor spreading rates are faster in the Pacific, where most researches have been made, but recently a few sites of venting and associated animal life have been discovered in the Atlantic at 26°N and there are areas of submarine hot springs off Iceland where the local shallow water fauna is enriched by the hydrothermal activity (Rona *et al.* 1986; Fricke *et al.* 1989).

Typical deep sea vent communities have been described from a number of sites in the Pacific, ranging from 20°S through the Galapagos area to the Juan de Fuca-Explorer Ridge off Vancouver Island at 44° to 50°N (Grassle 1986, Tunnicliffe 1988). The vents occur in a very narrow strip, 1 to 2 km wide, along the axes of ridges where new sea floor is formed by extrusion of hot basalt. Where spreading rates are lower (6 to 9 cm/year compared with up to 18 cm/year) they occur in a rift valley up to 200m deeper than the ridge crests. There are a number of forms of venting (Figure 13.2). At 'black smokers' the water issues at 350°C and on mixing with surrounding deep sea water builds chimneys up to 30 metres high made of precipitated metallic sulphides. These chimneys frequently collapse into fragments that become incorporated in the sea bed, but are constantly replaced by new outgrowths. Other chimneys with less elevated temperature outflow are built by 'white smokers,' much of the precipitate being made of gypsum. At other places venting is more diffuse through cracks and crevices in the lava, but even so, temperatures in excess of 40°C have been detected among clumps of animals growing at such vents, though the heated water is rapidly mixed with surrounding water and much of the associated fauna experiences typical deep sea bottom temperatures of 2°C or lower. A more diffuse type of venting occurs in a few places where accumulated sediments overly the ridge, as for example off Vancouver Island, off Oregon and in the Gulf of California (Simoneit *et al.* 1986). The fluid issuing from all types of venting begins as sea water whose chemical composition has been altered by passage through the heated basalts. Sulphate becomes reduced to sulphide, magnesium is replaced by barium, calcium and the alkaline Earths, while dissolved silicate and the heavy metals such as manganese are greatly increased (Table 13.1). Concentrations of methane and helium

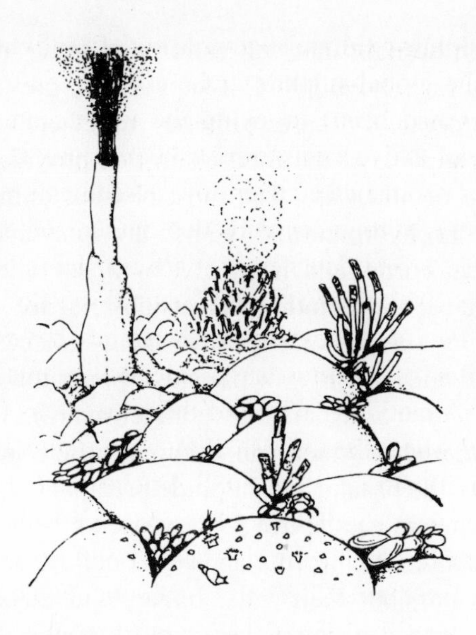

Figure 13.2. Sketch of typical hot vent animals, as found on the East Pacific Rise. There is a black smoke chimney (right), a white smoker with alvinellid worms (centre back), and pillow lava with diffuse venting in the foreground. Among the symbiont containing animals in the crevices are the large tube-worm (Riftia), large clams (Calyptogena), and smaller mussels (Bathymodiolus). The crabs, browsers or predators that depend on the symbiont-containing animals or on free-living chemoautotrophic bacteria for food.

are also much higher than in normal sea water. Hydrothermal sites are thought to remain active for several decades. However, individual vents appear to have shorter lives, from ten to twenty years, as judged by lack of accumulation of precipitated sulphides and occurrence of dead shells of clams. From the faunistic point of view vents have to be seen as short-lived and ephemeral habitats, occupied mostly by fast-growing opportunistic animal species. As a corollary, hydrothermal vent species will require a high output of larval stages or young to maintain themselves and allow 'jumping' to new vents as old vents close down, but even so there is probably a high extinction rate. This idea of an opportunist community is supported by the relatively low diversity of species at each vent region. But because of the high degree of endemicity of species the overall diversity of the vent fauna is higher than would be expected of such ephemeral habitats.

In reviewing what is known of the communities of life at the vents (Grassle 1986, Tunnicliffe 1988; see Figure 13.2) we start with the very large populations of free-living bacteria in and close to the vents. Some of these have been brought into cultivation and some indeed can live at elevated temperatures (above 100°C if kept at high pressures comparable to those in the depths). These bacteria, together with the internal symbionts, form the base of the food chain that provides organic matter for the abundance of other life. The most obvious animals, occuring in great abundance at hydrothermal vents, are polychaete worms, the pogonophoran tube-worms, and the bivalve molluscs (clams and mussels), but various crustaceans, including squat-lobsters are present in good number and several species of fish have been collected (Figure 13.2). Various jellyfish and acorn worms have been reported. The most abundant polychaete worms are the pompeii-worm *Alvinella* and the palm-worm *Paralvinella,* which can occur in large clusters attached to other animals or to the basalts and sulphide precipitates. Some species of both can live at temperatures above 25°C, close to the hot black smokers. Both groups of polychaete worms appear to collect and eat free-living bacteria in the water, but their gills, bodies and tubes are sometimes coated with filamentous bacteria whose nutritional value to the worm remains to be established. The large pogonophoran *Riftia,* which can reach 2 m tube length and a body diameter over 20 mm is abundant at the vents in the tropical eastern Pacific; smaller types of tubeworms can co-occur with *Riftia,* but may alone be present at other vents such as the Juan de Fuca-Endeavour Ridge *(Ridgeia).* The vestimentiferans show a high degree of endemicity, different species and genera being encountered at different areas of venting.

The most obvious molluscs at the hydrothermal vents are bivalves, the mytilid *Bathymodiolus* and species of *Calyptogena* (Vesicomyidae), some of them more wide-ranging in distribution than other vent groups. Primitive gastropod molluscs (archaeogastropods) are also abundant at vents, in the form of 'limpets' and 'periwinkles;' some graze on bacterial films while others have symbiotic bacteria that grow on their gills. A newly-discovered venting area in the western Pacific near the Marianas Trench, has an abundant population of a snail-like mollusc (a mesogastropod), whose gills harbour internal symbiotic sulphide oxidizing bacteria (Hessler *et al.* 1988).

Other groups of animals found at hydrothermal vents are indirectly dependent on the symbioses. The most noticeable crustaceans are scavenging decapod crabs (*Bythograea* and *Cyanograea),* often seen among the colonies of pogonophorans, on which they can prey. Waters near the vents may swarm with copepods (the deep-water family Spinocalanidae), while squat-lobsters, shrimps and amphipods are among other crustaceans seen at vents. Barnacles at the vents are represented by primitive members of the Scalpellidae (goose-barnacles), Verrucidae, and Brachylepadidae, sometimes forming something approaching a barnacle zone, as for example in the western Pacific venting areas off the Mariana Islands. Evidently the vents can provide a refuge for ancient life forms as well as a habitat for faster evolving opportunists.

A few fishes are exclusively found at hydrothermal vents, chiefly blenny-like and eel-like species (*Zoarcidae* and *Bithytidae*). Their biology and feeding habits remain to be investigated, but they depend on the symbioses for shelter and probably for food. The animal groups not represented at vents, or reported only from the periphery in small numbers are sponges, echinoderms (sea-urchins, starfish etc) and attached corals and whip corals. These groups lack a well-developed blood vascular system which may be a disadvantage in the fluctuating conditions at the vents, while the colony formers may be unable to adapt to the short life of the individual vents.

The existence of life in the hot water of the hydrothermal vents has been compared with the conditions that may have existed on Earth before development of photosynthesis. Some scientists have even suggested that life on Earth could have originated in conditions comparable to the vents, at hot submarine springs, where the combination of heat and dissolved chemicals might result in the formation of amino acids and their subsequent polymerization into peptides (Baross and Hoffman 1985). It is suggested that primitive replicating organisms may have evolved in the form of loose symbioses, some of which have greatly altered from the original. Objections have been raised to this hypothesis (Miller and Bada 1988), but much depends on the velocity and mixing of the hydrothermal flow inside the crust (Corliss 1990), a subject for further measurement. Analysis of the ribosomal nucleic acids of present day bacteria does indeed suggest that some of the chemosynthetic bacteria living in hot springs are primitive and close to the hypothesized first self-replicating organisms on Earth.

The Pogonophora

Pogonophora are wormlike animals related to annelids that construct tubes of chitin (Southward and Southward 1988). They are important in the present context since all species contain symbiotic bacteria. The bacteria occur inside special cells located in the hind end of the body, which often constitutes the greater part of the tissues. There are two main subgroups. The recently discovered large vestimentiferans *(Obturata)* live attached to rocks and other hard materials around hydrothermal vents or cold seeps. Adult vestimentiferans have hundreds of tentacles joined together into a branchial plume surrounding a plug (obturaculum) which can close off the mouth of the tube when the plume is withdrawn. The smaller pogonophorans *(Perviata)* were the first to be discovered (in 1914). They have elongated narrow bodies, carry from one to a few hundred tentacles, and do not have a device for closing off the tube from the exterior. These smaller pogonophorans live in softer sediments of the outer shallow seas (continental shelf) and the ocean slopes and also in fjords and trenches. Their symbiotic bacteria are usually sulphur oxidizers that depend on particulate sulphides in the sediment but as already noted, one species *(Siboglinum poseidoni)* that occurs in the Skagerrak, uses methane as an energy and carbon source.

The pogonophore tissue that contains the bacteria (trophosome) develops from larval tissue that would otherwise form the digestive cavity. A functioning digestive system is not formed in the comparatively large larvae of the small (perviate) pogonophorans but has been found in the juveniles of a vestimentiferan that appears to have a swimming planktonic larval stage (trochophore). In this vestimentiferan the gut persists after the larva stops swimming and settles on the bottom, but is soon transformed to bacteria-containing tissue and the mouth is lost (Southward 1988). Thus, after the larval food supplies have been used up, a growing pogonophoran is virtually dependent on supplies of food from the bacteria it nurtures, possibly supplemented by uptake of dissolved organic compounds from the surroundings (Southward and Southward 1987). The symbiotic nature of the association between Pogonophora and bacteria is confirmed by stable carbon isotope assays of the host tissues which show transfer of carbon compounds from carbon dioxide fixed by the bacteria (Spiro *et al.* 1986).

Molluscs

A number of clams (bivalve molluscs), including species living at hydrothermal vents and others living in ordinary sediments, are now known to be wholly or partly dependent on symbiotic sulphide oxidizing bacteria located in the gills (Southward 1987). This is most evident in the species of the protobranch genus *Solemya* in which the gut is either very reduced or absent in the adult stage. These animals can flourish in sediments where there is no oxygen and where free hydrogen sulphide is abundant, places where other sediment burrowing life is sparse, for instance in mangrove swamps and close to sewer outfalls. Other bivalves with symbionts, including the mytilid *Bathymodiolus* and species of *Calyptogena,* already mentioned, live in abundance close to hydrothermal vents. Both can be found at some distance from the vents, where their growth rate is slower, and it seems that they may live partly heterotrophically by consuming the free-living bacteria associated with vent plumes. Certain mussel-like bivalves (mytilids) growing near hydrocarbon seeps have been shown to contain bacteria capable of oxidizing methane, and the carbon isotope ratio of the tissues indicates that most of the host carbon is derived from this source (Brooks *et al.* 1987). Most other members of the cold seep and hydrocarbon seep faunas that live in symbiosis rely on sulphur-oxidizing bacteria (Paull *et al.* 1985).

The most interesting group of clams from the aspect of chemoautotrophic symbiosis is the superfamily *Lucinaceae.* Most species have modified gills (single thick demibranchs each side of the body) and the digestive system is reduced or simplified compared with bivalves possessing 'normal' gills and which use them to sieve off small particles of food from the plankton. The problem as to how the bivalves with modified gills and reduced digestive systems could nourish themselves was solved when symbiotic bacteria were identified in the gills. The autotrophic nature of the gill bacteria in this group is shown by the occurrence of the autotrophic enzyme ribulosebisphosphate carboxylase that fixes carbon dioxide, and enzymes involved in oxidation of reduced sulphur compounds. Analysis of the stable carbon isotope ratios confirms that much of the host organic matter is supplied by the bacteria (Spiro *et al.* 1986). The carbon isotope values indicate different degrees of reliance on the autotrophic bacteria; recent assays suggest that younger stages feed mainly on particles and only when the animal is big enough to burrow deeply in the sand or mud does autotrophy become dominant *(personal communication,* P.R. Dando). The adult stages of the lucinid and thyasirid clams that are dependent on chemoautotrophic bacteria all live deeply buried in sediments, with the shell below the interface between the oxidized and reduced layers (Figure 13.1). The lucinids have an exhalant siphon running up to the sediment surface and use their vermiform foot to excavate an inhalant canal from the surface for supply of oxygenated water. The foot is also used to excavate tunnels below the shell; it is thought that the animal mixes oxygenated water obtained from the inhalant canal with water from the anoxic layers that contain reduced sulphur compounds and is thus able to supply the gill bacteria with the correct substrate levels for chemoautotrophy (Dando *et al.* 1986). The flow of water through the inhalant canal is thought to oxidize some iron sulphides, converting them to thiosulphate and hydrogen sulphide, which can be used by symbiotic bacteria.

Extent of the symbiosis and Gaian implications

The above bivalves offer one example of how the symbiont-containing animals that live in sediments are able greatly to extend the habitat available for bacteria that live by oxidizing reduced sulphur compounds. The inlet and outlet canals are extended to the sediment surface, while the foot obtains access to reserves of iron sulphide deeper in the sediment (see Figure 13.1). Free-living sulphur-oxidizing bacteria are limited to the narrow interface between the oxidized and reduced layers and this would be the only habitat available for such bacteria if it were not for their ability to live in symbiosis with many invertebrate animals. The small oligochaete and nematode worms already mentioned also bridge this gap by their migrations above and below the interface. Perviate pogonophores are also able to bridge the gap between the layers, but without moving very much, by virtue of their very elongated body whereby the tentacles are exposed to oxygen while the bacterial tissue is exposed to sulphide.

In contrast to these sediment-living animals with symbionts, the organisms that live at hydrothermal vents have simultaneous access to oxygen and sulphide, as a result of mixing of the vent efflux containing hydrogen sulphide with surrounding oxygenated sea water. The vent fauna depends on this mixing and the animals die if the flow slows down or stops. Sediments containing high amounts of particulate sulphides that can be mobilized for the symbiotic bacteria provide a more stable but less rich environment than at the hydrothermal vents, and the animals tend to be less 'opportunistic.'

The association of bacteria with invertebrate animals living in sediments where there is iron sulphide opens up a much wider habitat for the sulphur-oxidizing bacteria. They would otherwise be restricted to the narrow interface between the upper layer with oxygen and the lower layers enriched in sulphides. Thus, the scope of the reaction is much extended and the amount of sulphide oxidized and returned to the sea water greatly enhanced. The ordinary animals that live in sand or mud also contribute to this feedback mechanism, though in a less positive and less controlled manner (Figure 13.3). Some crustaceans, clams and worms that live by collecting particles of food, for instance living plankton from the overlying water or dead organic particles from the sediment surface, obtain this food by pumping water through burrows formed in the sedi-

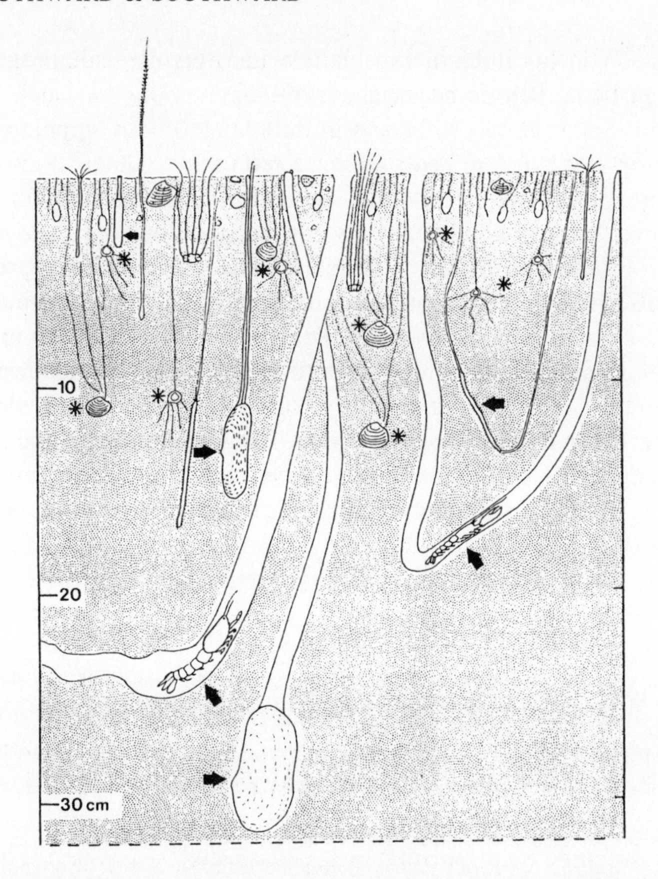

*Figure 13.3. Representation of the arrangement of burrowing animals (infauna) in a shallow water sediment, as found by taking large core samples. This example is from muddy sand in Plymouth Sound. There is a mixture of symbiont-containing clams (marked *, there are two species present) and animals that feed on particles filtered off from water pumped through burrows (marked by arrows). The deeper burrows include those of two species of callianassid crustaceans and two species of large clams (Lutraria). Shallower burrows include polychaete worms. Also shown are buried brittle stars with arms stretching to the surface.*

ment. They filter the water through gills or hirsute appendages to strain off the plankton and particles, which they eat. The water flowing through the burrows also carries with it oxygen which encourages the growth of sulphur-oxidizing bacteria on the walls of the burrows; in addition, the very passage of a stream of water also encourages chemical oxidation of the iron sulphides to thiosulphate and dissolved sulphide. Together with the activity of the symbiont-containing animals, this activity ensures that a large part of the particulate sulphides are returned to the sea. Many of these animals without symbionts are unable to live in sediments where the sulphide content is high, especially where dissolved hydrogen sulphide is present. But some of the symbiont containers, such as the protobranch *Solemya* can withstand millimolar levels of sulphide as can *Thyasira sarsi.* When sediments are rendered toxic to other forms of life, whether by natural events or human pollution, these resistant forms can still colonize the damaged habitat. By continued activity of the symbiotic bacteria they are able to lower the sulphide levels to those permitting recolonization by the rest of the fauna. The symbiont containers may then find there is not enough sulphide in the habitat to maintain the previous high populations, and they either have to migrate away to richer patches of sediment or die, leaving the less tolerant animals to regulate the sulphide levels *(personal communication,* P.R. Dando). Such interactions are all components of the regulatory system for sulphide in sediments, part of the pathway of sulphur cycling in the sea, and possibly of Gaian regulation of the global sulphur cycle.

References

Baross, J.A. and S.E. Hoffman. 1985. Submarine hydrothermal vents and associated gradient environments as sites for the origin and evolution of life. *Origins of life and evolution of the biosphere.* 15:327–45.

Brooks, J.M., M.C. Kennicutt, C.R. Fisher, *et al.* 1987. Deep-sea hydrocarbon seep communities: evidence for energy and nutritional sources. *Science.* 283:1138–42.

Burgh, M.E. de, and C.L. Singla. 1985. Bacterial colonisation and endocytosis on the gill of a new limpet species from a hydrothermal vent. *Marine Biology.* 84:1–6.

Cavanaugh, C.M. 1983. Symbiotic chemoautotrophic bacteria in marine invertebrates from sulphide-rich habitats. *Nature.* 302:58–61.

Childress, J.J. (ed). 1988. Hydrothermal vents. A case study of the biology and chemistry of a deep-sea hydrothermal vent of the Galapagos Rift. *Deep-Sea Research.* 35(10/11A).

Corliss, J.B. 1990. Hot springs and the origin of life. *Nature.* 347:624.

Dando, P.R., A.J. Southward, E.C. Southward and R.L. Barrett. 1986. Possible energy sources for chemoautotrophic prokaryotes symbiotic with invertebrates from a Norwegian fjord. *Ophelia.* 26:135–50.

Edmond, J.M., K.L. von Damm, R.E. MacDuff and C.I. Measures. 1982. Chemistry of hot springs on the East Pacific Rise and their effluent dispersal. *Nature.* 297:187–91.

Endow, K. and S. Ohta. 1990. Occurrence of bacteria in the primary oocytes of vesicomyid clam *Calyptogenae soyae. Marine Ecology Progress Series.* 64:309–11.

Felbeck, H., J.J. Childress and G.N. Somero. 1981. Calvin–Benson cycle and sulphide oxidation enzymes in animals from sulphide-rich habitats. *Nature.* London. 298:291–93.

Fricke, H., O. Giere, K. Stetter, *et al.* 1989. Hydrothermal vent communities at the shallow subpolar Mid-Atlantic ridge. *Marine Biology.* 102:425–29

Giere, O. and C. Langheld. 1987. Structural organization, transfer and biological fate of endosymbiotic bacteria in gutless oligochaetes. *Marine Biology.* 93:641–50.

Grassle, J.F. 1986. The ecology of deep-sea hydrothermal vent communities. *Advances in Marine Biology.* 23:301–62.

Hessler, R.R., P. Lonsdale and J. Hawkins. 1988. Patterns on the ocean floor. *New Scientist.* 117:1605.

Jannasch, H.W. 1985. The chemosythetic support of life and the microbial diversity at deep-sea hydrothermal vents. *Proceedings of the Royal Society.* B. 225:277–97.

Jones, M.L. (ed). 1985 Hydrothermal vents of the eastern Pacific; an overview. *Bulletin of the Biological Society of Washington.* 6:1–545.

Kelly, D.P. 1982. Biochemistry of the chemolithotrophic oxidation of inorganic sulphur. *Philosophical Transaction of the Royal Society.* B 298:499–528.

Kelly, D.P. and J.G. Kuenen. 1984. Ecology of the colourless sulphur bacteria. pp.211–40 in G.A. Codd. *Aspects of microbial metabolism and ecology.* London: Academic Press.

Kulm, L.D., E. Suess, J.C. Moore, *et al.* 1986. Oregon subduction zone: venting, fauna and carbonates. New York: *Science.* 231:561–66.

Margulis, L. 1981. *Symbiosis in cell evolution.* San Francisco: Freeman.

Miller, S.L. and J.L. Bada. 1988. Submarine hot springs and the origin of life. *Nature.* 334:609–11.

Muscatine, L. and J.W. Porter. 1977. Reef corals: mutualistic symbiosis adapted to nutrient poor environments. *Bioscience.* 27:454–60.

Olsen, G.J., D.J. Lane, S.J. Giovanni and N.R. Pace. 1986. Microbial ecology and evolution: a ribosomal RNA approach. *Annual Review of Microbiology.* 40:337–65.

Paull, C.K., A.J.T. Jull, L.J. Toolin and T. Linick. 1985. Stable isotope evidence for chemosynthesis in an abyssal seep community. *Nature.* 317:709–11.

Rona, P.A., G. Klinkhammer, T.A. Nelsen, J.H. Trefry, and H. Elderfield. 1986. Black smokers, massive sulphides and vent biota at the Mid-Atlantic Ridge. *Nature.* 321:33.

Schmaljohann, R. and H.J. Flügel. 1987. Methane oxidizing bacteria in Pogonophora. *Sarsia.* 72:91–98.

Simoneit, B.R.T., P.F. Lonsdale, J.M. Edmond and W.C. Shanks. 1990. Deep water hydrocarbon seeps in Guaymas Basin, Gulf of California. *Applied Geochemistry.* 5:41–49.

Somero, G.N., J.J. Childress and A.E. Anderson. 1989. Transport, metabolism, and detoxicification of hydrogen sulfide in animals from sulfide-rich marine environments. *CRC Critical Reviews in Aquatic Sciences.* 1:591–614.

Southward, A.J. 1988. Pogonophora: tube-worms dependent on endosymbiotic bacteria. *ISI Atlas of Science: Animal and Plant Sciences.* 203–7.

Southward, A.J. and E.C. Southward. 1987. Pogonophora. Vol.2, pp.201–28 in T.J. Pandian and F.J. Vernberg. *Animal Energetics.* New York: Academic Press.

Southward, E.C. 1982. Bacterial symbionts in Pogonophora. *Journal of the Marine Biological Association of the United Kingdom.* 62:889–906.

—— 1987. Contribution of symbiotic chemoautotrophs to the nutrition of benthic invertebrates. pp.83–118 in M. Sleigh (ed). *Microbes in the sea.* Ellis Horwood.

—— 1988. Development of the gut and segmentation of newly-settled stages of *Ridgeia* (Vestimentifera): implications for relationship between Vestimentifera and Pogonophora. *Journal of the Marine Biological Association of the UK.* 68:465–87.

Spiro, B., P.B. Greenwood, A.J. Southward and P.R. Dando. 1986. C^{13}/C^{12} ratios in marine invertebrates from reducing sediments: confirmation of nutritional importance of chemoautotrophic endosymbiotic bacteria. *Marine Ecol. Progress Series.* 28:233–40.

Taylor, F.J.R. and P.J. Harrison. 1983. Ecological aspects of intracellular symbiosis. pp.827–41 in H.E.A. Schenk and W. Schwemmler. *Endocytobiology II.*

Tunnicliffe, V. 1988. Biogeography and evolution of hydrothermal-vent fauna in the eastern Pacific Ocean. *Proceedings of the Royal Society.* B 233:347–66.

Acknowledgments

The authors are indebted to many colleagues for discussions on this topic. They would particularly like to thank Dr P.R. Dando, Professor D.P. Kelly and Professor V. Tunnicliffe for help and advice.

– 14 –
Mutualism and Soil Processes: a Gaian Outlook

Patrick Lavelle

Soil is a complex environment that comprises intimately mixed solid, liquid and gaseous elements. As a result of its structural characteristics, primordial soil became the first of terrestrial environments to be colonized by aquatic organisms. Soil organisms still bear the imprint of that ancient colonization. They include many primitive invertebrates and high densities of micro-organisms seldom observed in other habitats.

Soils have two complementary functions: to be the physical and nutritional support for plant production and to recycle dead organic matter through decomposition processes.

Abiotic factors are essential in determining the rates and pathways of decomposition. Nonetheless, decomposition is essentially a biological process that is realized through a cascade of complex interactions among all the organisms. These interactions may take any form. Mutualism, however, is largely dominant. This paper explains how constraints of living in soils have led to the differentiation of distinct adaptive strategies among soil organisms, and the establishment of mutualistic relationships between organisms with contrasted strategies. The role of mutualism in soil functions and the implications regarding the Gaia hypothesis are further discussed.

Adaptive strategies of soil organisms

Soil invertebrates have to face three major constraints in their environment: feeding in relatively low-quality organic resources; moving in a dark and compact environment; and resisting occasionally unfavourable conditions of temperature and/or moisture.

Feeding

The average nutritive value of resources available in soils is relatively poor. They mainly comprise decomposing material with a low nutrient content and the presence of highly polymerized molecules, for example lignin, humic acids and tannin-protein complexes). As an example, 80 per cent or more of the nitrogen of leaf cytoplasm forms complexes with tannins and polyphenols released in cells at the death of the leaf. Thus, fresh leaf-litter may well have a high overall nitrogen content, but the nitrogen be inaccessible to most invertebrate decomposers. Higher quality resources such as the microbial biomass or freshly-dead invertebrates are much less abundant, dispersed in the soil profile, and made partly inaccessible by physical protection in microhabitats.

Movements

Soil is a compact environment and movement is only possible through a labyrinth of pores and channels. These comprise a relatively low proportion of the whole soil volume and decrease in size as a proportion of the soil volume with increasing depth.

Moisture regime

This semi-aquatic environment is theoretically suitable for fauna with high moisture requirements. However, it may have highly variable patterns of water availability in time and space owing to climatic variation and to capillary forces which, depending on the mean size of pores, may hold fast to the water and prevent its extraction.

Temperature

Temperature is the ultimate regulator of metabolic activity in soil organisms, which are all heterothermic. Temperature operates as an ultimate factor through its absolute extremes, and as a relative factor in the short term. Temperature and moisture regimes determine the intensity and distribution of activity periods along the year. In that respect, they largely determine the viability of any particular adaptive strategy. Strategies based on the use of low-quality resources are only viable if long and intense periods of activity are possible; if this condition is not fulfilled the life cycle must be completed in a shorter time, by using higher-quality resources.

Water availability and temperature usually become more favourable and predictable with depth while food availability and quality decrease as well as the exposure to predators. As a result, selection by species of a depth at which to live is a significant parameter of their adaptive strategy.

The way and the extent to which soil animals face constraints of their environment largely determine their abundance and the ultimate role they play in any particular soil system.

Three main strategies of movement may be observed depending on the size of animals.

1. Swimming in the water films which fill soil capillaries and pores and cover soil particles. This is the way *hydrobiont* fauna moves about within the soil. Such movements are limited to a few millimetres owing to the small size of the animals and the frequent discontinuity of the water phase.
2. Moving in the air-filled pore space. This strategy is adopted by most mesofauna and some slender, worm-shaped macrofauna (for example, *Chilopoda, Geophilidae* and some thin polyhumic earthworms). Epigeic* macroinvertebrates do the same in the leaf-litter layers; a large number of litter invertebrates may shelter in the upper centimetres of the soil using macropores or the galleries of burrowing animals.
3. Removing the soil. Only large soil animals have the strength to do so and this behaviour is therefore observed in anecic and endogeic earthworms, termites, ants and a few insects with transformed forelegs, for example cicada larvae, *Gryllotalpidae, Hemiptera* or *Coleoptera.* The ability to dig gives invertebrates a great selective advantage. Like anecic earthworms or termites, these invertebrates are able to feed in leaf-litter — where the highest-quality resources are found — and avoid the frequently unfavourable climatic conditions and high density of the predators present in this environment. Some of these invertebrates are active root-feeders.

Adaptations to unfavourable climatic conditions

Soil organisms are all the more resistant to drought and frost as they are small and can shelter in favourable microsites when overall conditions are unfavourable. This is especially true of bacteria and protozoa which may

* *Epigeic* describes those invertebrates that feed on and live in surface litter; *endogeic* those invertebrates such as earthworms and termites that live in soil; and *anecic* those that feed on litter but live in burrows or galleries or at the surface.

soak in the water of micropores 1 or less microns in diameter, in soils with water tensions of up to pF 5. In the same soils large invertebrates as earthworms would not survive long for want of an efficient defence against drought.

However, in some instances, organisms may modify the environment to get better protection. This is especially true of social insects, as ants and termites that build nests with remarkably buffered conditions of temperature and moisture.

Mutualistic digestive systems

A major constraint for soil organisms in general is the relatively low quality of the major feeding resources, inclusive of leaf and root litter and soil organic matter. The major drawbacks associated with most of these resources are: *(i)* a high content of carbohydrates with high molecular weight such as cellulose and lignin, *(ii)* sequestration of nitrogen in tannin-protein complexes and therefore poor availability, *(iii)* nutrient imbalances. Soil invertebrates rarely possess suitable enzymes to digest directly most of the substrates available, such as decomposing litter or soil organic matter (SOM). Equally, while roots are able to assimilate mineral nutrients from soil solutions they lack the capacity to extract nutrients directly in organic form.

In contrast, micro-organisms as a whole apparently have unlimited abilities to digest any natural substrate. The principal limitation to their activity is their dependence on a water film to survive and above all their limited ability to move. The latter characteristic is especially true for bacteria, whereas fungi may colonize new substrates by growing new mycelia and translocating cytoplasm towards the growing points. In addition, invertebrate activities probably enhance fungal activity by the active dispersal of spores.

Micro-organisms and invertebrates therefore have developed contrasting adaptive strategies. The former have developed considerable potential for digesting any kind of organic substrate and a strong ability to withstand adverse environmental conditions. By contrast invertebrates have well-developed locomotion in soil and can fragment decomposing resources, create structures which affect aeration and water infiltration, for example through creating galleries, macropores and casts, and finally break down organic matter either by digesting the soil during gut transit or as a result of their mechanical activity. On the other hand they may further sequester SOM in the compact structure of their faecal pellets and casts or in the walls of their nests. Roots may be considered as functional equivalents of macro-invertebrates as a result of their ability to move (by growing new tips) and their limited ability to use soil nutrient resources other than in mineral form.

Mutualistic relationships have developed among soil organisms with contrasting adaptive strategies for the exploitation of organic resources of the litter and soil system. These are digestive mutualisms in which micro-organisms generally associate with macro-organisms, for instance with macro-invertebrates and roots. In general these relationships may be designated as *anisosymbiotic* owing to the differences in size of both components, transient, the association being temporary and casual, and ex-habitational, hence by physical rather than organismic contact. Such mutualistic relationships have also been qualified as 'diffuse' by Howe.

Based on the intensity of the association between macro- and micro-organisms, four different digestive systems may be distinguished: direct digestion; the 'external rumen' type of digestion; facultative mutualism developed in the gut of invertebrates with ingested microflora; and symbiosis with a specialized microflora or microfauna, as observed in the gut of primitive termites. This ultimate system may be considered as the most evolved, although facultative symbiosis is considered a more flexible and efficient association.

1. *Direct digestion* is found in micro-organisms and predators. It seems to be extremely limited among saprovores. Higher termites have cellulase (Potts and Hewitt 1974). Cellulases have also been reported in earthworms, but it is still uncertain whether they are actually produced by the worm itself or by associated micro-organisms (Laverack 1963; Loquet *et al.* 1987).
2. In the *external rumen type* of digestion, invertebrates which do not produce endogenous cellulase, periodically reingest their faeces and thus take advantage of the release of assimilable compounds owing to microbial activity (Swift *et al.* 1979). They comminute, fractionate and humidify the ingested material, which enhances microbial activity. Most litter feeding epigeic arthropods use this digestive system. Termites or Atta ants which cultivate fungi on especially elaborated woody or leaf material may be also considered as using this 'external rumen' strategy.
3. *Facultative mutualism* with a non-specific microflora ingested with the soil or litter material is a close association in which invertebrates offer microflora suitable conditions for their activity in their gut and take advantage of assimilable metabolites released by the enhanced microbial activity.

Such a digestive system has been described in endogeic geophagous (soil-eating) earthworms (Barois and Lavelle 1986). The soil ingested is mixed with an equivalent amount of water and 5 to 16 per cent of intestinal mucus which is a readily assimilable mixture of low molecular weight glycoproteins, amino acids and osides (simple sugar molecules). Intense mixing in the gizzard disperses the soil and results in the formation of an homogenous suspension of bacteria, readily assimilable substrates (mucus) with soil mineral particles and soil organic matter whose physical protection in aggregates has been removed. Soil microflora first increase in activity by using mucus as an energetic substrate. In the middle part of the gut mucus is almost completely metabolized; microbial activity is high and bacteria through a priming effect (Jenkinson 1966) are able to digest soil organic matter. The digestive products are released in the gut and partly reabsorbed by the worm.

This facultative symbiosis has also been observed in a number of wood and leaf-litter feeding *Diptera* and *Coleoptera* larvae (Campbell 1929; Hassall and Jennings 1975 in SAH 79).

4. *Symbiosis* with a specific gut microflora is the ultimate stage of an obligate association between invertebrates and micro-organisms to digest lignocellulose. Phylogenetically 'lower' termites, have flagellated protozoa and bacteria in a bulbous 'paunch' of the proctodeum. They are unique species, found only in the gut of these termites and are attached to the gut wall by a holdfast organelle which secures them to the epithelial tissue. These protozoa digest lignin which is used by the termite. Bacteria provide growth factors for protozoa, but termites can survive without these bacteria. (Yamin 1981). In higher termites, filamentous bacteria attached to cuticular spines partly fill the proctodeum 'paunch.'

The efficiency of soil organisms in the exploitation of soil resources, especially the low-quality ones, their ability to move and their resistance to unfavourable temperature and moisture conditions are determined to a large extent by their size and individual or social behavioural responses to constraints. Small animals better adapt temperature and moisture extremes, but they are less able to use low-quality resources and modify the environment. Conversely, large animals make a better use of low-quality food and do not adapt to extreme environmental conditions although they sometimes have a great ability to transform their environment.

Individual size partly determines the ability to use microflora in mutualistic digestive systems: a minimum size is necessary to allow transport and temporary or semi-permanent sheltering of associated microflora in the gut. As a result, the ability of soil invertebrates to use low-quality resources tends to increase with size, all other environmental conditions being equal. Size also determines the ability of invertebrates to move. The smaller they are, the least far they can move, and the more they are dependent on the distribution and continuity of water films and/or porous space. Conversely, large animals may move on a wider scale, provided they have the ability to dig their way when their diameter is much larger than the average pore size. Finally, size partly determines the ability of invertebrates to resist temporarily unfavourable conditions. Small invertebrates may resist through specific biological strategies such as encystment and/or shelter into favourable microenvironments. Large invertebrates have much less efficient defences. Such different patterns would explain why distribution of micro- and, to a lesser extent, meso-fauna taxa is continuous whereas macrofauna, especially termites and earthworms have highly discontinuous distributions. The behaviour of individuals and populations may somewhat alter this general pattern. Aggregation and social organization are most important in that respect.

Mutualism among macro-organisms

Mutualistic relationships among invertebrates and between invertebrates and roots have rarely been directly addressed. Since most saprophagous invertebrates develop a transient mutualism with the free microbial community, the whole detritivorous community becomes linked by a general mutualistic relationship in which the activity of each individual component is likely to be beneficial to the whole community. In such conditions, food-webs tend to be diffuse. At a finer scale of resolution, however, evidences of niche partitioning among invertebrates may appear. Detailed analyses of gut contents of *Collembola* and *Acari* species show that resource partitioning may operate through the following mechanisms:

1. Species use different parts of a same resource;
2. They ingest the same food, but digest different parts owing to their specific association with bacteria with different digestive abilities;
3. They ingest distinct nutritive resources as a result of morphological differences (i.e., different types of mouths) and/or specific physiological traits (e.g., interruptions of feeding owing to moultings or diapauses or ecophysiological adaptations).

Predators may play a critical role, especially micropredators (protozoa and nematodes) which occasionally serve as intermediaries between microflora and macroinvertebrates or roots. They digest micro-organisms and are, themselves digested by larger invertebrates (e.g., earthworms) or release nutrients in forms available to plants, at their death or as products of their metabolism.

Relationships between soil invertebrates and plants are diverse. Results obtained in experimental situations are often complex since they result from a mixture of obviously mutualistic effects, for instance the release of nutrients in urine and faeces, improvement of soil physical conditions (infiltration and retention of water), and enhancement of microbial activity and the subsequent alteration of nutrient release, and detrimental effects such as rhizophagy.

Mutualism and the function of soil

Biological systems of regulation (BSRs): At the scale of the entire soil system, the food-web may be separated into a few large interactive systems based on mutualistic relationships between micro– and macro-organisms. The structure and activity of these BSRs are determined by abiotic factors operating at larger scales of time and space, for instance climatic and edaphic factors, including nutrient status, nature and abundance of clay minerals.

The relative importance of these factors, however, may greatly vary depending on the type of ecosystem (Lavelle *et al.* 1991). In the humid tropics, climatic and edaphic constraints may be greatly reduced owing to constantly high temperatures and moisture, and the low abundance and/or activity of clay minerals. In fact, under such conditions, biological systems of regulation become the main regulators of soil processes and hence, of the conservation of soil fertility.

Biological regulation

Four main biological systems of regulation may be distinguished. Their relative importance varies in different types of ecosystems. Their function is entirely based on mutualistic relationships.

Litter-superficial root system

This system has leaf-litter as the main feeding resource, a dominant community of arthropods as macroorganisms and a microflora dominated by fungi, and an occasionally dense fine root mat which serves as a sink for nutrients released from the decomposing litter. This system may be almost closed in some extreme instances, for example Amazonian forest on spodosols, but most often, hydrosoluble organic and mineral elements can leach towards lower soil horizons and litter may be exported in other decomposing systems by the anecic fauna, hence those that feed on litter but live in burrows or galleries built in the soil (earthworms, some termites) or at the surface or on trees (termites). Anecic invertebrates thus have a special role as they take away part of the litter and introduce it in different systems of decomposition, such as the termitosphere of termites and the drilosphere of earthworms.

Direct mineralization of litter by the root-fungi association is an extreme situation only found in some forests on sandy, heavily leached and desaturated soils. In better soils, this system of direct cycling is less important and the thickness of the surface root mat decreases. Other processes operate as for example direct decomposition by free micro-organisms, principally fungi, and also fractionation and digestion by invertebrates. In this process, an important (10 to 20 per cent) proportion of the minerals released and water-soluble elements are washed down into the soil. They are then consumed or insolubilized, and absorbed by soil colloids.

All the epigeic fauna, those invertebrates that feed on and live in the surface litter participate in the fragmentation and include large myriapods (diplopods and polydesmids), isopods and epigeic earthworms as well as the microarthropods and *Enchytraeidae* among the mesofauna. Microfauna is also represented in the litter system, but its relative importance is usually low except in extreme arid or cold environments.

The rhizosphere

The rhizosphere is defined as the part of soil which is submitted to the influence of roots. This system exploits soil organic matter resources around the live root through active mutualistic relationships between roots and soil microflora mediated by root exudates and regulated by the micropredator food-chain including protozoa and nematodes with bacteria as prey. In that system, roots regulate microbial activity by providing readily assimilable carbon sources which stimulates the activity of the free soil microflora and of a suite of obligate or occasional microbial symbionts. Rhizo-deposition represents 5 to 30 per cent of total photosynthates, therefore amounting to several thousand kilograms per hectare.

Micro-organisms develop first at the expense of exudates. They become further able to digest more complex substrates from soil organic matter by a priming effect and this results in a significant mineralization of soil organic matter.

These micro-organisms may directly release metabolites that are used by the plant. However, a large part of this release results from the activity of a micropredator food-chain which operates in the rhizosphere, hence the root zone. This food-chain includes bacteria as a food source, protozoa and free nematodes as predators. Micropredators release nutrients from bacteria as a product of their own metabolism or following their own death when food sources diminish as when the root system matures.

The root zone is also characterized by an intense activity of obligate or semi-obligate root symbionts, especially mycorrhizae and nitrogen-fixing micro-organisms (*Rhizobium* and *Frankia*) that play a considerable role in providing nutrients to the plant.

The drilosphere

Drilosphere (from the Greek *drillos* = earthworm) is defined as the part of the soil which is influenced by earthworm activities in particular the generation of casts and galleries; the energy source may be surface litter or SOM, depending on the ecological category of earthworms. Microflora become active as result of anecic litter-feeding species mixing litter with soil or breaking the physical protection of SOM in soil aggregates during their passage through the gut. The production of large amounts of intestinal mucus in the anterior part of the earthworm gut triggers an intense microbial activity which first develops by breaking down the mucus and then shifts to the middle section of the gut by acting on the SOM which was inaccessible to microbial degradation in the soil. Thus, the worm digests protozoa fed on bacteria or fungal hyphae grown in the cast. For endogeic earthworms which are strictly geophagous, an enhanced microbial activity in the gut results in the release of assimilable organic matter in the posterior part of the gut and its further assimilation by both the worm and soil bacteria. True endogeics do not appear to reingest their casts and thus forgo the possibility of feeding on microbial biomass.

The termitosphere

The termitosphere is that part of the soil system influenced by termite activities. Since there are more than 3,000 termite species with different overall requirements the range of habitats covered is considerable. In general termites may be divided into four main groups based on their feeding habits: (1) grass and leaf litter harvesting species, (2) wood feeders, (3) fungus cultivators, (4) humivorous species feeding on SOM.

These differences in feeding habit go along with different habitats;

grass harvesters and fungus cultivators, for instance tend to build large epigeic termitaria (termite mounds) whereas others make carton or soil nests on tree trunks (some xylophagous species) and a last group consisting of humivorous and some fungi cultivators makes purely subterranean nests with a complex array of chambers and galleries. Digestive systems also greatly differ among species. All termites have symbiotic microorganisms such as protozoa in the most primitive wood-feeding lower termites, and bacteria and fungi in the other groups.

These four biological systems of regulation have a few basic properties in common:

(i) their function is largely based on mutualistic relationships mediated by an highly assimilable compound such as root exudates and earthworm intestinal mucus which prime the activities of microflora;

(ii) they bring about associations of organisms which operate at different scales of time and space, for instance from weeks to months and at the millimetre scale for fine roots, and from hours to days and the micronscale for associated bacteria;

(iii) BSR's are not equally developed in all ecosystems and may involve both mutualistic and antagonistic relationships. Meanwhile, litter systems dominate in forest ecosystems especially when anecic earthworms and termites — that tend to export litter towards other decomposition systems — are absent. In contrast, in savannahs, an important drilosphere or termitosphere is normally present if biogeographic barriers or human activities do not eliminate them;

(iv) organisms of different sizes are likely to react differently to changing environmental conditions, such as the addition of a high quality organic substrate and/or water, or a change in temperature. The mutualistic digestive system of the geophagous endogeic earthworm *Pontoscolex corethrurus* that functions well at 25–27°C does not seem to do so well at 15°C. In fact, microbial activity in the gut is reduced by a factor of five at temperatures below 17°C, and at 15°C the worm no longer grows. Thus, in the humid tropics mutualistic relationships between soil microorganisms and macroorganisms are likely to be much more developed than in colder ecosystems.

Mutualism in soils and the Gaia hypothesis

Two major likely consequences of increased efficiency of mutualistic relationships as one moves towards the tropics are: first, an increased diversity of species and functions; second, the generation of communities that are more adaptable to environmental stress, but more sensitive to large disturbances.

Diversity of invertebrates and plants in the humid tropics

In the 'first link' hypothesis we consider that increased temperatures in soils give roots access to an enlarged base of nutrient resources by means of an increased efficiency of mutualistic associations in the rhizosphere. An enlarged corporate niche owing to increased nutrient resources would result in a larger number of plant species. This would be the first link of a cascade process in which the species richness along the foodweb of consumers and decomposers would become larger than in colder areas.

From higher latitudes towards the Tropics, taking soil temperatures into account, earthworms become able to use food resources of diminishing quality. Thus, whereas in the coniferous forests of northern Europe, earthworms only ingest litter, in lower latitude temperate areas, some of the earthworm community is also able to ingest soil, as long as its organic content is high, or can take in litter mixed with soil. Yet, as C^{13} labelling methods have demonstrated, little if any organic matter of the soil is assimilated. At lower latitudes, some earthworms become able to live on soils with poor organic contents, for instance representing more than 70 per cent of earthworm biomass in the humid savannas of Lamto in the Ivory Coast. In warm climates, earthworms are able to digest all the particle-size fractions of SOM.

There is a striking analogy in the function of the drilosphere and rhizosphere. This has been expressed in a straightforward way by Janzen who asserts that 'plants wear their guts on the outside.' They produce exudates, a mixture of assimilable carbohydrates and proteins which trigger microbial activity and subsequent nutrient release in their rhizosphere. In guts of earthworms, the intenstinal mucus is a functional equivalent of root exudates. The digestive system described in these worms is analogous to the mechanisms of nutrient release in the rhizosphere hypothesized by Trofymow, Coleman and Clarholm and further demonstrated by Billes *et al.* Thus, earthworms contribute considerable amounts of water (100 per cent of the weight of dry soil) and mucus (5–16 per cent) to ingested soil. An intense microbial activity develops in the anterior part of the gut, feeding on intestinal mucus, a mixture of highly assimilable molecules. By the median part of the gut, mucus has been metabolized and the ingested microflora is able to digest the more complex organic matter of the ingested soil. Typical of a priming effect as defined by Jenkinson after Broadbent and Norman, this mechanism is equivalent to that observed in the rhizosphere. In that system, exudates are the functional equivalent to mucus, and root elongation replaces the movement of soil through the gut.

Termites provide another good example of the extended efficiency of mutualisms between macro- and micro-organisms as temperatures increase. These insects entirely rely on micro-organisms for the digestion of cellulose and lignin plant materials that they feed on. The limitation of their distribution, with a few exceptions, to tropical areas and their increased species richness towards the equator may be considered a result of the increased efficiency of their mutualistic digestive systems as temperature rises.

Effect of temperature along a thermo-latitudinal gradient

Mesofauna reaches its high abundance in the non-extreme tundra soils and is fully developed, qualitatively and quantitatively in cold temperate and temperate ecosystems, with high organic accumulations. Where the leaf-litter turnover is more rapid, as a result of increased temperature and/or earthworm activity, their abundance decreases.

Thus two main, and contradictory effects of temperature are manifested. High temperatures favour high metabolic activity of both micro-organisms and fauna. As a result, highly efficient, mutualistic digestion systems become possible (Lavelle 1988) and give earthworms and termites access to a wide range of resources, including those that are recalcitrant or highly dispersed. This results in a decrease of the litter and epigeic macrofauna and mesofauna.

Extension of the vertical distribution of soil communities

The soil fauna communities of many tropical soils have colonized both the deep soil strata and canopy of trees and palm-trees. This is a result of the enlargement of the resource base and favourable climatic conditions. In a Mexican rainforest at Laguna Verde, for example, only 20 per cent of soil fauna were in the litter, while respectively 52 per cent and 18.2 per cent were in the 0–10 cm and 10–20 cm strata and a further 9.7 per cent was in the 20–40 cm stratum. Further south, at Bonampak, an old Mayan settlement close to the Guatemalan border, the same pattern was observed in soil. Furthermore, hanging soils of the epiphyte *Bromeliaceae* had a very diverse and abundant fauna. Such an extended vertical distribution may be closely related to the enlargement of the resource base thanks to enhanced mutualistic digestive systems and to the permanently wet climatic conditions as well as high diversity of plant species.

Increased sensitivity to major disturbances

One striking feature of soil fauna communities in the humid tropics is their extreme sensitivity to vegetation changes such as when forests are replaced with cultivated crops. A similar decline has been observed in mesofauna and microfauna communities in deforested areas of the Amazonian forest in French Guyana. In contrast, soils of temperate areas, arable land and pastures may have rather diverse and sometimes abundant communities of macroinvertebrates.

Examples of earthworm communities clearly show the differences in the structure of tropical communities as compared to colder areas. Earthworm communities have been studied in a variety of natural and cultivated soils of temperate regions and it has been found that their abundance and biomass in cultivated soils is generally lower than in permanent pastures. However, in systems with limited tillage, high organic inputs (especially of cow manure) and no application of pesticides toxic to earthworms, communities may have a high abundance and be species-rich. In a Brittany cornfield, fertilized with 40 tonnes per hectare per year, Binet found a rich and diverse community of earthworms that was comparable to results obtained in temperate forests.

In temperate regions, earthworm faunas appear to be composed of a low number of species with large geographical distributions: most of the 28 species which constitute the fauna of the British islands are spread all over northern Europe and several of them have colonized temperate areas worldwide. In contrast, India has 365 species and 38 of the 58 genera are endemic.

Termites, absent from temperate soils, are a key component of tropical soil fauna with 2,200 species and a large diversity of functions in the ecosystem. Endemism is dominant and communities are extremely sensitive to biogeographical factors. As a result of such extreme specializations, most species do not adapt to the drastic changes of the environment following deforestation or cultivation. When a forest is cleared for pasture, or for a crop, most forest species do not adapt to the new savannah-like conditions nor, in general, do savannah species move in as colonizers. In that context, modified systems which conserve some tree components, such as the plantation of peach-palm with a cover of legumes, are better able to conserve soil fauna communities.

Conclusion

Biological interactions in soils are highly dominated by mutualism especially when abiotic parameters of the environment are not limiting. The establishment of such relationships may be considered as the result of a long period of coevolution which began with antagonistic relationships and gradually transformed into a global mutualism. The result is an increased turnover of organic matter and nutrients and, in the end, an increased diversity of species and life-forms. It is likely that organic matter and nutrient cycling are not the only processes that have been enhanced. There is growing evidence that soil formation itself is influenced by soil organism activities, far beyond that commonly believed. Alteration of the bedrock and the further elimination, or conservation, of nutrients and silica are partly determined by biologically mutualistic systems. There is some evidence that silica may be retained in the upper horizons by biological manipulation. Silica is a major constituent of clay minerals that themselves play a key role in the conservation of nutrients.

It is likely that the development of mutualism in soils has increased the importance of life as a major regulator of planetary processes. Nonetheless, it seems in the humid tropics that the increase in specialization has made communities more sensitive to large disturbances resulting from human activities.

References

Anderson, J.M. and I.N. Healey. 1972. Seasonal and interspecific variation in major components of the gut contents of some woodland Collembola. *J. Anim. Ecol.* 41(2):359.

Anderson, J.M. and P.W. Flanagan. 1989. Biological processes regulating organic matter dynamics in tropical soils. pp.97–122 in D.C. Coleman, J.M. Oades and G. Uehara (eds). *Dynamics of soil organic matter in tropical ecosystems.* Honolulu: University of Hawaii Press.

Barois, I. and P. Lavelle. 1986. Changes in respiration rate and some physicochemical properties during transit through *Pontoscolex corethrurus (Glossoscolecidae, Oligochaeta). Soil Biol. Biochem.* 18:539.

Cayrol, J.C. 1975. Importance des relations entre Nématodes et Bactéries dans la vie des sols. *Pepin. Hort. Maraich.* 158:43.

Elliott, E.T., H.W. Hunt and D.E. Walter. 1988. Detrital foodweb interactions in North America grassland ecosystems. *Agriculture, Ecosystems and Environment.* 24:41.

Garnier-Sillam, E., G. Villemin, F. Toutain and J. Renoux. 1986. Contribution a l'étude du rôle des termites dans l'humification des sols forestiers tropicaux. In N. Fedoroff, L.M. Bresson and M.A. Courty (eds). *Micromorphologie des sols.* Paris: AFES.

Howe, H.F. 1984. Constraints on the evolution of mutualisms. *Am. Nat.* 123:764.

Ingham, E.R., J.A. Trofymow, R.N. Ames, H.W. Hunt, C. Moley, J.D. Moore and D.C. Coleman. 1986. Trophic interactions and nitrogen cycling in a semi-arid grassland soil. I. Seasonal dynamics of the natural populations, their interactions and effects on nitrogen cycling. *Journal of Applied Ecology.* 23:597.

Janzen, D. 1985. The natural history of mutualisms. In D.H. Boucher (ed). *The Biology of Mutualism.* Beckenham: Croom Helm.

Lavelle, P. 1986. Associations mutualistes avec la microflore du sol et richesse spécifique sous les tropiques: l'hypothèse du premier maillon. *C.R. Acad. Sci. Paris.* 302(III,1): 11–14.

Lavelle, P., E. Blanchart, A. Martin, S. Martin, F. Toutain, I. Barois and R.A. Schaefer. 1991. Hierarchical model for decompositon in terrestrial ecosystems: Application to soils of the humid tropics. *Biotropica.*

Lee, K.E. 1985. *Earthworms: their ecology and relationships with soils and land use.* London: Academic Press.

Lee, K.E. and T.G. Wood. 1971. Physical and chemical effects on soils of some Australian termites, and their pedological significance. *Pedobiologia.* 11:376.

Lewis, D.H. 1985. Symbiosis and mutualism: crisp concepts and soggy semantics. In D.H. Boucher (ed). *The Biology of Mutualism.* Beckenham: Croom Helm.

Margulis, L. 1981. *Symbiosis in cell evolution: Life and its environment on the early earth.* San Francisco: Freeman.

Martin, A. 1991. Short-term and long-term effect of endogeic earthworm *Millsonia anomala Omodeo (Megascolecidae, Oligochaeta)* on soil organic matter of tropical savannas. *Biol. Fertil. Soils.*

Mills, J.T. and R.N. Sinha. 1971. Interactions between springtail, *Hypogastrura tullbergi,* and soil-borne fungi. *Journal of Economic Entomology.* 64:398–401.

Moore, J.C. 1988. The influence of microarthropods on symbiotic and non-symbiotic mutualism in detrital-based below-ground food-webs. *Agriculture, Ecosystems and Environment.* 24:147.

Piearce, T.G. and M.J. Phillips. 1980. The fate of Ciliates in the earthworm gut: an *in vitro* study. *Microb. Ecol.* 5:313–19.

Ponge, J.F. and M.J. Carpenteir. 1981. Etude des relations microflore-microfaune: expériences sur *Pseudosiniella alba* (Packard), *Collembole mycophage. Rev. Ecol. Biol. Sol.* 18(3):291–303.

Rouelle, J., M. Pussard, J.L. Randriamamonjizaka, M. Loquet, and M. Vinceslas. 1985. Interactions microbinnes (Bacteries, Protozoaires), alimentation des vers de terre et minéralisation de la matière organique. *Bull. Ecol.* 16(1):83.

Swift, M.J., O.W. Heal and J.M. Anderson. 1979. Decomposition in terrestrial ecosystems. *Studies in Ecology.* 5:372.

Vannier, G. 1983. The importance of ecophysiology for both biotic and abiotic studies of the soil. In Ph. Lebrun *et al.* (eds). *New trends in Soil Biology.* (VIII Int. Coll. Soil Zool.) Louvain-la-Neuve: Dieu-Brichart.

—— 1985. Modes d'exploitation et de partage des ressources alimentaires dans le système saprophage par les Microarthropodes du sol. *Bull. Ecol.* 16(1):19–34.

Zinkler, D. 1971. Carbonhydrasen steubewohnende Collembolen und Oribatiden. In *Organismes du sol et production primaire.* (IV Colloquium Pedobiologiae, Dijon 1970). Paris: INRA.

– 15 –
Gaia and the Evolution of Coherence

Mae-Wan Ho and Fritz-Albert Popp

The Ufaina Indians in the Colombian Amazon believe in a vital force called *fufaka* which is present in all living things. The source of this vital force is the Sun. From the Sun, it reaches Earth and is constantly recycled among plants animals and human beings. Each group of beings requires a minimum of the vital force in order to live, and is seen to be borrowing the energy from the total energy stock. When any being dies, the energy is released and goes back to the stock. Similarly, when a living being consumes another, for example, when a deer eats the leaves of the tree, or a tree extracts nutrients from the soil, or when people cut down trees to make a clearing, the consumer acquires the energy of the consumed. What is of importance to the Ufaina is that the vital force continues to be recycled from one species to another in such a way that not too much accumulates in any one of them, since this could deprive another of its vital force, and upset the natural balance (von Hildebrand 1988).

It is a remarkably coherent cosmology: a natural ecological wisdom that understands nature as a dynamically balanced whole linked by energy flow, with the energy arising ultimately from the Sun. This cosmology is based on a total understanding that comes not just by scientific observations, but from an intimate experience of nature from within. It took western science hundreds of years with many sophisticated instruments and a number of false starts and turns in order to arrive at a similar picture. As Peter Bunyard (1989) says, 'The Indian conception ... is not in principle far removed from ... [our own] notion of energy flows and foodweb and chains, with the Sun providing the necessary energy.' The major difference between them and us is that whereas they live by their wisdom and see themselves as part of nature, we have placed ourselves above nature, to the peril of all.

What we want to do in this paper is to present a vision of ecological balance from contemporary western biophysics which shows just how intimately we are connected with one another and with nature; how all nature is one resonating and intercommunicating whole. We shall be drawing from the work of many, including ourselves, who have derived inspiration from the union of biology and physics.

Let us begin with the western ecological version of energy flow. The energy of sunlight is absorbed by *chlorophyll,* the colour pigment in green plants, in individual packets or quanta called *photons.* This energy in each quantum goes into an excited electron, which, in the course of falling back to the ground state, travels around the body, its energy meted out to support all vital activities such as growth and differentiation, sensations, and movements. When animals feed on plants or on other animals, they are taking in the energy stored in the food to serve their own growth and development and all the activities that constitute being alive. Hence, the energy absorbed from the Sun is circulated a long way round all the organisms in the biosphere, with fractions of the total being lost as heat on the way till finally it becomes spent, or reaches the ground state. The energy cycle is accompanied by the parallel cycling of chemicals. Both cycles branch and anastomose in a very complicated way as ecologists who study foodwebs or nitrogen and carbon cycles are well aware. But it leaves us in no doubt that all life is a dynamic unity, it is the consequence of sunlight streaming through an open system, to maintain it far from thermodynamic equilibrium. Albert Szent-Györgi (1960), a founding father of modern biochemistry, had a nice way of putting it: that life is an interposition between two energy levels of an electron: the ground state and the excited state, and furthermore, as it is the electron that goes round the circuit, life is really a little electric current going round and connecting up all nature with the Sun and the Earth. This fundamental unity of physics and biology has indeed inspired a lot of people who felt that here was the key to unlocking the mystery of the living state. But as Szent-Györgi remarked then, and it is still largely the case now, biochemistry and molecular biology do not address such questions. They tell us a great deal about the molecules that make up living organisms, but very little about how they are supposed to act; how the energy plucked originally from the Sun is translated so very efficiently into various forms of work — chemical, mechanical, electrical and osmotic — and in organizing matter into the splendid diversity of organisms in the biosphere. Szent-Györgi suggested that we can only begin to understand these characteristics of living systems if we take into account the collective properties of the molecular aggregates in terms of solid state physics. There, we would find a clue to the mystery of life.

We know, for example, that even at ordinary temperatures the molecules in most physical matter have a high degree of uncoordinated, or random motion. The situation can change when the temperature is lowered to beyond a critical level. At that point, all the molecules so to speak, condense into a collective state, and exhibit the unusual properties of superfluidity and superconductivity. In other words, all the molecules of the system move as one, and conduct electricity with zero resistance (by a coordinated arrangement of all the electrons). Liquid helium at a temperature close to absolute zero is the first and only superfluid substance known. And various pure metals and alloys superconduct at liquid helium temperatures. Recently, technology has progressed to materials that can superconduct at much higher temperatures above absolute zero. The solid-state physicist Herbert Fröhlich (1968) in Liverpool was among the first to point out that something like a condensation into a collective mode of activity may be occurring in living systems, such that living organisms are in effect, superconductors working at physiological temperatures. He suggested that much of the metabolic energy, instead of being lost as heat, is actually stored in the form of coherent electromechanical vibrations in the body. He called these collective modes, coherent excitations.

Coherence refers to highly correlated activities in both space and time. In physics, it is usually understood as the ability of electromagnetic waves to interfere. For instance, in a version of Young's pioneering experiment, two narrow slits are illuminated by light from a light source. The light beams, on passing through the slits, fall on the screen and form an interference pattern of differing brightness in accordance to where the oscillations in the two light beams are in phase or out of phase. The ability to form interference patterns depends on the stability of the oscillations in the two light beams, or more specifically on their phase relationships. This phase stability is referred to as coherence; the more coherent the light, the sharper the interference pattern. The coherent state is fluctuationless and has the further characteristic that it is *factorizable* (Glauber 1969). This means that the parts paradoxically behave statistically independently of one another while maintaining a coherent pattern as a whole. In other words, coherence does not imply uniformity, or that every individual part or molecule of the system is necessarily doing the same thing all the time. An intuitive way to think about it is in terms of a grand symphony, or a grand ballet; or better yet, a jazz band in which individuals are doing different things and are yet in tune or in step with the whole. It is a state of cooperativity in which the individuals cooperate simply by doing their own thing.

What are the consequences of coherence? It results in properties that are characteristic of biological systems. These include the highly efficient energy transfer and transformation which often approaches 100 per cent;

the ability to communicate at all levels within cells, between cells and between organisms capable of resonating to the same frequencies; the possibility for sensitive, multiple recognition systems utilizing coherent electromagnetic signals of different specific frequencies, such as for example, the organization of metabolic activities within the cell, the operation of the immune network and a host of other biological functions involving specific recognition between hormones or ligands and their receptors; and finally, the stable persistence of the working system arising from the inherent stability of coherent states. A more detailed description of coherence is given in Ho (1993a).

Biophotons and coherence in living systems

Evidence for the existence of coherent excitations in biological systems came from the study of biophotons (see Popp *et al.* 1981, Popp 1986). Practically all organisms emit light at a steady rate from a few photons per cell per day to several photons per organism per second. An increasing number of observations within the past fifteen years from different laboratories all over the world suggest that biophotons are emitted from a coherent photon field within the living systems. Organisms are thus emitters and, most probably, also receivers of coherent electromagnetic signals which may be essential for their functioning.

The nature of the light emitted from living organisms is best studied after a brief exposure to weak illumination. It has been found, without exception that the re-emitted light from living tissues follows, not an exponential decay curve as characteristic of non-coherent light, but a hyperbolic decay function which is exhibited only by coherent light (see Figure 15.1). This unusual behaviour can be intuitively understood as follows. In a system consisting of non-interacting molecules emitting at random, the energy of the emitted photons are lost completely to the outside or converted into heat, which is the ultimate non-coherent energy. If the molecules are emitting coherently, however, the energy of the emitted photons are not completely lost to the outside. Instead, part of it is coherently reabsorbed by the system. The consequence is that the decay is very much delayed, and follows characteristically a hyperbolic curve with a long tail. This result can be derived rigorously from both classical and quantum mechanical considerations (Popp 1986). A coherent system stabilizes its frequencies during decay whereas a non-coherent system always suffers a shift in frequencies. That, and the capability to reabsorb emitted energy, account for the stability of coherent states.

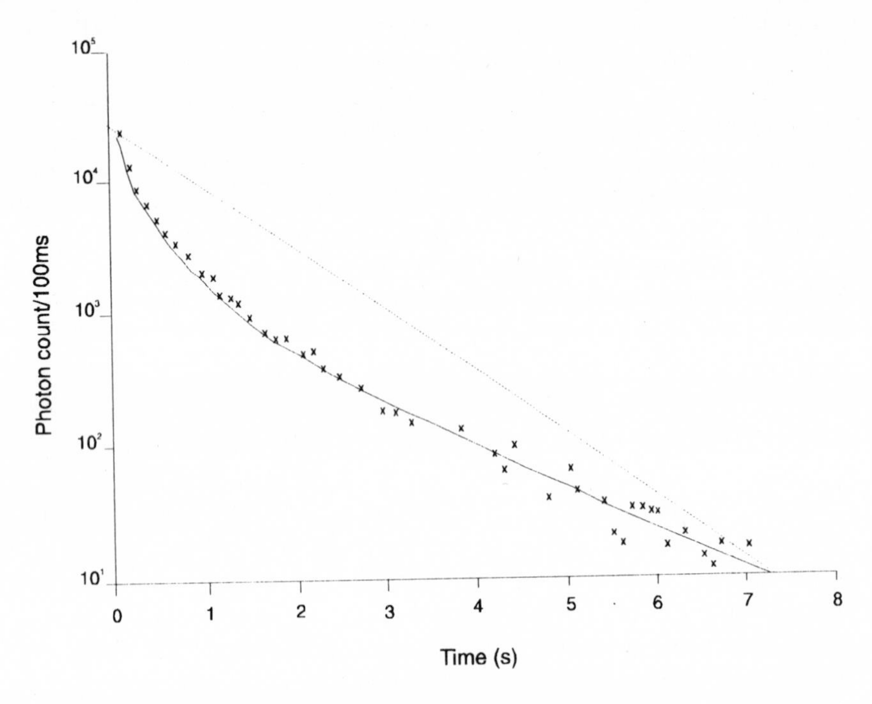

Figure 15.1. Hyperbolic decay of re-emitted photons from a synchronously developing population of Drosophila embryos. (From Ho 1993a).

The characteristics of biophotons

Where do biophotons really come from? We know that all sorts of excited molecules can emit light when they relax back to the ground state, the frequency of the emitted light being specific for each kind of molecules. When the spectrum of biophotons is examined, however, we find that the light is always in a broad band of frequencies from the infra-red to the ultraviolet, with approximately equal numbers of photons distributed throughout the range. This is very different from the Boltzmann distribution which characterizes a system at thermodynamic equilibrium at the physiological temperature of the biological system, thus indicating that the latter is far from thermodynamic equilibrium (see Figure 15.2). Not only is there an excess of photons at the high energy (short wave-length) end of the spectrum, but the distribution is very nearly flat. The distribution does not depend on the wavelength: $f(\lambda) = \text{const.}$ This means that the light is emitted from all kinds of molecules all over the cell. The photons are stored in a delocalized manner within the sys-

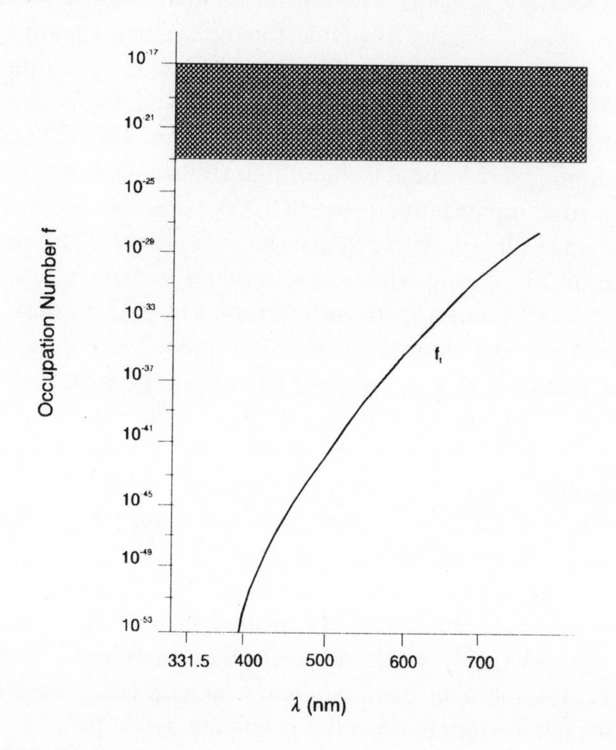

Figure 15.2. Spectral distribution of biophoton emission, upper zone, compared to the Boltzmann distribution, f_t *of a system at thermal equilibrium at physiological temperatures.*

tem, and all the frequencies are coupled together to give a single degree of freedom.

Evidence for the delocalization of coupled photons comes from the observation that the emitted light retains its broad spectral distribution when organisms are stimulated with monochromatic light or light of limited spectral composition. Moreover, the hyperbolic decay kinetics has the same form over the entire spectrum of emitted light (see Popp 1986; Musumeci *et al.* 1992).

The Boltzmann distribution characteristic of a system at thermodynamic equilibrium arises from the maximization of entropy (molecular disorder, or degrees of freedom) under the constraint of a fixed energy in a closed system. As biological systems are open instead of closed, the constraint of a fixed energy does not apply. This does not mean that energy conservation is violated, as the biological system plus surroundings are still subject to energy conservation. Nor does it mean that there is always an overflow of energy within the system. It only means that there is always enough energy available for the system. Living systems store energy (or photons) over the whole range of space and time scales — from 10^{-10} m to more than metres in length, and 10^{-9} s to days or longer time intervals — in a readily mobilizable form. They do not suffer from energy shortage on account of their high storage capacity within the intricate space-time organization (see Ho 1993a; 1993b for details).

The $f(\lambda)$ = const. distribution can also be seen as the consequence of the maximization of entropy when the constraint of fixed energy is removed in an open system far from equilibrium. The $f(\lambda)$ = const. profile looks somewhat like the expression of 'white noise' within the system, but this is far from the case. As this distribution represents the highest possible entropy in a system far from equilibrium, fluctuations cannot be interpreted in terms of noise — in contrast to a system at thermal equilibrium. Rather, they are 'signals' generated within the system. In other words, by maximizing entropy according to $f(\lambda)$ = const., the signal/noise ratio of the biological system is optimized over all wavelengths (Popp 1989). On the other hand, as the frequencies are all coupled together, the absolute value of entropy representing the maximum can also become arbitrarily small, theoretically even zero.

In summary, the fact that there is always enough energy available in the biological system confers on it the following properties:

1. Optimal signal/noise ratio for communication;
2. Existence at a phase threshold between a chaotic ($S \to \infty$, $N \to \infty$) and a coherent ($S \to 0$, $N \to 1$) regime, where S is the entropy, and N is the number of degrees of freedom; and
3. The possibility to extend energy storage, or the $f(\lambda)$ = const. distribution to longer and longer wavelengths in the course of evolution, and hence to expand the range of communication from distances between molecules within the cell all the way to distances between individuals in a population.

Long range communication

The hypothesis that the $f(\lambda)$ = const. distribution of biophotons can extend into infinitely long wavelengths is admittedly an extrapolation from measurements within and near the visible range. However, it can explain a variety of phenomena such as cancer development or group formation in organisms. We are postulating the existence of very weak, long-range (long wave-length) interactions between living systems. These weak long-range emissions cannot be detected directly with the instrumentation now available. However, this is not a sufficient reason for excluding them from consideration, as there are methods of obtaining indirect evidence of their existence, as we shall describe below.

Normal and cancer cells in culture

A first experiment of this kind was performed by Schamhart and van Wijk (1987). They exposed suspensions of cultivated rat liver and rat hepatoma cell lines H35 and HTC for some seconds to white-light from a 150W tungsten lamp and registered the re-emitted light afterwards. The decay curves are, as usual, hyperbolic rather than exponential. On altering the number of cells in the suspension, they found that normal cells exhibit decreasing light re-emission with increasing cell density, whereas tumour cells show a highly nonlinear increase with increasing cell density (see Figure 15.3). If there were no long-range interactions between the cells, the intensity of re-emitted photons would increase linearly with increasing number of cells, corrected by a term for self-absorption within the population. Neither the nonlinear increase of re-emission intensity from tumour cells nor the significant *decrease* of re-emission from normal cells could be explained unless there are long-range interactions between the cells, which are furthermore, correlated with their differing social behaviour, the tendency of tumour cells to disaggregate as opposed to the tendency of normal cells to aggregate.

These phenomena can be interpreted in terms of Dicke's (1954) theory of photon emission from an ensemble of emitters. He showed that photon emission tends to bifurcate into the two branches of *superradiance* and *subradiance* as soon as the wavelength of the emitted light is large compared to the distances between the emitters which are also absorbers. Superradiance is the increase of emission intensity concomitant with a shortening of the relaxation time. The opposite branch describes the regime of subradiance where emission intensity decreases with a prolonged decay time, corresponding to photon storage within the system.

In terms of Dicke's theory, normal cells have a greater capacity for subradiance the closer they are together, while the malignancy of tumour cells is associated with the opposite behaviour, that is, the loss of subradiance. This suggests that long-range interaction is based on the coherence of the subradiance system, with the coherence volume extending over the entire cell population. By changing the degree of coherence, the cells can control and regulate their social activities. According to this model, tumour cells, unlike normal cells, seem unable to communicate.

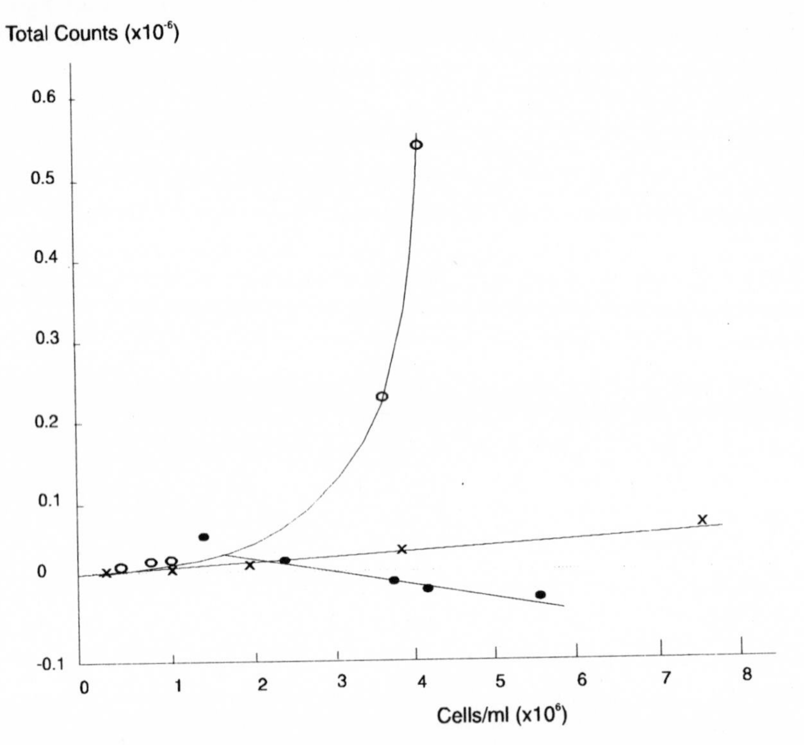

Figure 15.3. Total photon counts within the first seconds after exposure of cell suspensions to white light. Malignant HTC cells, –o–o–; normal heptocytes, –●–●–; and H35 cells which are only weakly malignant, –×–×–;

This may account for the repulsive forces that are responsible for metastasis in the malignant cells as opposed to the attractive forces responsible for population formation in normal hepatocytes (for further details see Nagl and Popp 1987).

Populations of Daphnia

Even more clear-cut results are obtained in organisms, such as *Daphnia,* where self-emission is measured instead of stimulated re-emission. Figure 15.4 depicts the results of measurements made by Galle *et al.* (1991). Instead of the expected linear increase in photon intensity with increasing number of individuals, a pattern of maxima and minima is observed, where the maximum and minimum values or photon intensity can be reproducibly assigned to definite numbers of individuals in the cuvette. It turns out that they invariably correspond to integer ratios of the average distances between individuals to their body size. The results cannot be

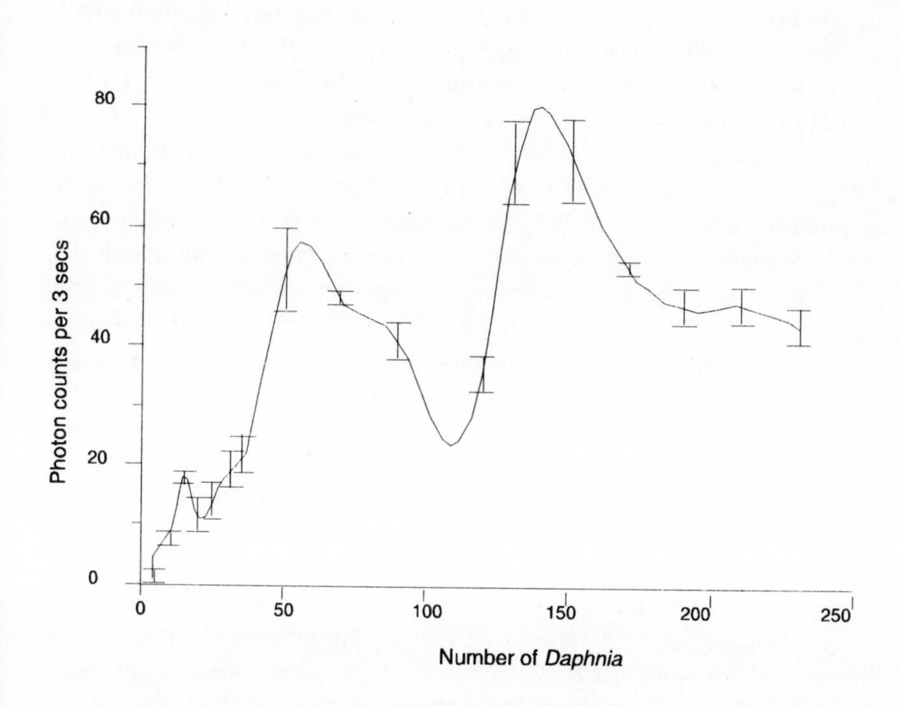

Figure 15.4. Self-emitted photon count-rate in Daphnia as a function of population density.

interpreted in terms of ordinary biochemistry. Instead, by treating the *Daphnia* as a population of antennae interacting by means of resonance wavelengths related to their geometrical dimensions, a good fit to the experimental data is obtained. Regardless of whether the details of the hypothesis are correct, the experiments clearly demonstrate the existence of long-range interactions between individuals in a population. These interactions may be the basis for swarming and the regulation of growth and other collective functions. The link to body size indicates communication wavelengths in the microwave to millimetre range.

Superdelayed luminescence in *Drosophila*

We have recently discovered the remarkable phenomenon of superdelayed luminescence in synchronously developing populations of early *Drosophila* embryos, in which intense, often prolonged and multiple flashes of light are re-emitted with delay times of one minute to eight hours after a single brief light exposure. Some examples are presented in Figure 15.5 (see Ho *et al.* 1992). The phenomenon depends on the existence of synchrony in the population, and furthermore, the timing of light exposure must fall within the first 40 minutes of development. However, the occurrence of the flashes themselves do not obviously correlate with specific embryonic events. They give information concerning the physical state of the embryos at the time of light stimulation — such as the existence of a high degree of coherence — rather than at the time during which the flashes themselves occur. Superdelayed luminescence bears some formal resemblance to the phenomenon of superradiance described above in which cooperative interactions among embryos within the entire population lead to most, if not all, the embryos emitting light simultaneously. This implies that each embryo has a certain probability of re-emitting after light stimulation, so that it can either trigger re-emission in other individuals, or alternatively its re-emission could be suppressed by them. Only when the population is re-emitting at the same time is the intensity sufficient to be registered as the intense flashes that are detected by the photon-counting device. On the other hand, re-emission in the entire population could also be suppressed (i.e., in the subradiant mode), such that in approximately 30 to 40 per cent of the cases, there is no clear indication of any superdelayed re-emission.

We do not know if any functional significance can be attached to superdelayed luminescence. *Drosophila* females typically lay eggs just before sunrise, so the external light source could be used as an initial synchronizing signal or *Zeitgeber,* which maintains the circadian and other biological rhythms. The superdelayed re-emission could then be a means of maintaining communication and synchrony among individuals in the population. On the other hand, the flashes may simply be the embryos' way to inform us of their globally coherent state at the time when light stimulation is applied, enabling the embryos to interact non-linearly to generate light that is coherent over the entire population, as well as being orders of magnitude more intense than the spontaneous emission background (see Ho *et al.* 1992, and Ho 1993a).

Coherence and the evolution of consciousness

What does the study of coherence contribute to our understanding of the unity of life? To return to our overview on the cycle of life, we can see that sunlight is the most fundamental source of energy, which is supplied at the high frequency end, and biological systems as a whole display the

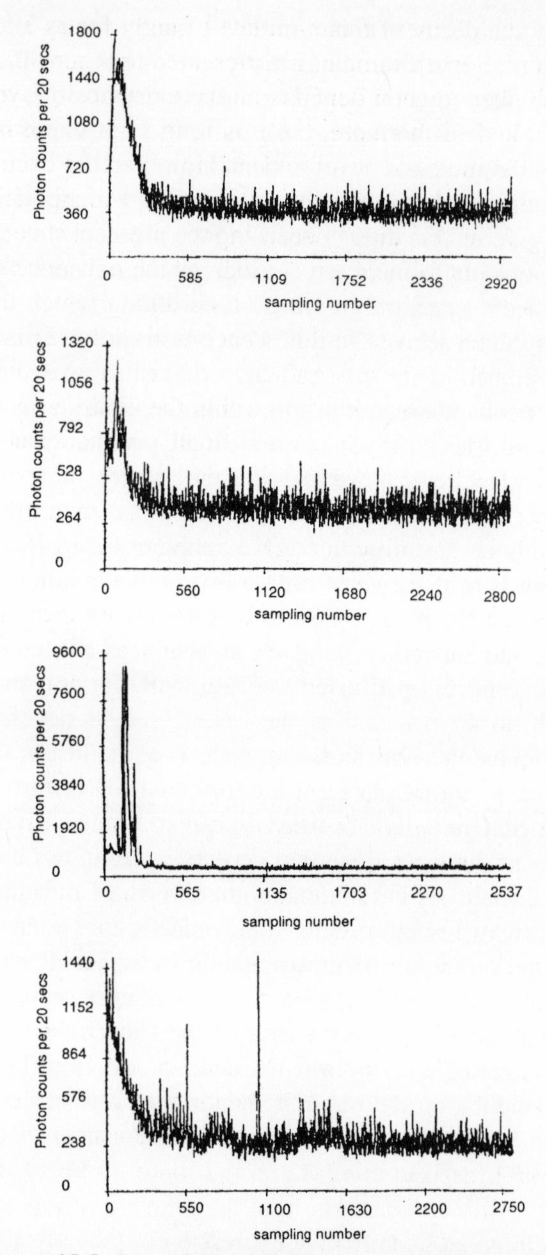

Figure 15.5. Superdelayed luminescence in Drosophila. continuous recordings of emissions from synchronously developing batches of embryos. Each data point on the graphs represents the aggregate photon count for 20 seconds. Top trace, control batch not exposed to light. The other traces are from batches which have all been exposed to white light for one minute before the recording, and show different forms of superdelayed luminescence. (From Ho, et al. *1992).*

natural tendency to delay the decay of this high level energy for as long as possible. This is why the Earth's natural biosphere is not a monoculture, indeed, it is the very diversity of life that is responsible for delaying the dissipation of the Sun's energy for as long as possible by feeding it into ever longer chains and webs and multiple parallel cycles in the course of evolution. But that is not the entire story, for the most effective way of hanging on to this energy for as long as possible is by the formation of a coherent platform of oscillations which expands the photon field into a coherent state of growing bandwidth. This is the $f(\lambda)$ = const. distribution which allows the Sun's energy to spill over into longer and longer wavelengths. This may be why organisms have such different life-spans; the trend in evolution is towards the emergence of organisms with longer and longer life-spans and finally in the case of social organisms and human beings, we see the emergence of social traditions that span many generations. The link with social tradition is the clue to the meaning of this energy flow through a coherent field of ever increasing bandwidth. For it is at the same time a flow and a creation of information. Electromagnetic signals of different frequencies are involved in communication within and between organisms, and between organisms and the environment. The coherent platform is a prerequisite for universal communication.

Thus, it seems that the essence of the living state is to build up and extend the coherent spatio-temporal platform for communication starting from the energy of the Sun initially absorbed by green plants. Living systems are thus neither the subjects alone, nor objects isolated, but both subjects and objects in a mutually communicating universe of meaning. In contrast to the neo-Darwinist point of view, their capacity for evolution depends, not on rivalry nor on might in the struggle for existence. Rather, it depends on their capacity for communication. So in a sense, it is not individuals as such who are developing but living systems interlinked into a coherent whole. Just as the cells in an organism take on different tasks for the whole, different populations enfold information not only for themselves, but for all other organisms, expanding the consciousness of the whole, while at the same time becoming more and more aware of this collective consciousness. Human consciousness may have its most significant role in the development and creative expression of the collective consciousness of nature.

References

Bunyard, P. 1989. *The Colombian Amazon: Policies for the Protection of the Indigenous Peoples and Their Environment.* Bodmin: Ecological Press. p.68.

Dicke, R.H. 1954. Coherence in spontaneous radiation processes. *Phys. Rev.* 93:99–112.

Fröhlich, H. 1968. Long-range coherence and energy storage in biological systems. *Int. J. Quantum Chem.* 2:641–49.

Galle, M., R. Neurohr, G. Altman, and W. Nagl. 1991. Biophoton emission from *Daphnia magna:* A possible factor in the self-regulation of swarming. *Experientia.* 47:457–60.

Glauber, R.J. 1969. Coherence and quantum detection, p.22. in R.J Glauber (ed). *Quantum Optics.* New York: Academic Press.

Hildebrand, M. von. 1988. In P. Bunyard and E. Goldsmith (eds). *Gaia, the Thesis, the Mechanisms and the Implications — Symposium 1.* Wadebridge Ecological Centre.

Ho, M.W. 1993a. *The Rainbow and The Worm. The Physics of Organisms.* Singapore: World Scientific.

—— 1993b. *Bioenergetics.* Milton Keynes: Open University Press.

Ho, M.W., X. Xu, S. Ross and P.T. Saunders. 1992. Light emission and re-scattering in synchronously developing populations of early *Drosophila* embryos — evidence for coherence of the embryonic field and long range cooperativity. pp.287–306 in F.A. Popp, K.H. Li and Q. Gu (eds). *Advances in Biophotons Research.* Singapore: World Scientific.

Musumeci, F., M. Godlevski, F.A. Popp and M.W. Ho. 1992. Time behaviour of delayed luminescence in *Acetabularia acetabulum.* pp.327–44 in F.A. Popp, K.H. Li and Q. Gu (eds). *Advances in Biophotons Research.* Singapore: World Scientific.

Nagl, W. and F.A. Popp. 1987. Opposite long-range interactions between normal and malignant cells. In T.W. Barrett and H.A. Pohl (eds). *Energy Transfer Dynamics.* Springer.

Popp, F.A. 1984. *Biologie des Lichts.* Berlin: Paul Parey.

—— 1986. On the coherence of ultraweak photon emission from living systems. pp.207–30 in C.W. Kilmister (ed). *Disequilibrium and Self-Organization.* Reidel.

—— 1989. Coherent photon storage of biological systems. In F.A. Popp, U. Warnke, H.L. Konig and W. Pescha (eds). *Electromagnetic Bio-Information.* Munich: Urban Schwarzenerg.

Popp, F.A., K.H. Li, W.P. Mei, M. Galle and R. Neurohr. 1988. Physical aspects of biophotons. *Experientia.* 44:576–85.

Popp, F.A., B. Ruth, W. Bahr, J. Bohm, P. Grass, G. Grolig, M. Rattemeyer, H.G. Schmidt and P. Wulle. 1981. Emission of visible and utraviolet radiation by active biological systems. *Collective Phenomena.* 3:187–211.

Szent-Györgi, A. 1960. *Introduction to a Submolecular Biology.* New York: Academic Press.

– 16 –
The Mechanical and the Organic: Epistemological Consequences of the Gaia Hypothesis

David Abram

Biologist Steven J. Gould, speaking on evolution several years ago to a packed auditorium at the State University of New York at Stony Brook, fielded a question from the back of the room. 'Could you please,' asked the small voice, 'could you please comment on the Gaia Hypothesis?' 'I'm glad you asked that,' said Gould, and he went on: 'After each of the last five lectures that I have given at universities, at least one person has asked a question about the Gaia Hypothesis. Yet nothing that I said in those lectures had anything to do with the Gaia Hypothesis! This is very interesting,' he said, 'people are obviously very curious about the Gaia Hypothesis. Yet I myself can't see anything in it that I didn't learn in grade school. Obviously the atmosphere interacts with life; its oxygen content, for instance, is clearly dependent on living organisms. But we've known this a long time. The Gaia Hypothesis says nothing new, it offers no new mechanisms. It just changes the metaphor. But metaphor is not mechanism!' And that was his final word on the matter.

What Gould failed to say is that 'mechanism,' itself, is nothing more than a metaphor. It is an important one, to be sure. Indeed the whole process of modern science seems to get underway with this metaphor. In 1644 the brilliant philosopher René Descartes wrote 'I have described the earth, and all the visible world, as if it were a machine.' In his various writings, Descartes, developing a notion already suggested by other philosophers, effectively inaugurated that tradition of thought we call 'mechanism,' or, as it was known at that time, the 'mechanical philosophy.' And his metaphor is still with us today.

But let us see how this metaphor operates upon us. What are the assumptions, explicit and implicit, that we wittingly or unwittingly buy into when we accept the premise that the visible world and, most specifically, the Earth, is best understood as a very intricate and complex machine?

First, the 'mechanical philosophy' suggests that matter, itself, is ultimately inert, without any life or creativity of its own. The great worth of the machine metaphor is that it implies that the material world is, at least in principle, entirely predictable. According to this metaphor, the material world operates like any machine according to fixed and unvarying rules; laws that have been built into the machine from the start. It has no creativity, no spontaneity of its own. As a watch or a clock ticks away with complete uniformity until it runs down, so the material world cannot itself alter or vary the laws that are built into it. (We don't commonly think that the gears of our clocks can mischievously mutate and thereby alter the time.) The laws of a mechanical world are fixed and unchanging; if we can discover those laws, we will be able to predict with utter certainty the events of the world. Or so the mechanical philosophers thought in the seventeenth century.

Mind you, a thing does not have to be a machine for it to be predictable. Most people that I know are fairly predictable. Other animals and plants are 'roughly' predictable. About as predictable as, say, the weather. But Descartes and his followers chose to view the weather as, in principle, entirely predictable. For the material world was not an organism — it was a machine. It had no life of its own, nor sensitivity, intrinsic power, or motive force of its own.

Which brings us to the second assumption implicit in the mechanical metaphor, an assumption rather more hidden than the first. A machine always implies someone who invented the machine, a builder, a maker. A machine cannot assemble itself. Clocks, carriages, or steam-engines do not assemble themselves from scratch — if they did, they would be very wild and magical entities indeed, and we could not ascribe to them the fixity, uniformity and predictability that we associate with any strictly mechanical object. If we view nature as a machine, then we tacitly view it as something that has been built, something that has been made from outside. This is still evident in much of the language that we use in our science today: we speak of behaviour that has been 'programmed' into an animal's genes, of information that is 'hardwired' into the brain. But who wrote the programme? Who wired the brain? As mechanists we borrow these metaphors from our own experience of built things, things that have been invented and constructed by humans, and then we pretend that the inventor or the builder (or the programmer) does not come along with the metaphor. But, of course, he does. It is a necessary part of the metaphor. You don't get a machine without someone who built the machine.

I am asking you to begin to recognize the way that metaphors work upon us implicitly, even unconsciously. Yet what is largely unconscious today was quite obvious in the seventeenth century. If the material world is like a machine, then this world must have been constructed from outside. A mechanical world implies a maker. And that is precisely why the mechanical philosophy and mechanism triumphed in the seventeenth and eighteenth centuries to become part of the very fabric of conventional science. Mechanism gained ascendancy not because it was a necessary adjunct of scientific practice, but because it disarmed the objections of the Church, the dominant social and political institution of the time. The mechanical philosophy became a central facet of the scientific world-view precisely because it implied the existence of a maker (a divine inventor, if you will), and thus made possible an alliance between science and the Church.

We moderns tend to assume that the adoption of the mechanical metaphor was a necessary precondition for the growth and flourishing of experimental science. Yet an attentive study of the various conflicts and debates that gave rise to the scientific revolution quickly calls such assumptions into question. Until the latter half of the seventeenth century, the tradition of experimentation was not associated with the mechanical philosophy. On the contrary, the method of careful experimentation was associated with those who practised it, those who developed and refined it to the level of an art, individuals who had a very different perspective from that of the mechanists. For these were those who called themselves 'natural magicians,' and often, 'alchemists.' They viewed the material world and, indeed, matter itself, as a locus of subtle powers and immanent forces, a dynamic network of invisible sympathies and antipathies. For the Renaissance natural magician, Marcilio Ficino — the great translator of Plato's works into Latin — for the Hermetic natural magicians Giordano Bruno and Tommasso Campanella, for the brilliant physician and alchemist Paracelsus (the real father of homeopathic medicine) and, indeed, for the entire alchemical tradition, material nature was perceived as alive, as a complex, living organism with which the investigator — the natural magician, or scientist — was in relation. The experimental method was developed and honed as the medium of this relation, as a practice of dialogue between oneself and animate nature. Experimentation was here a form of participation, a technique of communication or communion which, when successful, effected a transformation not just in the structure of the material experimented upon, but in the structure of the experimenter himself (Easlea 1980, Yates 1969).

Many of the great discoveries that we associate with the scientific revolution and, indeed, many of the scientists themselves, took their inspiration from this participatory tradition of natural magic. One need only mention Nicholas Copernicus, who wrote of the Sun as the visible

God, quoting the legendary Egyptian magician Hermes Trismegistus; Johannes Kepler, whose mother was imprisoned and nearly executed for practising witchcraft, on the evidence of Kepler's own writings; William Gilbert, the great student of magnetism, which he termed 'coition' as if it were a type of sexual intercourse that matter has with itself, and who, in his book *De Magnete,* wrote of the whole earth as a living body with its own impulse for self-preservation (Easlea 1980, Ch.2–3). And, of course, we must mention Francis Bacon, the 'father' of experimental science, who saw his scientific method as a refinement of the tradition of natural magic and wrote that through his work the term 'magic,' which 'has long been used in a bad sense, will again be restored to its ancient and honourable meaning' (Easlea 1980: 128).

How is it that we have forgotten this intimate link between experimental science and natural magic? How or why was this link with magic so obscured by the subsequent tradition of natural science? Why did Isaac Newton, arguably one of the greatest of all natural magicians, find it necessary to hide and even publicly deny the vast alchemical researches that occupied him throughout his life (researches that almost certainly influenced the development of his theories regarding the mutual attraction between material bodies — that is, gravity)?

Clearly, the Church in the sixteenth and seventeenth centuries felt itself threatened by this powerful tradition which held that the material world was a source of itself, this tradition which spoke of the enveloping earth as a living being, a living matrix of spiritual powers and receptivities. Such a way of speaking threatened the theological doctrine that matter itself is passive and barren, and that the corporeal realm of nature was a fallen, sinful realm, necessarily separated from its divine source. (I am not referring here, of course, to Christian doctrine in general, but only to the institutionalized Church of the sixteenth and seventeenth centuries — a period, let us remember, that saw hundreds of thousands, if not millions of persons, most of them women, tortured and executed as witches by the ecclesiastical and lay authorities.)

The true source, according to the Church, was radically external to nature, outside of the earthly domain in which we are bodily immersed. The teachings of natural magic, however, with their constant reference to immanent powers, implied that the divine miracles reported in the Old and the New Testaments might be explained by subtle principles entirely internal to material nature. This was heresy — heresy of the first order — since it enabled one to doubt the very agency and existence of the God outside nature.

Clearly then, if natural experimentation was to become a respectable or even a permissible practice it would have to find a new rhetoric for itself. It would have to shed its origins in the magical and participatory world-view and take on a new way of speaking more in line with Church doctrine.

It was 'mechanism,' or the 'mechanical philosophy,' that provided this new and much safer way of speaking. For again, a metaphorical machine entails a metaphorical builder, a creator. Like the Church, the mechanical philosophy necessitated an implicit belief in a creative source entirely outside of the material or sensible world. And, like the Church, the mechanical philosophy involved a denigration of corporeal matter, not exactly as fallen, sinful and demonic, but as barren, inert and ultimately, dead.

Here, then, was a perfect cosmology for the experimental scientists to adopt — one that would allow them to continue to investigate nature without fear of being persecuted, or executed, for heresy. The mechanical metaphor made possible an alliance between seventeenth century science and the Church. And thus mechanism became a central tenet of the scientific world view (see endnote).

We are now in a position to discern the third and most powerful assumption implicit in the mechanical metaphor. The only true machines of which we have direct experience are those that have been invented by humans. Hence, if the world really functions as a complex machine, then the one who built that machine must be very much like us. There is, in other words, an implied isomorphism between humans and the one who built or programmed the complicated, vast machine of the world. We are, after all, made in his image. Hence, we alone have a heavenly mandate to manipulate the rest of this world for our own benefit. If the material earth is a created machine, it falls to us — since we are not just created, but creators in our own right — to figure out how the machine works.

The mechanical metaphor, then, not only makes it rather simple for us to operationalize the world, by presenting nature as an assemblage of working parts that have no internal relation to each other — a set of parts, that is, that can be readily taken apart or put back together without undue damage — it also provides us with a metaphysical justification for any and all such manipulations. Since machines are invented by humans, the human mind necessarily retains a godlike position outside of the mechanical world that it analyzes. This is still evident today. It is neatly illustrated by two recent headlines in the *New York Times,* from a single week in 1987. The first, from April 14, 1987, reads 'Physicist Aims to Create A Universe, Literally.' The article relates the progress of Alan Guth and his colleagues at the Massachusetts Institute of Technology in their ongoing attempt to create a universe 'from scratch' in the laboratory. The second headline, three days later on April 17, reads 'New Animal Forms Will Be Patented.' This article goes on to describe some of the newly 'invented' animals awaiting patenting, such as the pigs whose genome now contains a human growth hormone gene to make them grow faster. 'The animals are leaner than naturally bred pigs, but they suffer from several debilitating ailments, including crossed eyes, severe arthritis in the joints and susceptibility to disease.' Hmmm. At any rate it is instructive to string these two headlines from a single week together, in order to see how they read. 'Physicist Aims to Create A Universe In The Laboratory: The New Animal Forms Will be Patented.' It is like reading the daily newspaper on Mount Olympus!

Within the mechanical metaphor, there is always this implicit parallel between the creative human mind and that which created the universe, between humans and God. The human researcher thus has a divine mandate to experiment on, to operate upon, to manipulate earthly nature in any fashion he or she sees fit. The inertness of matter, the clear lack of sentience in all that is not human, absolves the researcher of any guilt regarding the apparent pain he may happen to inflict upon animals or ecosystems (such pain, as Descartes told us, is entirely an illusion, for automatons cannot really feel anything).

The mechanical world-view implicates us in a relation to the world which is that of an inventor, an operator, or an engineer to his machine (many biologists, for instance, now think of themselves as 'genetic engineers'). It is this privileged position, the licence it gives us for the possession, mastery and control of nature, that makes us so reluctant to drop the mechanical metaphor today. If mechanism rose to prominence in the seventeenth century owing to its compatibility with the belief in a divine creator, it remains in prominence today largely due to the deification of human powers that it promotes.

But this deification, this human privilege, comes at the expense of our perceptual experience. Let me explain. If we suspend our theoretical awareness in order to attend to our sensory experience of the world around us (to our experience not as disembodied intellects but as intelligent, sensing animals), we find that we are not outside of the world, but entirely in it. We are thoroughly encompassed by the world, immersed in its depths. Hence our sensory relation to the world is hardly that of a spectator to an object. As sensing animals, we are never disinterested onlookers but participants in a dynamic, shifting and ambiguous field.

Maurice Merleau-Ponty, the philosopher who has perhaps most carefully analyzed the experience of perception, underscored the participatory nature of this experience by calling attention to the obvious but easily overlooked fact that our hand, with which we touch the world, is itself a touchable thing, and thus is itself entirely a part of the tactile field that it explores. Likewise the eyes, with which we see the world, are themselves visible. They are themselves entirely included within the visible world that they see — they are one of the visible things, like the bark of a tree, or a stone, or the sky. For Merleau-Ponty, to see is also, at one and the same time, to feel oneself seen, and to touch the world is also to be touched by the world! Clearly a wholly immaterial mind could neither see nor touch things, could not experience anything at all. We can experience things, can touch, hear, and taste things, only because, as bodies, we are ourselves a part of the sensible field, and have our own textures, sounds, and tastes. We can perceive things at all only because we are entirely a part of the sensible world that we perceive. We might just as well say that we are organs of that world, and that the world is perceiving itself through us (Merleau-Ponty 1968; 1962).

But here the main point to get from Merleau-Ponty is that, from the perspective of our lived, embodied awareness, perception is always experienced as an interactive, reciprocal participation. The event of perception is never instantaneous — it has always a duration, and in that duration there is always a movement, a questioning and responding, a subtle attuning of the eyes to that which they see, or of the ears to what is heard, and thus we enter into a relationship with the things we perceive.

When, for instance, my hand moves over the surface of a stone newly found on the beach, my fingers must adjust themselves to the particular texture of the stone's surface, they must find the right rhythm, the right way to touch it if they are to discover its subtle furrows and patterns, as my eyes must find the right way to look at and focus that stone's surface if they wish to disclose the secrets of its mineral composition. It is in this way that the stone teaches my senses and informs my body. And the more I dwell with that stone, the more I will learn. There is a mutual engagement of my body by the stone, and of the stone by my body. And so it is with everything that we perceive, constantly, continually — the paved streets we walk upon, the trees that surround our home, the clouds that catch our gaze. Perception is always an active engagement with what one perceives, a reciprocal participation with things. As such, our direct perception always discloses things and the world as ambiguous, animate presences with which we find ourselves in relation. That this is our native, human experience of things is attested by the discourse of virtually all indigenous, oral, tribal peoples, whose languages refuse any designation of things, or of the sensible world, as ultimately inanimate. If a thing has the power to 'call my attention' or to 'capture my gaze,' it can hardly be thought of as inert. 'If this stone was not in some sense alive, you could no longer see it,' I was told by an old shaman in the desert near Santa Fé. By which he meant to say, I think, that simply to see something is already to be in an active relationship with that thing, and how could one be in a dynamic relationship with something if it were entirely inanimate, without any potency or spontaneity of its own? How indeed? By implying that matter is utterly passive and inert, mechanism denies our perceptual experience. It denies our sensory involvement in the world.

The scientist who holds to a fundamentally mechanistic view of the natural world must suspend his or her sensory participation with things. He strives to picture the world from the viewpoint of an external spectator. He conceives of the Earth as a system of objective relations laid out before his gaze, but he does not include the gaze, his own seeing, within the system. Denying his sensory involvement in that which he seeks to understand, he is left with a purely mental relation to what is only an abstract image.

Likewise with any particular object or organism that the mechanist studies. There as well, she must assume the position of a disinterested onlooker. She must suppress all personal involvement in the object; any trace of subjectivity must be purged from her account. But this is an impossible ideal, for there is always some interest or circumstance that leads us to study one phenomenon rather than another, and this necessarily conditions what we look for, and what we discover. We are always in, and of, the world that we seek to describe from outside. We can deny, but we cannot escape being involved in whatever we perceive. Hence, we may claim that the sensible world is ultimately inert or inanimate, but we can never wholly experience it as such. The most that we can do is to try to render the sensible world inanimate, either by killing that which we perceive, or by deadening our sensory experience. Our denial of participation thus manifests as a particular form of participation, one that does violence to our bodies and to the Earth.

Mechanism, then, is a way of speaking that denies the inherently reciprocal and participatory nature of perceptual experience. It thus constricts and stifles the senses; they are no longer free to openly engage things like trees, bird-song, and the movement of waves. We grow more and more oblivious to the animate Earth as our body becomes closed in upon itself; our direct intercourse with the sensible world is inhibited. Mechanism sublimates our carnal relationship with the Earth into a purely mental relation, not to the world, but to the abstract image of a finished blueprint, the abstract ideal of a finished truth.

This mentalistic epistemology, with its fear of direct relationship and its intolerance of ambiguity, is the mark, I suggest, of an immature or adolescent science, a science that has not yet come into its own. Although it sporadically fosters grandiose feelings of power and godlike mastery over nature, science as mechanism is inherently unstable, since it is founded upon a denial of the very conditions that make science possible at all. Such a science cannot last — it must either obliterate the world in a final apotheosis of denial, or else give way to another mode of science: one that can affirm, rather than deny, our living bond with the world that surrounds us.

The Gaia Hypothesis may well signal the emergence of just such a mature science — a science that seeks not to control the world but to participate with the world, not to operate upon nature, but to co-operate with nature. If the chemical composition of the air that we are breathing is being sensitively monitored and maintained by the sum of all of the Earth's biota acting in concert, as a single, coherent, autopoietic or living system, then the material world that surrounds us is not, in any sense, inert or inanimate. Nor are these insects, these trees or even these boulders entirely passive and inert. For material nature can no longer be perceived as a collection of detachable working parts — it is not a created machine but rather a vast, self-generative, living physiology, open and responsive to changing circumstances. In short, it is an entity.

Of course, we may still attempt to speak of Gaia in purely mechanical terms, or try to conceive of Gaia as a strictly objective set of processes, straining thus to hold our science within the old mechanical paradigm to which we have become accustomed. We may be reluctant to give up the dream of a finished objectivity, and of the fixed reality to which it would correspond. Nevertheless, Gaia will never fit very neatly within the discourse of mechanism. A mechanism is entirely determined. It acts, as we have seen, according to a set of predictable and fixed rules and structures that it itself did not generate. Yet it is precisely such a formulation that Gaia, as a self-generating system, resists. Of course, we may say that Gaia is a machine, or a set of mechanisms, that is building itself. Fine! But then we have given up, perhaps without realizing it, that part of the metaphor that makes mechanism so compelling. That is, a machine that creates itself is never entirely predictable. For it is generating itself as it goes, creatively. (We have no guarantee, for instance, that the so called 'mechanisms' that Gaia employs to regulate the salinity of the oceans, or to limit the influx of ultra-violet radiation into the atmosphere, are precisely the same that she will be employing a hundred years from now.) Gaia, as an autonomous self-generating entity, is no more and no less predictable than a living body, and we might as well simply speak of it as such and stop pretending that it is anything like a machine that we could build. The Gaia Hypothesis indicates that the world we inhabit is rather more like a living organism than a watch, or a spaceship, or even a computer.

And we are entirely inside of, circumscribed by this organic entity. For the Gaia Hypothesis indicates that the atmosphere in which we live and think is itself a dynamic extension of the planetary surface, a functioning organ of the animate Earth. As I have stated in an earlier article:

> It may be that the new emphasis it places on the atmosphere of this world is the most radical aspect of the Gaia Hypothesis. For it carries the implication that before we as individuals can begin to recognize the earth as a self-sustaining organic presence, we must remember and reacquaint ourselves with the very medium within which we move. The air can no longer be confused with mere negative presence or the absence of solid things — henceforth the air is itself a density — mysterious indeed for its invisibility — but a thick and tactile presence nonetheless. We are immersed in its depths as surely as fish are immersed in the sea. It is the medium, the silent interlocutor of all our musings and moods. We simply cannot exist without its support and nourishment, without its active participation in whatever we are up to at any moment.
>
> In concert with the other animals, with the plants, and with the microbes themselves, we are an active part of the Earth's atmosphere, constantly circulating the breath of this planet through our bodies and brains, exchanging certain vital gases for others, and thus monitoring and maintaining the delicate makeup of the medium (Abram 1985).

So simply by breathing, we are participating in the life of the biosphere. But not just by breathing! If the biosphere is really a coherent, self-sustaining entity, then everything we see, everything we hear, every experience of smelling and tasting and touching is informing our bodies regarding the internal state of this other, vaster physiology — the biosphere itself. Sensory perception, then, is really a form of communication between an organism and the living biosphere. (And this can be the case even when we are observing ourselves, noticing a headache that we feel or the commotion in our stomach caused by some contaminated water. For we ourselves are a part of Gaia. If the biosphere is a living entity, then introspection, listening to our own bodies, can become a way of listening and attuning to the Earth.) Perception is a communication or even a communion — a sensuous participation between ourselves and the living world that encompasses us. Yet we have seen that this is precisely the way that we commonly experience perception — as an interaction, a participation or intertwining between ourselves and that which we perceive. Perception is never strictly objective, since to perceive anything at all is to involve oneself in that thing and to feel oneself influenced by the encounter. We have seen that mechanism denies this dialectic by assuming that the world is a created object, fixed and unchanging, incapable of creative response. The Gaia Hypothesis, on the other hand, ultimately affirms the participatory nature of our perceptual experience since it defines the physical environment as something animate and alive, which is precisely the way that our bodies experience it. Thus the Gaia Hypothesis enables, quite literally, a return to our senses. We become aware, once again, of our sensing bodies, and of the bodily world that surrounds us.

If this world we inhabit is really a machine — a fixed and finished object — then it cannot respond to our attention; there is nothing to participate or to communicate with except ourselves, our own 'creative human minds.' If, however, the Earth is not a finished object, but is continually creating itself, then everything is open to participation. We are drawn out of that ideal, platonic domain of thoughts and theories back into this realm we inhabit with our bodies, this land that we share with the other animals and the plants and the microbial entities who vibrate and spin within our cells and within the cells of the spider. Our senses loosen themselves from the mechanical constraints imposed by an outmoded language — they begin to participate in the ongoing life of the land around us.

We are now in a position to contrast succinctly the epistemology of mechanism with the epistemological implications of Gaia. The mechanical model of the world entails a mentalistic epistemology, the assumption that the most precise knowledge of things is a detached, intellectual apprehension purged of all subjective, personal or perspectival (that is, bodily) involvement. It is an abstract, disembodied knowledge. Meanwhile, the Gaian understanding of the world, that which speaks of the biosphere not as a machine but as an autopoietic, living physiology, entails an embodied, participatory epistemology. As the Earth is no longer a machine, so the human body is no more a fixed machine but a thinking, feeling, sensing physiology, a microcosm of the autopoietic Earth. It is hence not as a detached mind, but as a living body that I can come to know the world, participating in its processes, feeling my life resonate with its life, becoming more a part of the world. Knowledge, here, is always carnal knowledge, a wisdom born of the body's own attunement to that which it studies, and to the Earth.

This view is entirely akin to that of Ludwig Fleck, the great epistemologist and sociologist of science, who wrote in 1929 that:

> Cognition is neither passive contemplation nor acquisition of the only possible insight into something given. It is an active, live interrelationship,a shaping and being reshaped, in short, an act of creation (or, we might add, co-creation). (Fleck 1929).

We may wonder what science will come to look like if such an epistemology were to take hold and spread throughout the human community. It is likely that scientists would soon lose interest in the pursuit of a finished blueprint of the Earth, in favour of discovering ways to better the relationship between humankind and the rest of the biosphere, and ways to rectify current problems caused by the neglect of that relationship. I have spoken of a science that seeks not to control nature but to communicate with nature. Experimentation would come to be recognized once again as a discipline or art of communication between the scientist and that which he or she studies (an interpretation which is not unlike the original understanding of experimental practice, as we have seen). Indeed, I am sure that many scientists are already familiar with the experience of a deep communication or communion with that which they study, although current scientific discourse makes it rather difficult to acknowledge or to articulate such experience. (Unless, of course, one is a physicist. The physicists are freer to articulate such experiences only because their objects remain transcendent to the world of our immediate experience. To participate mystically with subatomic quanta or even with the ultimate origin of the universe does not really force science to alter its assumptions regarding the inert or mechanical nature of the everyday sensible world, and so does not really threaten our right to dominate and manipulate the immediate world around us. But biologists, who study this very world — the world that we can directly perceive, often with our unaided senses — are in a much more precarious position politically.) However, in a genuinely Gaian science, or in a Gaian community of scientists, it will become manifestly evident that one is already involved in that which one studies, and so it will no longer be necessary to try to avoid or to repress this involvement. On the contrary, scientists may begin to openly develop and cultivate their personal rapport with that which they study as a means of deepening their scientific insight.

Biologist Barbara McClintok, who was awarded the Nobel Prize in 1984 for her discovery of genetic transposition, exemplifies the participatory epistemology implied by a Gaian science. She insists that a genuine scientist must have 'a feeling for the organism' — and not only for 'living' organisms but 'for any object that fully claims our attention' (Keller 1985, 166). McClintok describes a rather magical shift in her orientation that enabled her to identify chromosomes that she had previously been unable to distinguish. It is the shift to a participatory epistemology:

> I found that the more I worked with them, the bigger and bigger the chromosomes got, and when I was really working with them, I wasn't outside, I was down there. I was part of the system. I was right down there with them and everything got big. I even was able to see the internal parts of the chromosomes — actually everything was there. It surprised me because I actually felt as if I was right down there and these were my friends. As you look at these things, they become a part of you. And you forget yourself. (Keller 1985, 165).

As Barbara McClintok came to perceive herself inside of the living system she was studying, so the Gaia Hypothesis situates all of us inside of this world that we share with the plants and the animals and the stones. The things around us are no longer inert. They are our co-participants in the evolution of a knowledge and a science that belongs to humankind no more, and no less, than it belongs to the Earth.

Endnote

On this reading mechanistic science went hand in hand with a Christian metaphysics. The schism that we have come to assume today between the scientists and the theologians, or between science and religion, only really gets underway with the publication and dissemination of the *Origin of Species*. For Darwin was beginning to speak of a sort of creative power inherent in nature itself; he spoke of a natural selection — a selective power not outside of nature but internal to nature. Of course, by using the metaphor of selection he was still propagating a metaphysics somewhat similar to that of the Church (in which he had been steeped as a young man). 'Selecting' is the kind of thing that an anthropomorphic divinity does; and we can see from newspaper articles of that time that many readers interpreted Darwin's use of the term 'selection' as a sort of indirect argument for the existence of God. His correspondence indicates that Darwin, himself, remained somewhat attached to the idea of a transcendental divinity: the use of the term 'selection,' with all its associations of humanlike will or choice (see Robert M. Young, *Darwin's Metaphor.* 1985, Cambridge University Press, pp.79–125). Nevertheless, Darwin's work was the first to imply a creativity inherent in nature itself, and this was a blow to the Church. We now are beginning to discern that if the environment 'selects' the organisms that inhabit it, so those organisms also 'selectively' influence that environment, and so maybe 'selection' is not such a great term. This interaction is a much more reciprocal phenomenon than that suggested by the metaphor of selection — it is more a sort of dialogue wherein the environment puts questions to the organism and the organism, in answering those questions, puts new questions to the environment which the environment, in turn, answers with further questions. It is precisely this sort of open dialectic, this mutual participation between the body and the Earth, that the Gaia hypothesis is beginning to thematize and articulate.

References

Abram, David. 1985. The Perceptual Implications of Gaia. In *The Ecologist.* 15(3).

Descartes, René. Principles of Philosophy. Part IV, principle CLXXXVIII. In 1931. *The Philosophical Work of Descartes.* Translated by Haldane and Ross. Cambridge University Press.

Easlea, Brian. 1980. *Witch Hunting, Magic, and the New Philosophy: an introduction to the debates of the scientific revolution 1450–1750.* New Jersey: Humanities Press.

Fleck, Ludwick. 1929. On the Crisis of 'Reality.' pp.47–57 in Robert Cohen and Thomas Schnelle (eds). 1986. *Cognition and Fact: materials on Ludwik Fleck.* Boston: Reidel.

Keller, Evelyn Fox. 1985. *Reflections on Gender and Science.* Yale University Press. p.166.

Merleau-Ponty, Maurice. 1986. *The Visible and the Invisible.* Edited by Claude Lefort, translated by Alphonso Lingis. Northwestern University Press. See also Merleau-Ponty's seminal text 1962. *The Phenomenology of Perception.* Translated by Colin Smith. London: Routledge & Kegan Paul.

Yates, Frances. 1969. *Giordano Bruno and the Hermetic Tradition.* Vintage Press.

– 17 –
Gaia and Culture: Reciprocity and Exchange in the Colombian Amazon

Martin von Hildebrand

Tribal peoples throughout the world have survived until this day because they learnt to live in relative ecological harmony with their natural environment. Such survival has not been the simple result of brute adaptation, but instead the consequence of profound cosmological experiences in which seasonal changes and cycles have not only been noted but sanctified in ritual and tradition. Indeed, tribal peoples' concepts of the Earth are quintessentially Gaian in so far as they conceive of the whole as being made up of balances that must be maintained for the health of the planet and its inhabitants.

A malocan model

The indigenous peoples of the Mirití Paraná and Lower Apaporis rivers of the Colombian Amazon still basically follow a local economic model which, in recognition of the specific cultures of the region, the anthropologist Elizabeth Reichel has called *a malocan means of production.* This model, centred within each extended patrilineal family inhabiting a communal house or *maloca,* derives its basis of existence from sustainable management of the ecosystem and is characterized by a simplified technology, a division of labour defined by sex and age, an equitable distribution of food and access to basic natural resources.

Obtaining its inspiration from the dynamic and spatio-temporal diversity of natural ecosystems, within which the community and its members are located, this economic model is governed by the principal of exchange and reciprocity of surplus within the natural and social environment. In essence the aim is to manage the flow of basic substances so as to permit the survival of each individual as well as of the whole unit. Given that the economy of today's global market is characterized by a maximization of production, by exchanging goods of commercial value and accumulating surplus for unlimited needs, then in sharp contrast the local economic model of the indigenous communities of the Colombian Amazon is *antimarket.* Thus, in the malocan economy the exchange of an object only has value for the relationship of reciprocity that it establishes between people, without the objects having any intrinsic value in themselves. Moreover, surpluses are distributed to reinforce ties within the community, while to accumulate is considered antisocial as it denies the reciprocity established through exchange. In fact, the community's needs are clearly limited by the considered need of the ecosystem to survive as a whole.

How the local economic model functions is to be seen in the relationship of the behaviour of the communities with their ecosystems; indeed how they organize their societies so as to permit them to utilize natural resources.

Natural resources

The indigenous groups in the Colombian Amazon obtain their natural resources through four main activities: horticulture, hunting, fishing and the gathering of forest products, the latter in particular being essential for providing materials that can be used for elaborating cultural material. The development of these activities is determined by the biological and spatial heterogeneity of the ecosystems. Thus the territories covered by any one group will include rivers, creeks, ponds, clear and muddy lakes, salt licks (salados), savannah, swamps, secondary growth forest, slash and burn gardens, each ecosystem within the whole offering different opportunities for obtaining plant and animal resources in differing quantities according to season.

Winter

During the months of April, May, June and July the majority of wild fruits mature. This is the season when the rivers swell and flood the river banks, creating areas of stagnant water and small islands *(restingas)* where animals take refuge. During these months the Indians consume large quantities of wild fruit such as palm nuts, including *canangucho, milpeso* and *asai.* They fish in the pools, using wild fruits such as *guamito* and *caimo* of *boa* as bait, while hunting is restricted to the *restingas* and the *pepeaderos* where the wild fruits fall. The community tends to remain longer in the vicinity of the maloca and dedicates itself to the fabrication of domestic and ritualistic utensils. During the months of August, September and October, the remaining wild fruits mature, the last being *yeche (Micandra epraceano).* At the end of the period, when the wet season gives way to the drier, the first of the cultivated fruits begins to ripen, such as pineapple.

Seasonal transition

While the rivers are high the Indians continue to hunt in the *restingas* and fish in the pools, but when the waters go down they resort to fishing in the rivers and in the streams, as well as occasionally in the lakes. Hunting is at night, along the river banks when the agoutis *(borugo)* comes down to search for food in those areas that have emerged from the waters. When several days have passed without rain the Indians hunt tapir or deer among the *salados*. In August they slash down forest in preparation for new gardens and it is during that month, according to them, that the *guardian of the fertility of gardens* — the cricket *Kankonaifi* — comes down, bringing with him energy or fertility and in compensation taking away the energy of those people who have recently died. To manage this exchange, the Indians celebrate great rituals such as the dance of *Werabaja.*

Summer

The period of November, December, January, February and March is the period when the rivers go down to their minimum and the cultivated fruits such as pineapple, *chontaduro* (palm nuts), *caimo* and *uva* (a tree fruit that resembles a grape) ripen. The Indians then take up fishing with traps and with barbasco *(Phyllantus sp.)* in the small rivers and lakes, and hunt along the banks of the rivers and in the salt-lick areas *(salados).* This period of abundance they consider healthy and the community dedicates itself to domestic activities such as the preparation of the gardens and the construction or repair of the malocas.

In April the waters of the rivers begin to rise and the last cultivated fruits ripen. Fishing and hunting are now difficult and the communities hunt in the forest of the *tierra firme* (dry land). The Indians calls this the period of not eatingand it includes the largest and most important ritual, known as *Yurupari,* when they fast for more than fifteen days.

Social organization and production

To bring about such productive activities the Indians practise a clearly defined division of labour by sex as well as by specializations. In effect the division of labour is the following:

The women occupy themselves with gardening, reproduction and the raising of children, the preparation of food and the manufacture of ceramics and hammocks. Just as food is transformed from the raw to the cooked, the period of pregnancy is seen as a period of 'cooking the unborn child.'

The men occupy themselves in the extraction and at times processing of wild resources, comprising fishing, hunting and the fabrication of canoes, baskets, weapons and the construction of malocas. They also concern themselves with the management of the relationships within the community and between the community and the natural environment. They hold the political power and concern themselves with shamanism. In this way they dedicate a good part of their time to meditating over the problems of the community, which are dealt with through the structure ordained by the myths, shamanism and rituals.

The other type of organization within the community is defined by specialization. The shaman cures or 'baptizes' children, assigning them a principal function for life. A boy may be ordained to become a shaman, *maloquero,* singer, responsible for pineapple beer, preparer of coca or simply gatherer of wood, a girl a sower of yuca, extractor of starch, maker of ceramics, or concerned with cooking. Today, given the new preoccupation with western education, shamans have begun designating children, of either sex, to become students.

For the males, specialization is generally based on a hierarchy that complies with the political structure of the group. The shaman and the cantor hold the functions of mediators between the community and the natural and supernatural world. The shaman specializes in the handling of cosmological models, and is trained to transform and adapt such models in accord with the social and natural changes that are generated over the course of time. He thus learns how to observe the behaviour of nature and hence to direct the community in the use it makes of the resources by determining the permissions and restrictions according to seasonal changes and ecological diversity. The authority of the *shaman* is thus based on his knowledge of the ecological changes during the course of annual cycles.

The *cantor* directs the singing in the rituals, during which, according to tradition, the songs take away the ills of this world. Above all this function carries with it more prestige than power insofar as it does not provide norms that can guide society.

The *maloquero,* as the third specialist in the triumvirate, is the administrator of the communal house. He is responsible for the well-being of the community, organizing the production of resources and the distribution of surpluses and managing the discords that surface between different members of the community. His permanent overseer is the shaman who directs him in his decisions; indeed the maloquero is the person responsible for effectively putting into practice that which is determined by the shaman. His authority depends on his understanding of tradition, his astute management of social relations, his discernment in the taking of decisions and his success in the administration of natural resources. As the person with the greatest authority in the community he nevertheless does not have the power to impose his will; his task is to orientate the community and each head of family is free to follow his advice, or not, as the case may be.

In general, the three functions of maloquero, shaman and cantor are held by three brothers, themselves the sons of the previous maloquero and so the tradition is passed on from generation to generation. Complementary to these three, another small group, consisting of a so-called aggressive shaman and two assistants of the maloquero, help direct the people in community work. The six people are considered the most important within the community.

Those who belong to the category of 'important people' are concerned with the distribution of surpluses and with orienting access of the members of the community to natural resources. But they do not themselves accumulate goods nor can they be distinguished from the remainder of the community in the carrying out of daily activities.

The 'ordinary people' too have members among them who specialize in mediating between the natural and supernatural, in this instance using their knowledge for the well-being of their own nuclear family and not necessarily for that of the community. Such people may try to usurp the power of the important people, for instance by putting up a separate maloca and manipulating the descendancy as delineated by lineage in order to legitimize their own aspirations.

Accumulation and the distribution of surpluses

As the centre of the community, the maloca is self-sufficient in economic terms and autonomous in political terms. Its internal organization, with spaces reserved for rituals, for communitarian activities and for domestic activities, as well as each space clearly defined for each nuclear family and for each specialist charged with different aspects of the community life, reflects the social structure of the whole.

Each family produces its own basic subsistence. The women have their area of cultivation from which they extract sufficient food to feed their families, while the men bring out foodstuffs from the forest according to the season of the year, utilizing above all the area around the maloca. This activity they need to do every three to four days so as to meet the basic requirements of their families. For this purpose they do not need to hunt large animals such as tapir or wild boar, nor fish in great quantities. Should they kill a large fruit-eating bird *(Cracidae)* such as a guan or curassow which gives a surplus, they then share that out with other families of the maloca or with some neighbouring relative without expecting any immediate return. In a similar manner, they exchange products such as baskets or ceramics.

Such distribution is not based on the responsibility for maintaining the well-being of others, but serves as a bond that reinforces friendship or some specific interest. Reciprocity effectively exists, but not in any formal way; hence, among the nuclear families of the maloca there is an exchange, a distribution and a reciprocity that generates a spontaneous collaboration.

The maloquero, situated at the western end, diametrically opposite the principal entrance, is responsible for the formal production and distribution of surpluses. Those he obtains from his cultivations, from hunting, from fishing and from gathering. Traditionally a maloquero has three wives, each one with her respective garden. The extraction and processing of these foodstuffs, particularly of *yuca,* produces surpluses that are distributed daily among the young bachelors who are no longer living with their parents, as well as among visitors should there be any.

Most families have their own production of food. In return for their food, the young unmarried men hunt, fish and gather fruits according to instructions given them by the maloquero; what they bring in is then handed over to him which he then distributes among all the inhabitants of the maloca in accordance with their needs. All families thus benefit, especially inasmuch as hunting and fishing are not always successful and for the most part young people obtain better results. According to the quantity obtained, children take precedence in the sharing out, next come the women and the old people and finally the men. Such distribution guarantees that the inhabitants of the maloca derive a basic sustenance and compromises them in a relationship of respect and reciprocity with the maloquero. The communal activities that result from this relationship ultimately benefit the whole community. Such a system of exchange is operating even today among the traditional malocas of the region.

The young bachelors also bring in and process the coca for the maloquero who then distributes it among the men during the night when they exchange impressions over the activities of the day and narrate myths that put these activities into the framework of a cosmological model, through which the maloquero is able to guide the group. Visitors, who generally remain for several weeks, receive food and coca from the maloquero and in return collaborate in the daily activities.

When the occasion arises for heavier activities, such as cutting down the forest to create new gardens or constructing or repairing the maloca, the maloquero invites people from other malocas to come and help. On these occasions the maloquero distributes food among the guests and should the food begin to run out, he sends everyone away even though the work may not be complete. In that way communities are invited to go from one maloca to another, thus facilitating communal work and production and the redistribution of surpluses. People are also invited to participate in collective fishing and in the gathering of wild fruits.

For the rituals, which are celebrated according to the season of the year, the maloquero accumulates large quantities of yuca, coca and meat for distributing among the guests. Usually two or even three communities arrive, hence more than a hundred people. Such rituals serve a cosmic function as well as one that is clearly economic and political. On such solemn occasions the maloquero and his assistants distribute the food and coca, asking the guests to sing and dance the sacred dances so as to clean the ills of the world. The invitation goes to each head of a maloca to come with his people; the maloquero then greets him and as part of the ritual invites him to the centre of the maloca where he publicly offers him a portion of food. The guest returns to his place and distributes the food among the heads of the nuclear families in his group.

A maloquero is considered good if he manages to distribute on an equitable basis. Meanwhile, each head of maloca offers a tin of coca to the host as a gesture of reciprocity and in recognition of his authority. The maloquero then mixes the coca in a bowl and once again distributes it among the visitors.

Such an act is similar to that which takes place on a daily basis when the bachelors pass over the game from hunting and fishing to the maloquero who then passes it round to all the families. However, in the context of the ritual the coca represents vital energy and therefore all are able to share in such energy when the host distributes it around.

Each ritual is also celebrated with *chicha,* a beverage derived from the fruit of the season. Large quantities are made and the guests are expected to partake so that the head of maloca can give and they can receive. This formal exchange takes place among the men; the women limit themselves to collaborating on a formal basis inasmuch as alliances are established between the men, the women being an essential part of such agreements.

The redistribution of food is also a form of sharing the surpluses from the garden, as well as from hunting, fishing and the wild fruits that are to be found in the neighbourhood of the maloca. Such rituals are celebrated according to season, those malocas with surpluses holding the ceremonies. As a result, the sharing of foods forms a vital part of the diet given that proteins are consumed for the most part during rituals whilst only small quantities are taken during daily life and then principally by the children.

To distribute implies reciprocity on the part of those that receive since during the course of the year different communities will hold the rituals. The rituals are also used to bring about exchanges of women according to the norms of exogamy, such exchanges establishing alliances and permitting the reproduction of the group.

Overall, we can observe three examples of production and exchange. The first, within the nuclear family, where the men bring in wild foodstuffs and the women cultivated ones in a way that each produces domestic elements that are exchanged between themselves. The exchange of these goods between a couple reflects the complementarity of conjugal life. When it does not exist, the relationship ends. The exchange of objects is defined by the needs of each one and it is carried out in a generous manner without expectation of a specific retribution.

The second example is the exchange between the maloquero and his community. Here the exchange is more formal and inasfar as he both gives and receives he is more aware of the various agreements that have been undertaken. On these exchanges depends the authority of the maloquero, the internal organization of the group and its continuity. The maloquero does not expect any equivalence in the reciprocity but rather collaboration in the running of the maloca.

The last example involving exchange between malocas by means of the rituals and communal activities is more formal. On it depend the alliances and the collaboration between the various ethnic groups as well as regional management of the natural resources. In this instance the exchange is finely balanced: one expects equivalence in reciprocity.

Norms that determine production and distribution

The norms by which the Indians govern exchanges, distribution and reciprocity are planted in their concept of the cosmos. For them exchanges at the social level are part of a cosmic system that exacts a permanent series of exchanges in nature. For them, overall, the existence of the universe is based on two types of vital energy that recycle between plants, animals and men and which manifest themselves in each group under the form of its members. One form of energy — *fufaka* — comes direct from the Sun and recycles directly through plants.

The other comes from the East, from *Ha-atike,* the original maloca, and recycles between animals and people. This energy of Ha-atike, exists in limited quantities and each group of animals and people requires a basic quota to exist and survive. For this, each group has a guardian. Each natural space of the forest also has its guardian, whether that be boa, frog, lizard, jaguar, that is responsible for those animals that live in its surroundings. Each time a member of a species consumes another, it is taking vital energy.

When, for instance, men hunt a peccary they are taking vital energy of that group and as far as the peccaries are concerned a member has died through a sickness sent by Man. Equally when men die through some sickness it is because they have been hunted by another group of animals. Given that the quantity of energy is limited it is dangerous that any one group accumulates too much, causing others to be deprived and their numbers threatened. Thus, to maintain an equitable distribution the guardians must communicate in altered states of consciousness, and transact energy quotas.

The shaman thus enters into contact with the guardians of the animals or of the biotypes and negotiates the hunting and fishing of a member of the group. In return he offers them coca or the energy of a member of his own group. If the guardian accepts the offer, then hunting or fishing can be undertaken without danger. These transactions are carried out principally during rituals. Should a group abuse or accumulate excessive energy then the guardians of the other groups will hunt, sending sickness so that people die; in that way the energy is recycled.

The maloquero therefore has to balance getting sufficient energy for maintaining his group but without exceeding the limits for fear that the animals will come and hunt in their turn. To manage this delicate situation the shaman must continually carry out assessments and indicate to his people how much, where and when they may hunt and fish. Control is by means of dietary and sexual restrictions. The aim, among others, is to control demographic growth and as a consequence social demand over natural resources. The restrictions are imposed during the ritual, after having made contact with most of the guardians of the forest and having achieved a settlement whereby the natural resources can be used in accordance with the season of the year. Those guardians with whom it has proved possible to reach agreement are given coca as payment. Those people that violate the restrictions expose themselves to sickness.

The importance of dietary and sexual restrictions is not limited exclusively to the administration of the use of nutrients and to social, economic and ecological exchanges: it also has implications for health and for symbolic interpretations.

The norms for production, distribution and consumption of resources are expressed for the most part in two ways. First, during daily life, when used in general arrangements of reciprocity within the maloca by means of which the social continuity of the group is reaffirmed, whether though exchange among the members of the nuclear family, or between families at the level of the community, as directed by the maloquero. The other is that involving balanced reciprocity, in which surpluses are distributed between other communities and maloqueros during the rituals. The exchanges with the guardians of the animals are also of this balanced form, that is to say the handing over of something to receive something. It could be described as payment in our terms but negotiation in their terms. Within the context of the group or of the maloca, there is no negotiation; that is reserved solely for dealing with communities outside one's own, exchanging foods, objects, women or with the guardians of the animals handing over coca or the vital energy of the group in return for food or other resources that are equivalent in terms of the vital energy of the animals.

The same cosmological concept of not accumulating vital energy in the group, of maintaining the recycling of energy between Man and animals applies to the exchange between Man and the other communities. One must not accumulate, one must instead recycle all the surplus, such recycling being enforced both by the dietary restrictions and the inability to preserve foods over a prolonged period. However, the capturing or passing on of vital energy, like the birth or death of a person, is an integral part of a permanent social relationship between Man and the natural environment. Thus distribution and reciprocity are but links in a chain of relationships that enable the economic, political and social existence of the communities. Equally, to hunt, fish, gather or cultivate, are links in a chain of relationships between Man and Nature. The person who does not want to exchange, or give and receive, hunt or fish breaks the social and ecological relationship, as the Indians relate in their myths. He who does not give is *mean* and will be shamed and die; that indeed is the basis of the exogamic rule and of ecology. One must give and receive one from the other and not consume one's own, and the person who accumulates and does not share exposes himself to death, whether social or physical, whereas the person who distributes and maintains the circuit actively extends his own being into the majority of men and animals, such integration with the immediate surroundings enabling him to live.

The surplus that one distributes is fundamentally of two origins: one of feminine work in the garden in which the woman effectively produces more than needed for her family to feed itself. The surplus is then distributed by the man to maintain his social relations and political power. The other comes from hunting, fishing and gathering, and when more is obtained than can be consumed by the family, or at the next stage up, by the maloca, then that is the time to distribute the surplus through a ritual. In this instance, the surplus has not come from work but as something that has been bought from a guardian. In all this the maloquero and the shaman are intermediaries, enabling the group to have access to the use of natural resources and to redistribute them by means of the same intermediaries in other groups. It is not the actual work of hunting and fishing that is important but rather the capacity of being able to negotiate with the guardians over the use of resources.

Thus, the basic dynamic of production and redistribution is based on a cosmic vision that holds that the resources (vital energy) are in limited quantity that neither grows nor diminishes. Each group or individual, whether animal or human, needs a basic quota, which, if not obtained will cause it to go out and seek it from another species, thus causing harm. Each group — human or animal — has an administrator, guardian or maloquero who is responsible for seeing that his group has its basic quota. He then brings about the exchange of a resource so that sufficient energy is accumulated, enabling the group to survive. The person or guardian who accumulates but does not redistribute denies the social and natural relations of reciprocity. The maloquero controls his group to respect the agreements of exchange with the guardians, human or animal, by means of dietary and sexual restrictions, attributing sickness to violations of these. His vision of the recycling of energy between the guardians of men, maloqueros and of animals, enables the control of social demand with regard to natural availability. It therefore functions both as a type of administration of natural resources over the long term and in the short term as a means of ensuring equitable distribution among the community. A major benefit of this system is the bringing about of social cohesion.

Ufaina

The general description of the malocan economy applies in principle to the Ufaina, a small ethnic group of some 150 people who live between the Lower Apaporis and Mirití rivers in the north-eastern part of the

Colombian Amazon. Their language belongs to the Tukano-oriental linguistic family, while their economy is based on horticulture, hunting, fishing and gathering. The land on which they live is poor, having lost most of its soluble minerals after millions of years of weathering and is either moderately or extremely acid. Hence the Mirití carries little sediment and is of low biological productivity. In this zone approximately half a degree south of the equator, the prevailing winds converge from either side of the equatorial line making it the most humid area of the Colombian Amazon (3,600 mm a year).

The rites and the annual cycle

For the Ufaina, the period of the *equinox* when the weather changes from dry to humid and humid to dry, is seen as favouring sickness. Conversely, the period of the *solstice* is considered a healthy one. The dry season ends and the rains start at the March equinox, a time when the rivers swell and drive from their banks snakes and other animals. *Yufurica,* the guardian spirit of wild fruit, now 'releases' the energy required for trees to bear fruit. To the Ufaina this period from dry to humid marks the transition from domesticated crops that are classified as female to wild food, classified as male. It is a dangerous and unhealthy period — it is also the period during which the ritual of *Yurupari,* which lasts 25 days or longer, is celebrated. At that ritual the Ufaina return to the Mother Earth the heat (a female attribute) accumulated during the dry (female) time. Indeed, the bodies of those participating are cleansed through the imposition of severe sexual and dietary restrictions of the energy accumulated as a result of the excessive consumption of domesticated crops. That way the tribal group can adapt to the exigencies of the transition. For the young, the *Yurupari* ritual also serves to initiate boys into the masculine world, leaving behind them that period when they were looked after by their mothers and other women of the group.

During the summer solstice the rivers remain swollen and the jungle flooded. It is a 'healthy' time but fishing and hunting are made difficult by the floods, and when the men fail to bring back solid foods, the women protest and refuse to go to the tilled fields to fetch 'yuca.' This is a source of tension in the community giving rise to much gossip which often leads to conflicts among couples. During these months, the Ufaina celebrate the 'white feather' or 'heron dance' ceremony, a ritual serving principally to reinforce community ties. Reciting the original myths and performing the appropriate rituals, they 'return' the gossip to the jungle and to the plants. It is then that the wild fruit ripens and is eaten in large quantities by the community.

The following period of the autumn equinox begins with rain, which on coming to an end leave behind mud holes, favouring the spread of various waterborne diseases. Now members of the community begin to select the area in the jungle which they will clear for their gardens or *chagras*. It is the time when the cicada sings, which according to the Ufaina is the guardian spirit, *Kankonaifi* of crops. The cicada then comes down from heaven carrying the vital force required to fertilize the new areas for tilling and in return takes away the *fufaka* of those who die. The Indians consider that during the winter their bodies accumulate an excess of vital force from wild fruit and that this is the reason for the sickness they experience during the time. Just as during the ritual of the *Yurupari* they must 'return' the female heat which can reduce the life-force and prepare for the world of rains and the cold of winter, so too, during the transition from moist to dry, ritual is required to 'return' the cold male vital force of winter which has sought to establish itself and to prepare the world for the female heat associated with cultivation. Thus, during the summer solstice, the community devotes itself to the preparation of land for tilling, to sowing, and when necessary to the construction of communal houses.

In December the pineapples ripen and the Ufaina celebrate a small dance or *guarapeada* when through shamanism and song they 'arrange' the recently opened areas for tilling so that they should cease to be lands where wild fruit grow and become instead fields where crops are cultivated. The second dance is celebrated at the end of the dry season, at the time of the maturation of the chontaduro palm *(Bactris gasipaes)* which grows all round the villages, and from which the beverage for the ritual is prepared. For this ceremony the community invites its allies who dwell in the world under the river from where crops arise, to come dressed up as animals. During the ceremony the water creatures who originally gave the vital force to the crops are invited to partake in the harvest. In short there are two great categories of ceremonies: dances for healthy times at the solstices considered 'gatherings to drink liquor' and which require little shamanistic activity; and dances for unhealthy times at the equinoxes, considered 'great dances or ceremonies' and which require a great deal of shamanistic activity.

The cosmos and life-energy: a Gaian imperative

When a being is born, the vital force enters it and the group to which the being belongs. The group is seen as borrowing the energy from the total stock of energy. When a being dies it releases this energy, and returns it to the stock. Similarly, when a living being consumes another, for example when a deer eats a bush, a man eats a deer, or a tree extracts nutrients from the soil or when people cut down trees to create a clearing, the consumer acquires the energy of the consumed, and it accumulates in its own body. Since the number of animals, plants, humans, trees and indeed of the amount of inhabited territory is 'limited' the amount of available energy is also limited, and must be treated as a scarce resource. This leads to competition among different species for the available energy, since each must maintain its quota of energy. Moreover, according to the Ufaina, it is important that the vital force continues to be recycled from one species to another, in such a way that not too much accumulates in any one of them, since this would cause another to be correspondingly deprived of its vital force. The delicate balance between a community and its environment makes it vulnerable to any disturbance, however slight.

For the Ufaina, each group of beings has a supernatural guardian who overseas that his 'flock' has enough life-energy to survive. The guardian of all hunted animals is the ant-eater, *Makuemari;* the guardian of wild fruit is the tapir, *Yafurica* and the *Yupari;* the guardian of the jungle is the jaguar, *Yifotsirimaki;* the guardian of the crops are the anaconda, *Okoaanafaki,* and the cicada, *Kankonaifi;* the custodian of the fish is the same anaconda and the captain is the ray, *Waibaifi,* the guardian of the land is the female Mother Earth, *Namatu;* and the guardian of the energy of each human group is the jaguar-man or sorcerer, *Yaiko.* In the tribe's mythology, four heroes who originally established the orders of time, of space and of the lives of men, animals and plants are responsible for the distribution of all the *fufaka.* They are called the *Imarimakana,* 'those who have always been.'

Fufaka or vital energy circulates through the cosmos, which is represented as a great pyramid composed of thirteen superimposed platforms. It is from the top six, referred to as the *Wehea* that the *fufaka* associated with males arises. From the lower six arises the feminine life energy of *Namatu* or Mother Earth. The centre platform where *Wehea* and *Namatu* meet is where Man and Nature are born and where the Ufaina live. The Sun revolves around the cosmos distributing energy to all equally, its summit lying between the abode of the four heroes and that of music. Thus, the four *Imarimakana* are there to administer the Sun's energy.

The jaguar-man and the handling of life-energy

The jaguar-man is the mediator between all these forces and the Ufaina community. He is selected for this role from birth and from that moment on is subjected to a strict diet forbidding the consumption of various animals and particularly salt, as well as either animal or vegetable fat. The apprenticeship is rigorous, requiring the study of the original myths, community life, animal behaviour, as well as the relationship and interdependence between men, plants, animals and Earth. At approximately the age of fifteen, having attained this knowledge, the apprentice retires for five years with a jaguar-man to specialize in meditation which will allow him access to other states of consciousness. The Ufaina do not take hallucinogens to attain this state, they simply use coca or tobacco as a stimulus. Their discipline implies little eating, little sleeping and abstention from sexual intercourse. The jaguar-man has profound theoretical and empirical knowledge of the environment in which he lives. One of his central objectives is to administer the handling of the nutrients in the natural environment such that the group can remain ten to fifteen years in a single place without the need to migrate. When the time comes it is he who decides when and in which direction to emigrate.

If the group needs to hunt, fish, collect wild fruit, extract minerals from the jungle for building or to open new areas of cultivation, it must consult with the jaguar-man before taking on the task. He concentrates and meditates on the state of the flora and fauna, on the carrying capacity of the area, and according to the need, invokes the 'owner' of wild fruit, or of hunting to request a loan of energy. If the answer to his request is positive, the jaguar-man offers coca in exchange for the animal or plant energy that the group will take for itself. Coca represents energy and has special qualities associated with shamanism like that of stimulating the mind, easing concentration, reducing sensation of hunger and sleep and reducing the need for sexual intercourse.

Restrictions and the control of energy

Mechanisms for purification as well as for preserving the purity of individual energy, are founded on obligatory rules which refer mainly to dietary and sexual restrictions. For instance, after the great rituals or certain feasts like that of the jaguar or the sparrowhawk *(Arpía arpía)* or after the birth of their child, men must abstain for long periods from eating certain foods, the exceptions being yuca in the form of cassava and white tucupi, red pepper and coca, as well as abstaining from sexual intercourse.

Figure 17.1. Matapí Maloca, overlooking the Caquetá River, Colombian Amazon.

By means of sexual restrictions demographic growth is controlled, and hence the administration of the carrying capacity of the area is made easier. After each ceremony the participants are forbidden to have sexual intercourse for a period of time equal to the duration of the ceremony, which can last for three days or as long as a month according to the type of ritual. Considering that a communal household may celebrate four rituals a year, and that its inhabitants participate in those of two other houses, the people are under sexual restrictions more then ten times a year.

Polluted energy and illness

When a man consumes an animal or a plant he acquires its energy. If the right amount is consumed the energy identifies with and strengthens the consumer. But if too much is consumed, the energy of the consumed animal or plant dominates the man's own energy which makes him vulnerable to illness or misfortune. Many people accumulate energy of other beings, establishing a dichotomy in body-energy. When this happens, the contaminated energy becomes visible to the 'owners' or to jaguar-men, not as the energy of the person, but as that of whatever was consumed, whether plant or animal. When the 'captains' or 'owners' want to take human energy they send snakes to bite the contaminated person or as spirits they hit the individuals over the head with a branch, make them fall off a tree, overturn a canoe in the river, or send ill-winds or sickness. Only a person with contaminated energy is visible and therefore susceptible to these evils.

The bodies of people who respect the restrictions are animated with their own energy and hence are invisible to the 'owners' and to jaguar-men, and no harm can come to them. For this reason the community must return energy which is not its own and purify itself through rituals, as well as respecting dietary and sexual restrictions imposed by the jaguar-man on the strength of his knowledge and of tradition.

Purification of energy as a healing system

Health through preventative medicine is expressed as an ecological relationship. But healing exists too, although for the Ufaina the individual's needs are secondary to keeping the community healthy. The sick are those who have accumulated alien energy and are suffering because the owner is trying to recuperate that which is his or hers. When healing an individual, the jaguar-man enquires about his or her daily conduct and establishes in what way restrictions have been violated. This is in order to decide who is sending the ill, whether the owner of hunting or of fish, or that of wild fruit. But he also does this to show those present at the healing ritual how the sick one is a victim of his or her own imprudence — as a salutory warning. The patient is thus the protagonist of a drama, the evidence of what happens when restrictions are not adhered to.

Today the jaguar-man is losing his powers. The Indians can cure themselves with 'white' medicine without submitting themselves to restrictions. Nor can the jaguar-man cure those diseases of colonization. The consequences clearly transcend the issue of individual health and affect group-cohesion, cultural identity, adaptation to the natural environment and involve the possible disintegration of the group and the irrational exploitation of the jungle.

Bibliography

Andrade, G. and J.P. Ruiz. 1988. *Amazonia Colombia: Aproximación ecológica y social del la colonización del bosque tropical.* FESCOL 4.

Castaño, C.U. 1989. *Políticas para el manejo y preseleccíon de parques nacionales fronterizos en Colombia: aproximación a la conservación de la Hylea Amazónica.* Mesa redonda sobre el manejo conjunto de areas fronterizas.

Fischer, J-M. 1989. *Proyecto de Salud para las Comunidades Indígenas del Rio Apaporis.*

Hildebrand, M. von. 1988. An Amazonian Tribe's View of Cosmology. In Peter Bunyard and Edward Goldsmith (eds). *Gaia, the Thesis, the Mechanisms and the Implications.* Wadebridge Ecological Centre.

——. 1989. *Conservation and Sustainable Development in the Putumayo Caquetá Area in the Colombian Amazon.* Fundación Puerto Rastrojo.

Imbert, E.G. 1986. Puesto que hablamos distinto ¿quiere Usted casarse conmigo? *Glotta-Bogotá (Colombia)* 1(3).

Palacios, P. 1987. Análisis de los usos y formas de manejo de algunas especies vegetales empleadas por las comunidades Andoque, Huitoto y Miraña asentadas en la ribera del rio Caquetá. *Colombia Amazónica.* 2(2).

Política del Gobierno Nacional para la Defensa de los Derechos indígenas y la Conservación Ecológica de la Cuenca Amazónica. *Republica de Colombia.* November 1989.

Primera Reunión de Capitanes y Líderes Indígenas de los Resguardos de Mirití, Yaigoje, Puerto Cordoba y Comeyafu. 1989. *Desarrollo sostenido, Conservación y Procesos autogestivos en el Area del Bajo Caquetá, Mirití y Apaporis.* Puerto Remanso del Tigre, Amazonas Colombia. April 3–8.

Reichel, E. 1987. *Asentamientos Prehispánicos en la Amazonia Colombiana.* Colombia Amazónica. Universidad Nacional de Colombia.

Reichel-Dolmatoff, G. 1987. The Great Mother and the Kogi Universe: A Concise Overview. *Journal of Latin American Lore* 13:1, 73–113.

Roldán, R. Esparragoza. A.F. 1984. *Fuero Indígena.* Bogotá: Presencia.

Schroeder, T. 1987. Estudio de un systema agrícola tradicional en Araracuara. *Colombia Amazónica.* 2(2).

Walschburger, A.C. 1987. Algunos aspectos generales sobre las repercusiones ecológicas del systema de tumba y quema de los indígenas Yacuna en la Amazonia colombiana. *Colombia Amazónica.* 2(2).

– 18 –
A Gaian Critique of Contemporary Social Theory

Alwyn K. Jones

In making the assertion that the Earth is one single 'living' organism, the Gaia hypothesis has implications that go well beyond the specific confines of the Natural Sciences. Indeed, the assumption in the hypothesis that humankind is an integral part of Gaia poses particular problems for mainstream social theory. This inability to reconcile Gaia with social theory can be attributed in no small degree to the attempts made by leading theorists of the late eighteenth and early nineteenth centuries to set their studies of society within a methodological framework closely identified with that of the natural sciences (Finger 1988). Two interrelated issues emerge from this presumption of unity between the natural and social sciences: firstly how has it arisen, and secondly what implications does it have for the construction of holistic ideas within social theory? To address these questions I shall first turn briefly to the work of two writers, Saint-Simon and Comte, both of whom have had considerable influence in establishing the scientific basis of social theory.

Saint-Simon (1760–1825)

There seems no doubt that Saint-Simon's thought had far-reaching implications for the subsequent development of social theory (Lukes 1969, Abraham 1977, Kumar 1978), but what particularly concerns us here is his belief that the study of society, or what he called 'social physiology,' could be put 'on the same sound footing as had been achieved in the sciences dealing with the natural world' (Kumar 1978). For him human societies had progressively evolved through various 'critical' periods, interspersed by 'organic' calm, until his own social epoch in which was emerging the third and final 'organic' period of industrialism. The industrial society, as Saint-Simon called it, was important because it reflected the final point in the development of human societies. With the advent of industrialism humankind no longer faced the capriciousness and unpredictability of the material world: its control and manipulation through the acquisition of scientific knowledge would be increasingly assured. But for humankind to reap the full benefit of these developments society itself must be rationally and scientifically organized. To achieve this would mean the demise of politics and the emergence of an industrial and scientific elite comprising:

> scientists, engineers, mathematicians and economists, with a leavening of those — bankers and industrialists — who could claim to be honest men of affairs with no political axes to grind and with special skills to offer. (Kumar 1978).

Though Saint-Simon did not systematize his ideas into a framework for the formulation of social theory, he nevertheless laid the groundwork for a reductionist, analytical and *instrumentalist* social science in which the individual was estranged from both nature and society.

Comte (1798–1857)

The importance of Comte lies not so much in his originality, but in the way in which he synthesized Saint-Simon's ideas to form the 'first comprehensive system of sociology' (Swingewood 1984). For him, like Saint-Simon, the human mind had progressively evolved through three stages of history ('The Law of the Three Stages') which he described as theological, metaphysical and positive. Each stage corresponded to a particular form of social structure, with the final and most developed stage being associated with what he called 'industrial *pacific* society.' This, the 'positivist' or science based modern age, was one in which human problems, whether social, political or cognitive, could for the first time in history be increasingly resolved not by resorting to violence, but by reference to rationally and reliably acquired knowledge. From hindsight it is difficult to share Comte's optimism as we approach the end of a century in which two world wars, environmental degradation, and escalating levels of violence and aggression seem to correlate directly with increases in scientific and technological skills!

According to Comte each science passes through historical stages similar to that of the human mind, finally freeing itself from the grasp of metaphysics when it reaches the positive and ultimate stage of its development. Sociology is the last science to make the epistemological break with its intellectual antecedents and stands at the top of an hierarchy of sciences which have evolved from high levels of generality to ever greater degrees of specificity and complexity (Giddens 1979).

Although, for Comte, each science is logically dependent on its predecessors in the evolutionary spiral, this is without prejudice to its status as a separate and discrete area of study. For instance biology

> presupposes the laws of physics and chemistry insofar as all organisms are physical entities which obey the laws governing the composition of matter; on the other hand, the behaviour of organisms as complex beings cannot be directly derived from those laws. (Giddens 1979).

Comte's assertion that biology immediately precedes sociology in the hierarchy of sciences is fundamental not only for understanding his thought, but for the implications it has had for the subsequent development of functionalism in social theory. In the study of the biological organism it is assumed that the whole is greater than the sum of its parts. Thus the focus of analysis is on the overall entity with its parts being understood in terms of their contribution to the maintenance of the whole. It was Comte's view that this approach should be used as the analogy for the development of appropriate methodological procedures in sociology. The institutions of society would therefore be studied not as isolated entities, but as parts which *relate* together to maintain the whole. This procedure is what Comte called 'statics' in contrast to 'dynamics,' the historical study of the evolution of human societies to which we have already referred in our discussion of the Law of the Three Stages. What concerns us here is the extent to which Comte's advocacy of a holistic perspective in sociology can be said to conform to Gaian principles.

At first sight it would appear that by giving priority to the whole over the parts there is some degree of conformity between the Comtean and Gaian positions. However the Gaia Hypothesis posits the Earth as one *single* organism in which parts and whole are inextricably interwoven: reference to one must imply reference to the other. Moreover, as Abram argues, humankind is uncompromisingly subsumed within Gaia thus collapsing all dualities, including subject/object, fact/value and society/nature (see Abram).

Comtean holism is synonymous with Gaian principles at only a very superficial level. First the existence of Society is externalized as objective reality. As we have seen both Saint-Simon and Comte were preoccupied with theorizing the conditions for social order, and using such theory for the rational reconstruction of society. Society thus becomes established almost by *diktat* with individuals fulfilling institutionally defined roles whose prime function is the maintenance of social stability. Such a scenario allows little latitude for a Gaian style resonance in which the parts interrelate *creatively* to ensure the continuance of the whole. Second the presupposition that the different sciences, despite the interconnections between them, have specific areas of knowledge exclusively within their particular domain reinforces scientific reductionism and discourages an inter-disciplinary approach upon which an understanding of Gaian mechanisms depends. Third the objectification of the *social* world as the framework for sociological analysis has not only estranged the individual from society, but has also precluded any meaningful consideration of humankind's interaction with nature.

Finally the instrumentalism we find in the work of both Saint-Simon and Comte, in which an objective value-free science is to be used to foster industrial growth and progress, limits the knowledge base in society to a consideration of the most efficient means by which to achieve such objectives (Weisskopf 1971).

The outcome of this narrowing of the intellect in which means take precedence over ends is the virtual silencing of any critical reflective debate over what the ends or goals of life should be. Weisskopf's observations relate to contemporary industrial society, but the influence of Saint-Simon and Comte in promoting an instrumentalist perspective in sociology when it was at a very early stage of its development should not be underestimated. Such a perspective, based as it is on a reductionist view of science, is as Finger claims clearly not reconcilable with Gaia (Finger 1988).

The social theory of Emile Durkheim

Durkheim (1858–1917) was arguably the theorist who made the greatest contribution to the development of sociology, by both establishing it as an autonomous discipline with a clearly defined subject matter, and constructing a methodology which aligned it closely with reductionist science.Two issues arising from Durkheim's sociology are of particular concern to us : firstly his methodological dictum that 'the first and most fundamental rule is: consider social facts as things;' (Durkheim 1966) and secondly his preoccupation with the problem of social order.

By making the assertion that social facts should be regarded as things Durkheim establishes what is for him the objective reality of the social world. Such facts which include laws, norms, mores and customs are *exterior* to individual human beings and act as a form of coercion which constrains them to conform to the collectivity. By demarcating the field in this way Durkheim protects a predominantly reductionist perspective in sociology by ensuring that sociological phenomena are not reduced to psychological, biological or other modes of explanation. In short he did what Comte had failed to do: he established the parameters for a framework of analysis in which sociology could develop as a discipline in its own right within a clearly identified sphere of endeavour.

In order to ensure that explanatory devices from other disciplines could not be imported into sociology Durkheim argued that the cause of a social fact could be explained only in terms of another social fact.

The extreme reductionism to which this gives rise, whilst it may be important for disciplinary purity, has been challenged by Catton *et al.* in a manner which is relevant to the argument being developed in this article:

> Sociology needs to break away from Durkheim's rules enough to take explicit account of certain facts of geology and ecology that shape social facts. It simply is not true any more, if it ever was, that the cause of a *social* fact is always another social fact. The non-renewability of resources upon which human societies became dependent through industrialization is too important to overlook. Because of it, human efforts to hold today's social fabric together make tomorrow's social fabric still more fragile. To understand this, we must acquire a clear grasp of the concept *carrying capacity.* Unfamiliarity with this ecological concept allows illusions about the social fabric's durability to persist (Catton *et al.* 1986).

It is not just boundaries between the natural sciences which must be breached as most of the contributors to the Gaian debate have so far assumed.

Though important we must go further than this. The only way in which we can face the future with any degree of confidence is to integrate the concepts of science, social science and the arts into a broad understanding of the difficulties that beset us in an over-industrialized world. Gaia has more than just physical dimensions: it has social, political, psychological, ethical, spiritual and cosmic ones as well. In short it means, as Mae Wan-Ho has so aptly put it, the emergence of a new paradigm which accords not only with empirical findings, but also with our deepest experience of nature as unity. In so doing, it re-establishes a fertile and harmonious relationship between the human spirit and the world we inhabit; and *that* may well be the very soul of Gaia (Ho 1988).

The problem of social order

For Durkheim the pre-industrial order was characterized by what he called 'mechanical solidarity' in which individuals were bound to the group by collectively shared sentiments and values. This was reflected in a minimal division of labour and a strong *conscience collective* in which 'there exists a social solidarity which comes from a certain number of states of conscience (consciousness) which are common to all the members of the same society' (Durkheim 1964). But the emergence of modern industrial society has meant the attenuation of the ties which linked the individual to the group with a resultant weakening of the *conscience collective:* how, then, in this radically different state of affairs can social cohesion be sustained? (Jones 1983).

For Durkheim the division of labour is the source of what he calls 'organic solidarity' in industrial societies. According to him it is the increase in both volume and material density — literally more people on a specific area of land *in regular and continuing interaction with each other* — which has given rise to industrialization. In such circumstances it 'is not that the growth and condensation of societies *permit,* but that they *necessitate* a greater division of labour' (Durkheim 1964). The vast increase in a whole range of specialisms and skills in both the occupational and social spheres of life meant that individuals had to become mutually interdependent if they were to survive. Thus mutualism through the division of labour was Durkheim's recipe for cohesion in the new industrial order.

It is true that Durkheim faces up to many of the problems of industrialization, but his whole orientation is to find remedies within the system the basic tenets of which he never really challenges. The division of labour is a case in point. The thrust of capitalist industrialism, in which achieving profitability in a highly competitive market was a prime objective, meant that tasks were subdivided to the point at which all meaning was drained out of work and the worker became, in Marx's words, 'an appendage of the machine.' For Durkheim, however, this was an abnormal and transient phenomenon, to be overcome when the division of labour more accurately reflected the natural distribution of talents and abilities in the population as a whole (Kumar 1978). But, notwithstanding Durkheim's contentious defence of inequality, it is difficult to share his optimism that the division of labour could ever play a role as an instrument of cohesion (similar to the Gaian regulatory mechanisms?), in an increasingly competitive, bureaucratized, politically centralized and urbanized society.

At best Durkheim's social theory gives us some insights into the shortcomings of industrialism. But, like functionalism, in which it reaches its ultimate expression, it must remain antithetical to Gaia because it fails to challenge the inherent progressivism which lies at the heart of the value system of industrial societies.

Marxist social theory

In contrast to the theoretical perspectives discussed above, Marxist social theory does not hesitate to cross the divide between society and nature because one of its fundamental postulates is that the human being interacts with nature in order to produce his or her needs (Marx 1975).

In the dawning of human history humankind faced a potentially hostile and negating physical world. Unlike other animals that are biologically equipped to survive in a specific self-sustaining ecological habitat, human beings are in a dialectical or contradictory relationship with nature and must transform it to survive. Through such transformation nature becomes humanized: this is what Marx calls 'species-being' in which human beings become consciously aware of a world they themselves have created. The duality between subject and object is collapsed and human beings are at one with nature.

For Marx the history of human societies can be understood in terms of the development of the human capacity to overcome the problems of production posed by the natural world.The situation is exacerbated by the coming into being of social classes at a very early stage of human development. Such classes arise from the social relations of production in which one class (the ruling class) owns the means of production, with the other being denied direct access to nature on which it depends for its livelihood. It cannot therefore realize its essence (species-being) through productive activity and is alienated from the natural world. However the enhancement of human productive powers cannot be furthered within the existing antagonistic relationships of production and 'From forms of development of the productive forces these relations turn into their fetters.

Then begins an era of social revolution' (Marx 1971). Hence, in each era of social revolution human productivity moves to a higher level of development until, with the overthrow of capitalism, and the ushering in of communist society production will be freed from all antagonisms which fetter its growth.

This is an over-simplified version of Marx's theory of history. But enough has been said to indicate the extent to which production through the transformation of nature is of overriding importance in the analysis. This raises serious questions for Gaia. In particular it would appear that the dialectic between humankind and nature is firmly in place even after the overthrow of industrial capitalism. Are we, however, to accept unequivocally the following comments Naydler made in his critical review of Pepper's *The Roots of Modern Environmentalism?* (Pepper 1986).

> Marxism is essentially positivistic and technocentric: Marx sought to unveil scientific laws operating in the economic and social spheres and his overall outlook was that of a severe scientific materialist. Likewise, he believed unquestioningly in industrialism and industrial expansion. How to hold on to these tenets of the Marxist credo while adequately addressing the environmental problems — and problems of consciousness — which we now face, is a formidable task. (Naydler 1987).

It may be that there is some ambivalence on ecological issues in Marx's writings which has not been brought out in the various interpretations of his work. By concentrating on the class struggle, and adopting an optimistic view of industrial growth and progress, with the prospect of fair shares for all in the eventual communist *Nirvana,* Marxist thinkers may have overlooked the extent to which Marx was aware of the need to protect and conserve nature. As Capra says:

> although Marx did not strongly emphasize ecological concerns, his approach *could* have been used to predict the ecological exploitation that capitalism produced and socialism perpetuated. One can certainly fault his followers for not grasping the ecological issue earlier, since it provided yet another devastating critique of capitalism and confirmed the vigor of the Marxist method. (Capra 1983).

It remains arguable, however, whether such a re-reading of Marx will provide a route through which mainstream social theory can be integrated into Gaian thought.

Gaia and social theory

The Gaia hypothesis presupposes that the Earth is one single 'living' organism in which all aspects of reality interrelate symbiotically together to create the whole. The relationship between the separate parts of Gaia is therefore a cooperative one in which no activity can be seen in isolation from any other. If we accept this hypothesis as the basis on which the natural world, including humankind, can be understood we can see immediately that it stands in contradistinction to mainstream social theory which supports the underlying anti-Gaian ethos of industrialism.

Such an ethos presupposes a universal, and virtually unequivocal, acceptance of industrial growth and expansion (Jones 1987a). Indeed it can be argued that the pursuance of unlimited material growth is the *raison d'être* of industrialism. As economic expansion depends on scientific and technological advance the control and manipulation of nature is given full legitimacy. It is axiomatic in such circumstances that nature will be regarded as *external* to humankind and defined as a resource to be exploited for human gain. It is clear that there can be no place here for the 'top down' holistic epistemology proposed by Lovelock in his Gaia hypothesis.

Though all of the social theorists to whom we have referred so far were by no means unaware of the extent to which industrialization had eroded the mutualistic and symbiotic values of traditional culture, they nevertheless seem to have accepted the inevitability of this process. Saint-Simon, Comte, and to a lesser extent, Durkheim were confident that substantial benefits would accrue to humankind from the industrialization of life as long as action was taken to ensure that the appropriate social arrangements were in place.

Such action would be based on rationally acquired scientific knowledge derived especially from the new science of society, namely sociology. Another important early theorist Spencer (1820–1903) gained considerable social acclaim in nineteenth century Britain for his particularly vigorous support for these ideas (Swingewood 1984). In an elitist, ethnocentrist and somewhat high handed manner, he closely identified social theory with biology and coined the term 'the survival of the fittest' to account for the evolution of human societies towards their ultimate industrialized stage of development.

There is a sense in which all these theorists, with the possible exception of Marx, can be included under the rubric of the 'ideologues of progress' (Kumar 1978) because they leave little room in their theories for the kinds of issues with which Gaia is concerned. What is lacking in social theory, therefore, as Illich argues, is a comprehensive theory of industrialization:

> Our present ideologies are useful to clarify the contradictions which appear in a society which relies on the capitalist control of industrial production; they do not, however, provide the necessary framework for analyzing the crisis in the industrial mode of production itself. (Illich 1975).

Our general disillusionment with classical social theory means that we must turn to Weber, Illich and other thinkers, some of whom are only on the periphery of social science, if we are to enter into any meaningful critique of industrialism from a Gaian perspective.

The eclipse of *Gemeinschaft*

We shall take the distinction Tonnies (1963) made between *Gemeinschaft* (community) and *Gesellschaft* (association) as our point of departure for a Gaian critique of industrialism. For Tonnies the pre-industrial social order is characterized by *Gemeinschaft* in which people interact together on the basis of reciprocal and whole person relationships which are to their *mutual* advantage. In such circumstances an organic or natural will, *Wesenwille,* embraces the whole of the individual's being; it places being before thought, and emphasizes the unity felt by individuals in *Gemeinschaft* relationships. In Kumar's words:

> Members of *Gemeinschaft* bodies follow collective sentiment, rather than calculating egotistical reason. They are governed by custom, folkways and religion. The social relations that these give rise to are best expressed in the family, the village, and the town, or the corporate organization of guilds, colleges churches and religious communities. Intimacy of scale is critical: large increments of numbers or of physical distances would destroy the texture of frequent daily contacts, in

> different places and for different purposes, that are the hallmark of *Gemeinschaft* life. (Kumar 1978).

But with the onset of industrialism the mutualism to be found in *Gemeinschaft* gives way to the competitive ethos of *Gesellschaft* society in which relationships are fragmented, self-motivated and egocentric. Rational will, *Kurwille,* comes into prominence over natural will: it puts calculative thought before being, is future-oriented and emphasizes means over ends. No longer do people treat each other as ends or whole persons, but as means by which to achieve particular objectives or purposes (Jones 1983). Moreover the 'intimacy of scale' to which Kumar refers is ruptured as large specialized institutions, detached and estranged from the culture as a whole, replace family and community in the meeting of the more essential human needs. Institutions thus become the settings for the establishment of associative relationships such as buyer/seller, doctor/patient and teacher/student in which individuals interact only in terms of that part of their being which is relevant to the accomplishment of the particular task. This loosening of the social fabric, and the fracturing of human relationships to which it gives rise, recalls a Hobbesian world of human individuals desperately trying to realize their desires in a perpetual 'war of all against all' (Pappenheim 1968).

It might be argued that this is drastically overstating the case, but once the ethical bonds are broken which tie people together in closely knit *Gemeinschaft* communities the way is clear for the atomization of social life in which the pursuit of self interest becomes the organizing principle for *Gesellschaft* society. Tonnies sees the loss of community, from which life derives its meaning, as the fundamental destabilizing force in the modern world.

But such ties have been torn asunder in the modern world by a rampant economism which attaches itself to limitless industrial growth and progress, within the framework of a free market economy informed by the ethos of competitive individualism. However our acceptance of *Gesellschaft* as a basis for understanding the mechanisms underlying human relationships in industrial society does not unequivocally imply a preference for a reversion to the *Gemeinschaft* of a pre-industrial social order. Indeed *Gemeinschaft* undoubtedly imposes many constraints on individual freedoms, especially those which can broadly be described as the 'tyranny of custom.'

But, as I have argued elsewhere, (Jones 1983) the industrial social order has imposed a new and perhaps more dangerous tyranny — a tyranny of *Gesellschaft* institutions which have become more and more detached from life at the community, or what Illich calls the 'vernacular' level of society. Not only has this meant the virtual eclipse of community life, but the fragmentation of society into discrete and relatively autonomous institutional complexes which are able to set standards in their respective areas of activity relatively free from public assessment and control.

The fragmentation of reason

If a future based on the Gaian principles of interdependence, mutuality and interrelatedness is to be contemplated a re-emergence of some form of *Gemeinschaft* must be a fundamental prerequisite. But this cannot be accomplished without the expansion of reason from the narrow, pragmatic and essentially instrumental role it serves in modern industrial society. As we have seen the division of the intellect in *Gesellschaft* society is exemplified for Tonnies by the ascendancy of 'rational' over 'natural' will, which denotes not only the dissociation of thought from being, but the *paramountcy* of thought over being in the modern world. Thought or reason thus becomes detached from its deep roots in culture and community from which are derived those values which give ultimate meaning and purpose to life. In such circumstances reason can no longer carry out its former critical all-encompassing role (Weisskopf 1971) in which judgements are made without making any distinction between ends and means. In his differentiation between 'ontological' and 'technical' reason, which respectively parallels Tonnies' 'natural' and 'rational' will, Tillich has put the point well:

> According to the classical philosophical tradition (ontological) reason is effective in the *cognitive, aesthetic, practical and technical* function of the human mind ... (but) in the concept of *technical* reason, reason is reduced to the capacity for *reasoning*. Only the cognitive side of the classical concept of reason remains, and within the cognitive realm only those *cognitive* acts which deal with the discover of *means* for ends. (Tillich 1971).

Whilst the fragmentation of reason may have had its origin in the development of instrumentalism in the natural sciences from the seventeenth century onwards (Jones 1987b) there seems little doubt that the narrowing of reason to primarily *technical* considerations has now become pervasive in the industrial culture as a whole. Weber (1864–1920) was perhaps the only major nineteenth century social theorist who recognized this as being central to the specific contradictions to which industrialism, as opposed to capitalism, gave rise.

Weber's critique of formal rationality

For Weber the relentless pursuit of profit and gain in the modern world, aided and abetted by developments in science and technology, has led to the displacement of 'substantive' rationality, *Wertrational* in which human actions are given meaning within a broad framework of values. In its place emerges 'formal rationality,' *Zweckrational,* similar to Tonnies' 'rational will,' and Tillich's 'technical reason,' in which means take precedence over ends. The implication of this is that instrumental, and predominantly economic, criteria such as efficiency, cost-effectiveness and utility become virtually redefined as ends whilst the actual goals being pursued remain predetermined, and very largely unevaluated insofar as they are assumed to be furthering industrial growth and expansion. As Schumacher argues:

> Call a thing immoral or ugly, soul-destroying or a degradation of man, a peril to the peace of the world or to the well-being of future generations; as long as you have not shown it to be 'uneconomic' you have not really questioned its right to exist, grow and prosper. (Schumacher 1974).

Weber recognizes, as does Tonnies, that the breakdown of community structures as a result of industrialization means that decisions can no longer be made with reference to the *totality* of social life. In cohesive community settings reason encompasses the whole culture, with no distinction being made between instrumentality on the one hand and the values, ends or purposes of life on the other. But an industrial system, orientated as it is to the single-minded pursuit of *material* progress, has no place for a rationality which takes the overall or substantive interests of humankind into account.

For Weber the outward manifestation of formal rationality is reflected in the emergence of specialized bureaucratic institutions which become the crucial mechanisms through which the material objectives of industrial society are pursued. Decisions made in any one institutional setting will tend to be made in isolation from other spheres of life, and will reflect what is expedient for the particular institution involved (Giddens 1971). Similarly the emergence of scientifically backed rationality, far from increasing our understanding of reality, precipitates a flight from religion, magic, folklore, legend and poetry from which alone the establishment of ultimate meanings in human life is possible. This is what Weber calls 'the disenchantment of the world,' which is well summarized by Brubaker as follows:

> The rise of modern science leads to the 'disenchantment of the world' and creates a deep tension between the basic demand that life and the world have a coherent overall meaning and the increasingly evident impossibility of determining this meaning scientifically. The extension of scientific knowledge, to be sure, enhances man's rational control over social and natural processes. But while this control has made possible dramatic improvements in material well-being, it has also made possible the development of increasingly sophisticated techniques for the 'political, social educational, and propagandistic manipulation and domination of human beings.' (Brubaker 1984).

Weber's critique of rationalization is important because it provides the first real sociological attempt to develop a theory of industrialization which goes beyond a specific analysis of capitalism. It is unfortunate that, because of his commitment to a value-free social science, Weber was not able to develop his ideas within the broad framework of a critical theory of society. However, his analysis of rationalization and Tonnies' notion of *Gesellschaft* give us crucial insights into the fragmented nature of social reality, and a basis for our discussion of Illich's critique of advanced industrial society.

Illich's critique of advanced industrial society

Illich has extended Weber's somewhat generalized critique of the rationalization and bureaucratization of modern life by placing the concomitant phenomenon of professionalization at the centre of his analysis. For him the rapid growth of a technocratic elite, equipped with professional and technological expertise from which the lay-person is excluded, has meant that institutions have increasingly become controlled by professionals who have been able to achieve a 'monopoly over the social imagination, setting standards of what is valuable and what is feasible' (Illich 1973). This is what Illich means by the 'institutionalization of values,' a process by which the institutional imposition of values (needs) abrogates a fundamental human freedom: namely the basic right of individuals to determine their own needs in a given social milieu. Most of the more important spheres of life have been affected by this process — for instance education, medicine, transport and religion, as well as industrial production.

Associated with the institutionalization of values is Illich's notion of 'radical monopoly' (Illich 1974; 1975). This is a situation in which human perception of reality is so constrained that there can be no perceived alternative to the meeting of a given need other than through the consumption of the product of a particular institution. This is not the same as an ordinary monopoly in which a specific product may dominate the market. For instance Coca-Cola might establish a monopoly in the soft drinks industry; but as long as people believe that they can quench their thirst in other ways the monopoly has not taken on a radical form. But it will take this form once people think that their thirst can be assuaged only by consuming coke (Illich 1975).

The Coca-Cola illustration is of course allegorical, but through it Illich adroitly makes explicit the process by which all the main areas of human need have been institutionalized in modern society. Thus for Illich education and professionalized health care are clear examples of radical monopolies in the service sector of industry. General Motors and Ford are comparable examples in manufacturing because they can so 'manipulate public taste' that there is hardly any conscious awareness of alternatives to the motor car as a means of transportation (Illich 1975). Radical monopoly, by turning people into consumers, thus encourages the unexpurgated expansion of the products of institutions (1977).

A Gaian social order — myth or reality?

From the writings of Tonnies, Weber, and especially Illich, we can discern certain broad principles which would have to be invoked if the anti-Gaian tendencies in modern society are to be overcome. All three writers argue that fragmentation is an inherent characteristic of the industrial social order. Tonnies' distinction between *Gemeinschaft* and *Gesellschaft* is particularly important because it exposes a fundamental paradox of industrialism: namely the extent to which the individual has been both centralized and marginalized in modern society (Tonnies 1978).

The breakdown of *Gemeinschaft* divorces individuals from integration into a cultural milieu from which life derives its meaning. The implication of this, as Illich has so forcefully argued, is that people increasingly come to associate the 'good' life with an ever-increasing supply of goods and services produced by the institutions of society (Jones 1987). Such a society is 'dynamically unstable. It is organized for indefinite expansion and the concurrent unlimited creation of new needs, which in an industrial environment soon become basic necessities.' (Illich 1975).

For Illich expansionism is the ultimate hubris of humankind. We are finite in our capacities, and face the certainty of death. Yet in our desire to manipulate and control the world we act as though we have the immortality of the gods. We arrogantly assume that the answers to our mounting environmental problems are forever in our grasp. By narrowing the scope of reason to purely instrumental considerations we extract lead from petrol, but keep cars on the road; introduce 'environmentally friendly' products onto the market, but encourage businesses to grow; and respond to an industrial disaster such as Chernobyl with the promise to tighten safety regulations, but take no steps to abandon the use of nuclear power.

We are indebted to Illich not only for his sharp insights into the counterproductivity of the institutional structure of industrial society, but also for his attempt to establish principles for the construction of what he calls a 'convivial' society. Illich's studies in health, education and transport are paradigmatic illustrations of his more general point that the industrial mode of production, with its *inherent* tendency to promote the meeting of need through institutional rather than personal or community direction, must inevitably lead 'to the degradation of the cultural ecology necessary for satisfactory activity outside commodity-monopolized spheres' (Illich 1979). What Illich is saying here, following Leiss (Leiss 1978) is that an individual's capacity to derive personal *satisfaction* from the meeting of need recedes in inverse ratio to the increasing prevalence of need 'satisfied' through the acquisition of commodities whether of goods or services.

As we have seen both Tonnies and Weber were concerned at the extent to which institutional growth had eroded basic human freedoms in the modern world. But Illich is not prepared to let the matter rest there. For him the discovery of 'natural scales and limits' to human endeavour in all spheres of life is of vital importance if we are to take the path towards 'convivial reconstruction' in which individual autonomy over the determination of need, and social and ecological balance, are to be achieved. Thus:

> We must come to admit that only within limits can machines

> take the place of slaves; beyond these limits they lead to a new kind of serfdom. Only within limits can education fit people into a man-made environment; beyond these limits lies the universal schoolhouse, hospital ward, or prison. Only within limits ought politics to be concerned with the distribution of maximum industrial outputs, rather than with equal inputs of either energy or information. Once these limits are recognized, it becomes possible to articulate the triadic relationship between persons, tools, and a new collectivity. *Such a society, in which modern technologies serve politically interrelated individuals rather than managers, I will call 'convivial.'* (Illich 1975).

A convivial society, which has no place for the externalization of authority and the heteronomous determination of needs, seems far removed from the structures familiar to those of us in industrial societies today. Similarly Illich's suggestion that our technologies should be fully accessible to every member of the community so that they would add to, and not detract from, each person's potential for self-development and creativity would be hard to reconcile with our everyday experience of modern life. For instance what control do we have over the giant machinery working on the new building or motorway site; or the high technology in use in the modern hospital or nuclear power station? But Kumar's comment on Illich's analysis is apposite:

> This may seem familiar utopian stuff. What gives it a concreteness and a foothold in contemporary reality are various indications that industrialism is in a state of genuine crisis, and that certain varieties of utopian thought, new or traditional, might now have a relevance previously denied them by the powerful currents of a developing and triumphant industrialism. (Kumar 1988).

Illich's notion of conviviality correlates closely with a Gaian perspective. Unlike mainstream social theory, it posits the interconnectedness between the individual and social and physical reality. As Illich argues:

> I choose the term 'conviviality' to designate the opposite of industrial productivity. I intend it to mean autonomous and creative intercourse among persons, and the intercourse of persons with their environment ... I consider conviviality to be

> individual freedom realized in personal interdependence and, as such, an intrinsic ethical value. (Illich 1975).

It seems that there is a creative resonance, or symbiosis, between individuals in a convivial society so that freedom for one is equated with a like freedom for all. Positive expression is thus given to the dynamics of freedom as it is lived in the *interrelatedness* of human beings both with each other, and with their physical and social environment. In such circumstances the presumed duality between individuals and social and physical reality collapses and cooperation, rather than competition, becomes the organizing principle for social life.

Expressed in this way conviviality comes very close to Gaia. Moreover the presumption of interdependence as an 'intrinsic ethical value' has important implications for a reappraisal of humankind's attitude to nature and society. Once we perceive ourselves as integrated into social and physical reality it would be absurd to claim that our actions towards those milieux are not ethically based. On what grounds, for instance, can we justify a course of action which disturbs irreversibly the delicate and complex interrelationships upon which we as part of the overall web of life depend?

Indeed if we assume that the whole of reality is interconnected, we must, as Schumacher has argued (Schumacher 1974), develop a holistic wisdom which passes beyond the mere acquisition of instrumental knowledge. Our ethical horizons must expand from the immediacy of our surrounds to embrace a planetary, even cosmic, consciousness. In his attempt to lift these horizons Roszak suggests:

> there is a planetary dimension to the spreading personalist sensibility which links the search for an authentic identity to the well-being of the global environment. The scientific status of this connection between person and planet can only remain speculative ... but I have little doubt that, within the next generation, there will emerge a well-developed body of ecological theory that illuminates this subtle interrelationship and gives it enough political force to displace the inherited ideologies of industrial society ... Perhaps even the hard sciences of the Western world will find their way to a personalist paradigm that unites the knower and known in a vital reciprocity ... Meanwhile ... my argument is that the needs of the planet are *the needs of the person. And, therefore, the rights of the person are the rights of the planet.* (Roszak 1981)

Since these words were published more than ten years ago Lovelock's Gaia hypothesis has come into prominence not only in the scientific community, but also in the broader social milieu. Perhaps the scientific status of Roszak's words has already passed from speculation to reality?

References

Abraham, J.H. 1977. *Origins and Growth of Sociology.* Penguin. pp.84–86.

Abram, D. 1989. The Mechanical and the Organic: Epistemological Consequences of the Gaia Hypothesis. In Bunyard, P. and Goldsmith, E. (eds) *Gaia, the Thesis, the Mechanisms and the Implications.* Wadebridge Ecological Centre. p.128. (Reprinted in this volume.)

Brubaker, R. 1984. *The Limits of Rationality.* Allen & Unwin. pp.3f.

Capra, F. 1982. *The Turning Point.* Wildwood House. pp.216–19.

Catton Jr., W.R., G. Lenski and F.H. Buttel. 1986. To What Degree Is a Social System Dependent on its Resource Base? In J.F. Short Jr. (ed). *The Social Fabric.* Sage. pp.177f.

Durkheim, E. 1964. *The Division of Labour in Society.* Free Press. p.109.

—— 1966. *The Rules of Sociological Method.* Free Press. p.14.

Finger, M. 1988. Gaia: Implications for the Social Sciences. In Bunyard, P. and Goldsmith, E. (eds) *Gaia, the Thesis, the Mechanisms and the Implications.* Wadebridge Ecological Centre. pp.201–14.

Giddens, A. 1971. *Capitalism and modern social theory.* Cambridge University Press. p.184.

—— 1979. Positivism and Its Critics. In T. Bottomore and R. Nisbet. *A History of Sociological Analysis.* Heinemann.

Ho, M-W. 1988. Gaia: Implications for Evolutionary Theory. In Bunyard, P. and Goldsmith, E. (eds) *Gaia, the Thesis, the Mechanisms and the Implications.* Wadebridge Ecological Centre. p.180.

Illich, I. 1973. *Deschooling Society.* Penguin. p.11.

—— 1974. *Energy and Equity.* Calder & Boyars. pp.55–61.

—— 1975. *Tools for Conviviality.* Fontana. p.11.

—— 1977. *Limits to Medicine.* Penguin. p.217.

—— 1979. Vernacular Values and Education. *Teachers College Record.* Columbia University. 81(1):66.

Jones, A. 1983. Beyond Industrial Society: Towards Balance and Harmony. *The Ecologist.* 13(4):141–47.

—— 1987a. The violence of materialism in advanced industrial society: an eco-sociological approach. *The Sociological Review.* 35(1):19.

—— 1987b. From Fragmentation to Wholeness: A Green Approach to Science and Society. Part 1. *The Ecologist.* Vol.17(6).

Kumar, K. 1978. *Prophecy and Progress.* Penguin. pp.27–44.

—— 1988. *The Rise of Modern Society.* Blackwell. p.65.

Leiss, W. 1978. *The Limits to Satisfaction.* Marion Boyars. (For Illich's reference to Leiss see pp.64–66).

Lukes, S. 1969. Saint-Simon. In T. Raison (ed). *The Founding Fathers of Social Science.* Penguin. pp.27–34.

Marx, K. 1971. *A Contribution to the Critique of Political Economy.* Lawrence & Wishart. p.21.

—— 1975. Economic and Philosophical Manuscripts. In L. Colletti introducing *Early Writings of Marx.* Penguin. p.329.
Naydler, J. 1987. *The Ecologist.* 17(2/3):124.
Pappenheim, F. 1968. *The Alienation of Modern Man.* Modern Reader Paperbacks. pp.66f.
Pepper, D. 1986. *The Roots of Modern Environmentalism.* Croom Helm.
Roszak, T. 1981. *Person/Planet.* Granada. p.25f.
Schumacher, E.F. 1974. *Small is Beautiful.* Abacus. p.34.
Swingewood, A. 1984. *A Short History of Sociological Thought.* London: Macmillan. p.40.
Tillich, I. 1951. Systematic Theology. Vol.I. University of Chicago Press. pp.72ff. in W.A. Weisskopf. 1971. *Alienation and Economics.* Duttton. p.37f.
Tonnies, F. Row. 1963. *Community and Society.* Trans. and ed. C.P. Loomis. Harper & Row.
Weisskopf, W.A. 1971. *Alienation and Economics.* Dutton. p.38.

– 19 –
Natural Being and Coherent Society

Mae-Wan Ho

Science is a system of concepts and tools for knowing and living with nature. As such, it should be integral to any human society, from the most primitive prehistoric culture to the industrialized nations of today. But whereas the primitive lived within nature, using the totality of personal and tribal experience to gain inner knowledge, civilized man is imprisoned outside nature, thereby denying himself real knowledge of her.

Cartesian mind-matter dualism and Newtonian mechanics began a process of the dissolution of our natural being, which Darwin completed by reducing organisms (including humans) to objects, isolated from the environment, and buffeted by blind selective forces. This deep alienation from nature and from our own natural being is the human condition of modern man. It is his paradise lost. From then on nature would become opaque, with man condemned to a knowing from without, to a life alone and devoid of meaning.

In this paper, I wish to deconstruct the myth of Darwinian man by re-examining the biological roots of human nature to show how it is inextricably bound up with the social. From studies on animal and plant communities to 'primitive' human societies, we see that sociality is at the basis of life: it is the direct consequence and expression of the fundamental unity and interconnectedness of all nature. The unity of nature is itself a universal, which the new biophysics of coherence in living systems, in particular, is validating in every aspect. Authentic knowledge is premised on this coherence and interconnectedness. Social and moral values arise explicitly and naturally in a life coherent with authentic knowledge. From this perspective, culture is the creation of meaning and knowledge in partnership with nature, in which every social being participates. The coherent society is the society of natural beings living in harmony with nature's creative process.

The conference of the birds

According to ancient legend in Persia, all manner of birds gathered for a conference one fine day and were persuaded to disperse to the four corners of the world in search of the meaning of life. After many long and arduous years, they returned home only to discover that what they were seeking had been right there all along. They were blind to it, and the journey away was necessary to open their eyes.[1] This is in many ways the parable of western science. After centuries of intellectual wanderings that increasingly led away from nature, we are irresistably drawn back in the realization that there is no authentic knowledge, and hence no meaning in life, apart from nature.

Perhaps the single most decisive factor in the evolution of the knowledge system of the west (and it is a knowledge system rather than science in isolation), is that it depends on severing our intimate, manifold connections with nature at the outset. Cartesian mind-matter dualism is simultaneously a division of mind from body as well as the isolation of observer, as disembodied mind, from an 'objective' nature observed. Newton clearly brought out the stark consequences of this dual separation when he proferred reality as a desolate universe of absolute space and time, where inert, indifferent bodies are acted on by the push and pull of extraneous forces. Green grass and trees, fins and wings, are so many illusory 'secondary qualities' added on by our senses. Human joys and pains, likewise, can have no dominion; relegated as they are, to the realm of poetic fancy that hangs ever like a veil over objective reality.[2]

But this exile is entirely self-imposed; and is neither necessary nor inevitable. Elsewhere, I try to show why this is the case, and how we may yet find our way back, if not to paradise, then surely to a more fulfilling and humane future through recovering our natural being, which is also the vehicle to authentic knowledge.[3]

The Darwinian metaphor and the Darwinian man

He bought white ties, and he brought dress suits,
He crammed his feet into bright tight boots.
And to start in life on a brand new plan,
He christened himself Darwinian Man!
But it would not do,
The scheme fell through,

For the Maiden fair, whom the monkey craved,
Was a radiant Being,
With a brain far-seeing,
While Darwinian man, though well-behaved,
At best is only a monkey shaved![4]

Darwin's theory states that organisms evolve on Earth as the result of the natural selection of random variations. There were three immediate sources for the theory.[5] The first was Paley's theological argument from design — how it is that organisms so perfectly adapted to their way of life could be explained naturalistically, without invoking, as Paley did, a supernatural 'Maker.' The second was artificial selection, practised by plant and animal breeders who selectively bred from organisms with the desired characteristics so as to create new breeds. The problem was how selection could take place in nature where no obvious selector exists. A chance reading of Malthus provided the third ingredient, which was just the natural mechanism required. Malthus noted that human beings, like all organisms, have the natural propensity to increase exponentially, generally outstripping the rate at which food supply can increase. Consequently, populations numbers are kept down by starvation, famine, disease and war which now and again take their toll. In Malthus' theory therefore, Darwin found the perfect solution to Paley's problem of how adaptation could be explained. All organisms have a natural propensity for exponential increase, outstripping the carrying capacity of the environment. Thus, only those organisms with characteristics that favour them in the struggle for existence will survive to reproduce. Heredity ensures that the offspring of those organisms will have the same favourable, or adaptive characteristics. In this manner, the population will become more and more adapted to the environment in subsequent generations. This then, is how natural selection is supposed to work.

As we shall see later, competition for scarce resources is hardly the norm for natural animal or human populations; in general they do not increase exponentially because many social and biological factors intervene (before those associated with food supply) to keep the reproductive rate low so that the Malthusian scenario is seldom realized. Nevertheless, the Darwinian metaphor took hold in the western world, and became incarnated in the Darwinian man, who proceeded to remake the world in his own image.

The full title of Darwin's epoch-making book of 1859 was, *The Origin of Species by Means of Natural Selection* or *The Preservation of Favoured Races in the Struggle for Life.* If Darwin liberated the Victorian era from the domination of religion and superstition, he also delivered it well and truly to a nature painted 'red in tooth and claw.' Our continuing disharmony with nature derives ultimately from this unedifying image, which Darwin clothed with the full dignity of a scientific theory. At the same time, the emphasis on competition between individuals and the implied superiority of the 'favoured races' in the 'struggle for life' were most easily taken to be justification — on the basis of natural law — for the economic exploitation of the masses as for the colonization and oppression of 'inferior' races.[6]

Thus, a metaphor borrowed from life in the Victorian English society, steeped in ideas of progress arising from unbridled competition in the free-market, of imperialist conquests and expansion, became enshrined as a scientific truth, dictating how we should see reality, and ultimately shaping reality in accordance to its dictate — that Darwinian man shall rule the world. Huxley invented a birthplace for him in the primitive society, where,

> ... the weakest and stupidest went to the wall, while the toughest and shrewdest, those who were best fitted to cope with their circumstances, but not the best in another way, survived. Life was a continuous free fight, and beyond the limited and temporary relations of the family, the Hobbesian war of each against all was the normal state of existence.[7]

This picture was directly echoed by Freud, whose theory of the savage, patricidal primal horde is so far-fetched and ridiculous that it hardly bears repeating. The modern Freudian man, nonetheless, is the bulwark of the western industrialized society. According to a summary given by a sympathetic exponent,

> Freud believed in the person as a social atom requiring community only as a means to the satisfaction of his needs; in a primary hostility so strong that only sheer necessity or common hatred directed elsewhere could join people in love; in a certain biological inevitability of hereditary constitution, anatomy, and development, which strictly limits human possibilities; in an inner private existence which, although in part the result of early personal relationships, seems in later life, to make only indirect contact with external reality ... and finally in civilization as the result of thwarted libidinous impulses which have been deflected to symbolic ends.[8]

Such a view of human nature continues to validate the competitive, profit-seeking consumerist society of the industrialized west that in turn reaffirms and reinforces it until no alternative is conceivable. The Darwinian man is the constant, unchangeable parameter that must enter into every social equation. There can be no consideration other than cost and benefit, which creates at best, an uneasy equilibrium poised between loveless, self-serving individuals. 'Scratch an altruist, and watch a hypocrite bleed,' so says a staunch defender of neo-Darwinism.[9] A more moderate, though no less revealing statement, is made in the opening pages of E.O. Wilson's book, *Sociobiology,* which applies neo-Darwinist principles to explain the evolution of social behaviour, thus creating the discipline of the same name:

> This brings us to the central theoretical problem of sociobiology: how can altruism, which by definition reduces personal fitness, possibly evolve by natural selection?[10]

Why do sociobiologists find such common and commonplace human qualities so difficult to accept, that they need to do their utmost to explain them away? It has been suggested that part of the reason lies buried in their own psychology, which reflects the warped society that has nurtured them.

The natural being

> We crave to be more kindly than we are.[11]

In reacting to the claims of some sociobiologists that competitiveness, aggression, and worse, the propensity for rape and murder in males are universal human characteristics, Clairborne points out that in reality, the overwhelming majority of human beings readily engage in activities to help or benefit others, whereas only a tiny minority have ever committed criminal acts. Therefore it may be argued that altruism, rather than aggression is the universal human characteristic. He does not regard altruism to be innate, however. Rather, he sees it as a learned behaviour based on the universal human capacity for empathy, that is, for deriving pleasure from other people's pleasure and distress from their distress. And hence, 'satisfying the needs of others, and thereby sharing their satisfaction, is intrinsically rewarding.'[12] This empathy, as I shall try to show, comes from the experience of connectedness with kin, with fellow creatures and ultimately with all nature.

Mutual aid versus mutual struggle

Kropotkin tells us that, under the influence of Darwin's *Origin of Species,* he began to study animal life in Siberia in order to find evidence of intraspecific competition. Two general features emerged from his observations. First, that there was indeed extreme severity of struggle for existence against inclement nature (as one would expect in Siberia); and second, that even under the most abundant animal life, there was no struggle for existence against one another.[13]

He went on to document at length numerous examples of mutual aid and mutual support among animals throughout the animal kingdom, from ants and termites to birds and mammals, quoting widely from published sources as well as from his own experience.[14] Thus, ants regularly regurgitate food to feed hungry comrades, while pelicans always fish together, typically forming a wide half-circle facing the shore, then narrowing it by paddling towards the shore.

Cooperation does not stop within species boundaries. Species may combine together to repel attacks, as the gulls and terns, who cooperate to drive away the sea-hen. Lapwings, *Vanellus cristatus,* attack birds of prey so bravely that the Greeks gave them the name 'good mother.' Cranes live in excellent relationships not only with their congeners but with most aquatic birds. Their sentries keep watch around a mixed flock which is feeding or resting together.

A considerable body of present-day sociobiological theory is devoted to explaining, or explaining away cooperation in terms of the selective advantage that after all, must accrue to the cooperating individuals (see Bateson[15]). But this is a misreading of nature. In many instances, help is freely given to others from whom no return can ever be expected, and with whom the individual shares no genetic relatedness. Among mammals, dolphins are well-renowned for their intelligence and friendship towards humans. They will actually help fishermen drive fish into their nets if, after a long day, the fishermen have netted nothing and they call to the dolphins for help. However, if the fishermen are greedy and do it too often, the dolphins will ignore their call.[16]

Goethe was once told by Eckerman that two little wren-fledgelings, who had run away from him, were found the next day in the nest of robin redbreasts who fed the littles ones together with their own. Goethe saw in this a confirmation of his pantheistic views.[17] It is surely this universal neighbourly tendency of birds to look after other's young that enables the cuckoos to exploit their hosts,[18] and not because the latter are too stupid or mesmerized to distinguish foundlings from their own offsprings. In my experience, female and even male domestic cats, too, will readily adopt and look after kittens that are not their own. The love of young is such among Indian langur monkeys that as soon as a newborn arrives, the troop's females will cluster around the mother, all reaching out gently to try and touch and lick the infant. During its first day of life, it will have passed through the loving arms of up to eight females.[19]

What appears much more fundamental than cooperativeness or helpfulness is that animals tend to seek out and enjoy the society of others. The crane is in continual activity from morn till night, of which only a few hours are devoted to finding food. All the remainder of the day is given over to society life.[20]

> And finally, we have that immense display of mutual aid among birds — their migrations. Birds which have lived for months in small bands scattered over a wide territory gather in thousands; they come together at a given place, for several days in succession, before they start ... Some species will indulge every afternoon in flights preparatory to the long passage. All wait for their tardy congeners, and finally they start in a well-chosen direction ... the strongest flying at the head of the band, and relieving one another in that difficult task. They cross the seas in large bands consisting of both big and small birds. And when they return next spring, they repair to the same spot, and, in most cases, each of them take possession of the very same nest which it had built or repaired the previous year.[21]

Similarly, social mammals are highly successful and associate in large numbers (until decimated by man). The numbers of solitary carnivores are trifling in comparison with the social herds of wild horses, donkeys, camels, and sheep that used to roam in central Asia; and elephants, rhinoceroses, monkeys, reindeer, muskoxen and polar foxes in northern Asia and Southern Africa.

> And how false, therefore, is the view of those who speak of the animal world as if nothing were to be seen in it but lions

> and hyenas plunging their bleeding teeth into the flesh of their victims! One might as well imagine that the whole of human life is nothing but a succession of war massacres.[22]

Most of all, animals derive pleasure and satisfaction from life in society. Society was not created by 'man' as our anthropocentric view would lead us to believe, but is antecedent to our own species. Sociability — the love of society for society's sake — is at the very basis of animal life. Not only do numerous species of birds assemble together habitually to indulge in antics and dancing performances, but according to Hudson, nearly all mammals and birds (probably with no exception) indulge frequently in more or less regular or set performances with or without sound, or composed of sound exclusively. One has only to listen to the chorus of birdsongs mornings and evenings that happen regularly as clockwork during the warm seasons. The habit of singing in concert is most strikingly developed with the chakar *Chauna chavarria.*[23]

Many years later, Allee[24] was stimulated to re-examine Kropotkin's thesis when, by chance, he discovered that even such lowly animals as isopods aggregate most eagerly to form social clusters. From this, he was led to review abundant evidence of swarm formation in the living world, starting with the single-celled photosynthetic organism *Euglena,* through to insects, birds and mammals. He concluded that sociality is indeed universal:

> The growing weight of evidence indicates that animals are rarely solitary; that they are almost necessarily members of loosely integrated racial and inter-racial communities, in part woven together by environmental factors, and in part by mutual attraction between the individual members of different communities, no one of which can be affected without changing all the rest, at least to some slight extent.[25]

As an example, he referred to the grassland bison community of the Great Plains in North America. The bison herds kept the grasslands closely cropped, preventing the invasion of herbs and shrubs. This provided a rich habitat for grasshoppers, crickets, mice and prairie dogs, all of whom converted the grass into meat, on which the plain Indians, buffalo wolves, hawks, owls and prairie chickens fed. The plants of the community, therefore, cannot be considered in isolation from the animals. This is but the age-old wisdom of ecological connectedness and interdependence of all living things that is universal to indigenous cultures all over the world.[26] The dominant modernist culture of the industrialized west is unique in its persistent denial of the unity of nature.

Allee and his colleagues also carried out numerous experiments demonstrating that society *per se* has important effects on the behaviour and physiology of individuals in it, not all of which can be interpreted as contributing to an increase in survival value. The ill-effects of crowding are well-known and clearly documented for animals such as fruitflies and laboratory mice. What is not so well-known is that under-crowding is also deleterious for the survival of individuals. Goldfish and planarians, when isolated, succumb to poisoning more readily than when grouped.[27] Embryonic development in sea urchins is significantly accelerated when the eggs are massed together.[28] And ciliate protozoa reproduce faster in groups than when isolated, the reproductive rate being also dependent on the density of bacteria on which they feed.[29]

Of especial interest is Allee's demonstration that goldfish learn faster in groups than as individuals, through a combination of imitation and group cohesion.[30] From this arises the concept of 'social facilitation' of behaviour which may have important implications for our own species that are as yet unexplored.

Having demonstrated that cooperativeness and sociality is for animals the most natural state of being, Kropotkin went on to cite abundant evidence of mutual aid, compassion and moral feelings among so-called primitive human societies. The relative lack of competition and strife in most traditional cultures have long impressed anthropologists. The point is not that competition or rivalry never occurs. Competition, like cooperation, is a social phenomenon; it does not follow that corresponding preformed human qualities of competitiveness and cooperativeness actually exist. There is, at bottom, a feeling of connectedness with other beings, a desire for society — sociality, or love. According to Kropotkin, sociality not only offers the greatest advantage in the struggle for life under any circumstances (as opposed to competition, which is only advantageous under some circumstances), but it also favours the growth of intelligence, language, social feelings and a 'certain sense of collective justice' akin to morality. Sociality, the desire, or propensity for society, is the regulating and cohesive principle in both animal and human society. It exists prior to any consideration of selective advantage. In a sense, Kropotkin, and also Bateson[31] (a strong advocate of cooperation among contemporary neo-Darwinists), invert cause and effect in trying to explain why cooperation or mutual aid could have evolved by natural selection. Qualities such as compassion or empathy, based on the same experience of connectedness with other beings, are also antecedent to life in organized society. Life in society may of course, reinforce and enhance those qualities, but they would never have arisen through any externally imposed social order were they not already heartfelt and integral to the natural state of being.

The origins of love and hate

In direct opposition to Freud and his many followers, for whom sex is the single most important human instinct on a par with survival, the Scottish psychologist Ian Suttie saw love as primary. The idea of love comes from the ministrations of the mother or caretaker during infancy. From this arises an emotion of tenderness which considers the whole world of people as possible companions, who are to be enjoyed and loved, and from whom apreciation is sought.[32] Hate or aggression has precisely the same source: it arises when love is lost, or threatened with loss, frustrated or thwarted. Thus, only the capacity to love predisposes us to hate; the stronger the love, the deeper the hatred that comes into being should love fail. Like Kropotkin, Ian Suttie came to his conclusions from studying social behaviour among animals as well as 'primitive societies.' Sociality is congenital to human beings as much as it is to all animals (even those that are not obviously social). And sociality is in turn, the root of culture and creativity.

Just as play is universal among animal societies, it is an integral part of human development. Play gives the individual reassuring contact with fellow human beings which is lost when the mother's nurtural services are no longer required or offered. From play arises creativity: play therefore, and not necessity, is the mother of invention. Donald Winnicott, a contemporary of Suttie, located play, and by extension, creativity and culture, in the 'potential space' that comes in being between mother and infant who, through the realization of love, remain connected as they become separate.[33] What is it to live? he asked. It is to live creatively. Thus, cultural and creative activities do not result from the sublimation or suppression of the sexual instinct, as Freud supposed. Instead, they are the *raison d'être* of human existence, the very meaning of life and a direct extension of the primal, irreducible feeling for love.

This is how I see the real original motive for gifts: they were not solely nor primarily exchanges, even less so a primitive form of trade, as most anthropologists seem to believe. The item given is above all a sign of love. It refers to all other loves by association.

The item given overflows with meaning referring without bounds to all of nature which is fully connected with, and accessible to the primitive consciousness. This meaning is irretrievably lost when exchange is reduced finally to money: money which changes hands impersonally and indifferently, obliterating all reference to value, to labour, or to love, because it is itself valueless and formless.

Suttie began his book with some questions for his colleagues:[34]

> In our anxiety to avoid the intrusion of sentiment into our scientific formulations, have we not gone to the length of excluding it altogether from our field of observation? Is love a fiction, an illusion of a weak mind shrinking from reality, and if so how and why should our minds ... ever have created the 'idea' of love?

Science, he argued, should be concerned with the whole range of our experience. In its failure to deal with sentiment and human attachments, mechanistic materialism is but a form of sublimated intellectual play. Suttie himself demonstrated that it is possible to have a science of feeling, but only with feeling. I suggest that the re-integration of intellect with feeling is essential to a full experience and understanding of nature, in other words, to an authentic knowledge of nature from within.[35]

What I propose is a knowledge system based explicitly and firmly on natural human values, a knowledge system which is already implicit in many aspects of contemporary western science, as I shall make clear in the next section. In claiming to be value-free and objective, western science has systematically obliterated human values and divorced us from our feelings and experiences, which however remain to haunt our dreams in hidden, subterranean forms, making us strangers to ourselves. We are constantly being fragmented into a rational thinking domain, opposed to an irrational domain of feeling: of head versus heart, with a strong emphasis of head over heart. Science and technology without value or purpose, that is, without heart, fall easy prey to the artificial value system of vested interests whose only criteria for validation are monetary cost and benefit; while cost to human life, plant and animal life, takes second place at best. The present global environmental crisis is a crisis of a materialistic lifestyle based on the ruthless exploitation of nature and of our fellow human beings. An exploitation which has been mediated, aided and abetted by the prevailing western science and technology. In that respect, it is also a crisis for western science and technology and a challenge to scientists to respond to the needs and sufferings of peoples all over the world.

Nature from within

To know nature from within is to recover the primitive natural wisdom that is sustaining of human life, that sees nature as she really is: the evolving plenitude that affords the existence of things, the source and sustenance of all life, and the ultimate inspiration for the human consciousness striving to know and to create. In a culture that has lost none of this feeling of real participation in nature's creative process, science, as much as art, is a quest for greater intimacy with nature that involves our whole being. The ideal state of true knowledge and inspiration is a state of total coherence with nature in which the knower and the known are mutually transparent. In ancient China, this entails the spiritual union of the knower with the *tao,* the creative principle that generates the multiplicity of things. As the *tao* is eternal, the knower partakes of the eternal in all things through the *tao.* Similarly, in ancient Greece, true knowledge is unobscured participation in the divine mind from which all creation springs.[36] In this coherent state, one's actions are guided not by a disembodied objective intellect, but on the contrary by a passionate total involvement and harmony of mind and body in nature.

The feeling for the unity and interconnectedness of nature is not just a romantic notion entertained by poets and mystics and the so-called primitive consciousness. It is an universal intuitive insight that contemporary science is driven to validate in all aspects.

In biology, by far the most tenaciously held dogma for the whole of the present century is that the genes of organisms are immune from environmental exigencies and are therefore passed on practically unchanged to the next generation. Within the past fifteen years, as the tools of molecular genetics become more and more precise, people begin to discover that the genes can change as readily as many other characters of the organism in response to the external environment. So much so that molecular geneticists have coined the term 'the fluid genome' to describe the large variety of processes that can chop and change the genes, expand or shrink different parts of the genetic material.[37] Recent experiments also indicate that adaptive genetic mutations are non-random in that they are much more likely to occur than non-adaptive ones.[38] All the evidence indicates that organism and environment are intimately interconnected, from the sociocultural domain right down to the genes. Stable inheritance depends on this very interconnection, rather than on a mythical, unchangeable genome. The process of heredity has a dynamic stability which resides in the feedback interrelationships that can propagate from the external environment through the physiological system to the genes. Organisms and environment, like figure and ground, engage in ceaseless rounds of mutual definition and transformation which is the essence of evolution.[39] Similar cycles of feedback between the biosphere and the physicochemical environment are the basis of stability for the global ecosystem.

The present global environmental crisis is the direct consequence of a knowledge system based on a denial of the unity of nature. And nature responds with a message that has become all too clear in recent years: she is one indivisible ecosystem, and whatever insult is perpetrated in one part of the globe will have repercussions, not only locally but globally as well. Lovelock's Gaia thesis encapsulates the ancient ecological wisdom in a contemporary form: the collective activities of the biosphere as a whole maintain the earth's atmosphere and temperature far away from thermodynamic equilibrium in conditions that are suitable for life.[40] In other words, instead of every individual organism working for its own selfish ends as envisaged in neo-Darwinian theory, it is the extent to which they effectively cooperate in cycles of mutual feedback and interdependency that life for all is possible. This is also a generalization of the principle of mutual aid among animals that Kropotkin and Allee expounded on. More importantly, organisms are not so much passively adapted to the environment by natural selection, as actively adapting the environment to themselves.[41] That is, they actively participate in shaping their own evolution. This arises naturally from the interconnectedness not only of all life-forms, but also between the biological and physical realms: each shapes the other in successive cycles of mutual stabilization and transformation. Every species is endowed with powers that are given by all the rest. In a very real sense, each is implicated in every other by material and energy flow, and possibly also the flow of information, as we shall see. There is an irreducible wholeness of being and becoming on earth. This wholeness encompasses our relationship to reality at the most fundamental physical level.

The inseparability of the observer and observed, or knower and the known, and the universal wholeness of being, are nowhere as clearly brought home to us as in quantum physics. Quantum physics is the culmination of a long series of attempts to fragment reality into the smallest particle; only when physicists got down to the infinitesimal, indivisible quantum, they find that the whole exercise was futile: it cannot be done at all! It turns out that in order to have a consistent representation or theory, it must be supposed that observer and observed are one indivisible system, and that the very act of observation transforms reality from an indefiniteness of multiple superimposed states of being to a state of definiteness, which however, cannot be predicted in advance. Moreover, the same act of observation can simultaneously determine the state of a system which is widely separated from the one observed, as though reality were indeed, an organic, universal whole. This has prompted David Bohm and his colleagues to reformulate quantum theory on the basis of universal wholeness: every particle or being is embedded in a field, or quantum potential consisting of the influences from every other being in the universe.[42] From this perspective, wholeness and interconnectedness are actual and primary, just as fragmentation and separation are illusory.

How then, can we think of reality at all? Nature has resisted all attempts to describe her simplistically, in terms of a flat, common sensible literalness. The reductionist, atomistic science whose aim it was to do just that, when pushed to the very limit, can only reaffirm that reality has breadths and depths beyond our attempts at description and comprehension. As our knowledge of nature deepens, so too the magic and the mystery; (the same magic and mystery that were accessible to our ancestors). She is both wave and particle, both here and everywhere at once. To know her requires not only the analytic intellect of the scientist, but also the vision of the mystic, the imagination of the poet, and the sensitivity of the artist. In other words, it requires our whole undivided being participating fully in knowledge.[43]

The coherence of being

I hinted that organisms may be interconnected with one another and with their physicochemical environment by information flow, as well as by material and energy flow. It is already generally accepted that physical parameters such as day length and other seasonal variables are informational in that organisms respond to them physiologically. One hypothesis, advanced by Brown,[44] is that the biological rhythms are closely attuned to the rhythms of the Earth (which are in turn attuned to those of the Sun and the Moon). Many of these natural rhythms are electromagnetic in nature. There is now a substantial literature on the sensitivity of organisms to weak electric and magnetic fields occurring either naturally, or close to power lines and other electrical appliances; although the mechanism involved in this sensitivity is not fully understood.[45]

Many molecular biologists assume that the answer to biological organization will come when all the molecules in organisms are isolated and analyzed. But biological organization is a dynamic, macroscopic order extending over astronomical numbers of molecules; spanning distances at least millions of times the size of individual molecules. This organization enables organisms to transform energy with the rapidity and efficiency rarely achieved elsewhere, and to be extremely sensitive to specific signals in the environment.[46] Thus, muscle contraction can be as efficient as 98 per cent in converting chemical energy to mechanical work; and it is estimated that our eye is sensitive to a single light quantum falling on the retina.

Some thirty years ago, the nobel laureate biochemist, Albert Szent-Györgyi[47] pointed out that we can only begin to understand the characteristics of living systems if we take into account the collective properties of molecules akin to superconductivity and superfluidity. This idea was developed at around the same time by solid-state physicist, Herbert Fröhlich,[48] who suggested that living systems may have collective modes of activity somewhat similar to superconductors operating at physiological temperatures. Metabolic energy, instead of being lost as heat, is stored in the form of collective, or coherent electromechanical and electromagnetic excitations. There coherent excitations could be responsible for generating and maintaining long-range order. They also make possible highly efficient energy transfer and transformation of energy and the detection of very weak electromagnetic signals (Ho and Popp).

Evidence for the existence of coherent excitations in living organisms come from the work of Fritz Popp and his co-workers,[49] who showed that practically all organisms emit light at very weak intensities, which can nonetheless be detected with a sensitive photomultiplier placed with the organisms in a dark chamber (see Ho and Popp). The nature of this light (biophotons) can also be studied as rescattered emission, or delayed luminescence, after brief illumination with an ordinary light source. As the result of more than fifteen years of experimentation, Popp advances the hypothesis that biophotons come from a coherent electrodynamical field within the living system. This field has a wide range of frequencies that are coupled together to give effectively a single degree of freedom, and that may be the basis of biological organization. Living systems are thus both emitters and receivers of electromagnetic signals originating from the physicochemical environment as well as from other organisms. We have recently demonstrated, for example, that synchronously developing fruitfly embryos can interact nonlinearly to generate coherent light emissions that are orders of magnitude higher than the self-emission rate.[50] This adds a whole new dimension to the interconnectedness in nature in terms of information flow as mentioned above.

Another important aspect of coherence is that it suggests a relationship between local and global (or individual and collective) that has previously been deemed contradictory or impossible. It turns out that a coherent field shows space-time correlations between different points; however, these cross-correlations are precisely the products of the self-correlations at each point. In other words, any number of points in a coherent field will behave statistically as though independent of one another.[51] A coherent state is thus one of maximum global cohesion and also maximum local freedom! The inevitable conflict between the individual and the collective, which serves as the starting point for all social (as well as biological) theories of western society, is not so inevitable after all. Perhaps it is time for social theorists to adopt a new set of premises.

The coherent society

Can we envisage a society that is consonant with our new, and hopefully, more authentic knowledge? I shall call it the coherent society to resonate with our knowledge of unity and coherence, in the hope that we can ultimately live and act coherently with our knowledge. It also carries the notion of a life coherent with nature, and with our own natural being.

Biological organization has long served as the metaphor of social organization for utopians and other social theorists alike, for example, Spencer, Comte, and Saint-Simon, to name but a few.[52] A mechanistic view of life thereby visits on society a whole set of unfounded and mistaken assumptions of which social Darwinism has had the most devastating influence.[53] Two unspoken, deeply ingrained beliefs, encapsulated in Darwinism are that 'man' is above all an isolated individual motivated solely by self-interest, if not aggression; and that in the absence of an externally imposed social and moral order, chaos will reign supreme.

From our vantage point of 'nature from within,' all nature is a unity in which we ourselves participate in shaping. Connectedness and sociality are primary, just as aggression and hate are the result of frustrated or failed love. The Darwinian/Freudian man is the product of a patriarchal, repressive society built upon the denial of love at every turn. It is neither the universal nature of human beings, nor the ineluctable human condition.[54] A consciousness fully indigenous to nature is grounded in nature, and connected to all being. It is never isolated nor alone; hence it roams freely and without fear. It is kind and loving and ever in possession of the highest of moral feelings; for morality itself is derivative of the experience of real interconnectedness with kin, with fellow creatures and ultimately with all nature. In this interconnectedness, the sufferings and joys of others are as those of the self. Such is the natural, heartfelt morality that needs no external schooling.

What do primitive, indigenous cultures tell us concerning human nature? One of the most relevant studies is that conducted by Margaret Mead and her colleagues on *Cooperation and Competition Among Primitive Peoples.*[55] They asked the question: what does the literature on primitive peoples yield on the subject of competitive and cooperative habits which throw light on the problem of culture and personality? It is a monumental work, and probably the only of its kind. In the book, cooperation is defined as the act of working together to one end; whereas competition is defined as the act of seeking or endeavouring to gain what another is endeavouring to gain at the same time. The usual way to define goal or end in the west is in terms of something accomplished, something gained. What can it possibly mean in a culture that does not value material gain *per se?* It is significant that in summarizing the studies, Mead admitted that 'cooperative' and 'competitive' were not opposites, and that a category of behaviour, 'individualistic' must be added, in the sense that collective versus individual behaviour refers to overt behaviour, and not to goals. Similarly, in summarizing the findings, one of the headings for character formation is 'ego development' in the sense in which Freud used it to contrast ego drives with sexual drives. Her co-worker Dr Kenworthy states:

> In the use of our term ego needs is implied the self-protective,
> self-maximating tendencies so often described under the
> caption of the self-preservative instinct.[56]

This perpetrates the greatest confusion of all. 'Self-preservating' and 'self-maximating' are entirely different things. None of the cultures which she has classified as 'weak' in ego development has any trouble in self-preservation, though they often regard self-maximating behaviour as socially abhorrent. In the west, people seem quite unable to distinguish between the 'sense of self' and 'selfishness;' and many indigenous peoples and foreigners alike are said to lack a sense of self simply because they do not value personal possessions and do not act selfishly. Significantly, Mead had to conclude from the studies that strong ego development can occur in individualist, competitive or cooperative societies.

Of the thirteen cultures examined, six were identified as cooperative, four, individualistic and only three were competitive. Mead arranged them in the form of a triangular diagram, the midpoint of each side representing the most intense development of that emphasis. Of especial interest are the cultures classified as individualistic. The Arapesh, for example, are a peaceable good-natured people, helpful to a fault. They minimize blood relations, fixed membership in any given group or rigid association with any piece of land. There is complete individual freedom of choice in association with any group, and the groups are extremely fluid, changing freely with the particular collective task involved. Their economic affiliations therefore cut across all boundaries of geography and kinship, and are based upon personal ties and friendship between individuals.

The Arapesh are classified apart from the cooperative cultures as 'individualistic' (although they engage in collective tasks almost all of the time!) simply because mere helpfulness without any personal gain or end in sight is considered other than cooperation. As in many natural animal societies, helpfulness is an expression of sociality for its own sake, which is more fundamental than cooperation towards a common end. In many respects, the Arapesh culture exhibits a coherent society where individual and collective are maximally expressed, and there is no conflict between the two. Mead attributed this to the elimination of the distinction between the self and the good of others, which is also achieved in all the societies classified as cooperative. To me, this is also a concrete demonstration of empathy: satisfying the needs of others and thereby sharing their satisfaction is itself intrinsically rewarding.

The most suggestive generalizations from the studies are that cooperative societies are those in which personal property is consistently undervalued and which have a strong sense of security afforded by kin group and other extension groups. There is no attempt to exercise power over other persons and all share a belief in an ordered universe. Competitive societies, on the other hand, place a high valuation on property for individual ends, have a low sense of security correlated with a strong will to power over others; and finally a belief in an arbitrary, disordered domain of the supernatural which is prevailingly antagonistic to them.

Mead concluded that the social structure itself has an overriding determinate influence on whether the culture is competitive or cooperative; whereas there was no correlation with the means of subsistence (whether food-gathering, hunting, agricultural or pastoral), nor with the state of technologies, or with the dictates of the natural environment.

In social structure, she suggested that competition was prevented by (1) a rigid hierarchical social system such that rank interposes between would-be competitors; (2) a social system through which the desired end is converted from an individual to a group end; and (3) cultural phrasing which displaces the emphasis from the objective situation to some other sphere in which competition is not so possible (for example, the Zuni and Arapesh transform the scarcity of land into a perception of the scarcity of labour and hence encourages cooperative labour). Inherent in this suggestion is the widely-held underlying assumption that competition is a pre-existing quality which must be mitigated, or ameliorated by some means.[57]

One might easily gain the impression from the foregoing description that cooperative societies are closed and hierarchical, and rigidly controlled by rituals. This is not the case. Although the Maori have a system in which status is inalienable, the Samoans have a system in which status is movable, the Zuni have no status at all, and the Dakota are quite egalitarian. What is more significant is that they all share an emphasis on natural kin relationship which can be very extended; and hence, I believe, they are best able to retain and express their natural sociality (and security) on which cooperation depends. In this light, the so-called competitive societies may be such because they have lost the means to express their natural sociality, resulting in a pervading sense of insecurity and hence in competitiveness.

Perhaps the most significant feature of cooperative societies, for the purpose of this essay, is that they all have a view of an ordered universe. Inherent in this belief is that nature is knowable and hence it is possible to live with her and within her. On the contrary, an antagonistic, disordered view of nature such as pervades western industrialized societies, gives rise to the idea that nature is ultimately unknowable, being governed solely by chance, and must hence be dominated or conquered.

Viktor Schauberger, an Austrian scientist who lived at the beginning of this century[58] was fascinated by the natural properties of water and water-flow. One of his many insights is that water naturally flows in a rolling and meandering fashion that has a coherence of its own, and that a river has the greatest carrying capacity when it is allowed to flow naturally. Under those conditions, it deepens its bed as it flows and does not silt up. However, when people started to control floods by building straight concrete banks along the river, the water, unable to roll and meander under its own impetus, begins to silt up the river bed, and sooner or later overflows the banks. Instead, he suggested that by installing flow-regulators on the river bed which encourages the natural flow, such disasters could be averted. The moral is in how to let nature take its course, to live creatively with her, rather than to exert control by stopping her in her tracks. In the same way, our coherent society must be such as to be mindful of our natural social being, to give it full expression in partnership with nature.

Schauberger already noticed, in the very early days of logging in the Austrian Alps, the intimate relationship between water and forest; and predicted that flooding and loss of ground water would follow when forest covering was removed. We are seeing the disastrous confirmation of his theory today in the destruction of tropical forests. In the Mae Soi Valley in Thailand, we saw 70 square kilometres of forest that had been turned into wasteland; and in the midst a mere acre of primary forest left as 'sanctuary.'[59] It was not until we entered this sanctuary that the impact of what had been lost struck home with full force. The sanctuary is a copse of giant trees surrounded by a shallow stream. Many of the trees are at least two persons armspan, standing perhaps a hundred feet tall. Thick curtains of epiphytes drape over their tops and sides, while below, the dappled sunlight catches now and then, the sheen of broadleaves in the undergrowth, or the occasional fluttering wings of butterflies. I came away with a distinct sense of having taken my last leave of Earth. We have yet to find the way to know nature as she really is, to be mindful of her being, so that we can live with her. It is in knowing her that we shall have intimate knowledge of ourselves.

Notes

1. Heilpern, J. 1989. *Conference of the Birds. The story of Peter Brook in Africa.* London: Methuen.
2. Ho, M.W. 1988a. Genetic fitness and natural selection, myth or metaphor? In E. Tobach and G. Greenberg (eds). 1988. *Evolution of Social Behavior and Integrative Levels.* New Jersey: Erlbaum.
3. Ho, M.W. 1993a. Towards an indigenous western science. In W. Harman (ed). *Reassessing the Metaphysical Foundations of Science.* Noetic Sciences Institute Publications.
4. Gilbert, W.S. 1962. Princess Ida. pp.321f in *The Savoy Operas.* Oxford University Press.
5. Young, R.M. 1985. *Darwin's Metaphor.* Cambridge University Press.
6. Barzun, J. 1958. *Darwin, Marx, Wagner.* New York: Doubleday Anchor.
7. Huxley, T.H. 1888. *Nineteenth Century.* (Feb. issue), p.165.
8. Brown, J.A.C. 1961. *Freud and the Post-Freudians.* Harmondsworth: Pelican. pp.13f.
9. Ghiselin, M. 1974. *The Economy of Nature and the Evolution of Sex.* University of California Press.
10. Wilson, E.O. 1975. *Sociobiology.* Cambridge, Mass: Belknap Press. p.3.
11. Brecht, B. cited in Clairborne 1974 (Note 12).
12. Clairborne, R. 1974. *How Homo sapiens learned to be good.* Horizon. pp.30–35. See also E.L. Khalil, 1990, Beyond self-interest and altruism, *Economics and Philosophy,* 6:255–73, for a recent interpretation of Adam Smith's frequently misunderstood, thesis *The Theory of Moral Sentiments.*

13. Kropotkin, P. 1914. *Mutual Aid: A Factor of Evolution.* Boston: Extending Horizon. p.x.
14. Kropotkin 1914 (Note 13), p.13.
15. See Bateson, P. in Gambetta, D. 1988. *Trust: Making and Breaking Cooperative Relations.* Oxford: Blackwell. pp.14–30.
16. Csányi, V. Personal communication.
17. Cited in Kropotkin 1914 (Note 13), p.xi.
18. I am indebted to P.T. Saunders for this suggestion.
19. Clairborne 1974 (Note 12).
20. Brehm, A. cited in Kropotkin 1914 (Note 13), p.28.
21. Kropotkin 1914 (Note 13), p.36f.
22. Kropotkin 1914 (Note 13), p.39f.
23. Cited in Kropotkin 1914 (Note 13), p.56.
24. Allee, W.C. 1951. *The Social Life of Animals.* London: The Book Club.
25. Allee 1951 (Note 24), p.23.
26. Prof. Khalil rightly points out to me that there is a distinction, at least at first glance, between social connectedness and ecological connectedness. However, to the truly indigenous (or ecological) consciousness which perceives most intimately the interdepence of all nature, every species of animal or plant is regarded as kin (brother or sister). Ho 1993a (Note 3).
27. Allee 1951 (Note 24), pp.38–44.
28. Allee 1951 (Note 24), pp.55f.
29. Allee 1951 (Note 24), pp.59–61.
30. Allee 1951 (Note 24), pp.138–47.
31. Bateson, P. In Gambetta 1988 (Note 15), pp.14–30.
32. Suttie, I. 1989. *The Origins of Love and Hate.* Harmondsworth: Penguin.
33. Winnicott, D.W. 1974. *Playing and Reality.* Harmondsworth: Pelican.
34. Suttie 1989 (Note 32), p.1.
35. See Ho, M.W. 1989b. Evolution in action and action in evolution. pp.14–28 in P. Bunyard and E. Goldsmith (eds). *Gaia and Evolution: Implications of the Gaia Thesis.* Wadebridge Ecological Press.
36. Barfield, O. 1956. *Saving the Appearances, a Study in Idolatry.* details?
37. Ho, M.W. 1986. Heredity as process: towards a radical reformulation of heredity. *Rivista di Biologia.* 79:407–44.
38. Cairns, J., J. Overbaugh and S. Miller. The origin of mutants. *Nature.* 335:142–45; also, B.G. Hall. 1990. Spontaneous point mutations that occur more often when advantageous than when neutral. *Genetics.* 126:3.
39. Ho, M.W. 1988b. How rational can rational taxonomy be? A post-Darwinian rational taxonomy based on a structuralism of process. *Rivista di Biologia.* 81:11–55.
40. Lovelock, J.E. 1979. *A New Look at Gaia.* Oxford University Press.
41. Saunders, P.T. 1994. Evolution without Natural Selection: Further Implications of the Daisyworld Parable. *Journal of Theoretical Biology.* 166:365–73.
42. Bohm, D., B.J. Hiley, P.N. Kaloyerou. 1987. An ontological basis for quantum theory. *Physics Report.* 144:323–48; 349–75.
43. Ho, M.W. 1990. A quest for total understanding. *Transcript of Saros Seminar on the Dilemma of Knowledge.* Bristol: Saros Book Club. See also Ho 1993a (Note 3), and Ho. 1993b. *The Rainbow and the Worm: The Physics of Organisms.* Singapore: World Scientific.
44. Brown, F.A. 1962. Extrinsic rhythmicality: a reference frame for biological rhythms under so-called constant conditions. *Annals New York Academy of Sciences.* 98:775–87.
45. Shulman, S. 1990. Cancer risks seen in electro-magnetic fields. *Nature.* 345:463. See also Ho 1993b (Note 43).

46. Ho, M.W. 1989a. Coherent excitations and the physical foundations of life. In B.C. Goodwin and P. Saunders (eds). *Theoretical Biology: Epigenetic and Evolutionary Order from Complex Systems.* Edinburgh University Press. See also Ho 1993b (Note 43).
47. Szent Györgyi, A. 1960. *Introduction to a Submolecular Biology.* New York: Academic Press.
48. Fröhlich, H. 1968. Long-range coherence and energy storage in biological systems. *Int. J. Quant. Chem.* 2:641–49.
49. Popp, F.A., K.H. Li, W.P. Mei, M. Galle and R. Neurohr. 1988. Physical aspects of biophotons. *Experientia.* 44:576–85.
50. See Ho, M.W., X. Xu, S. Ross and P.T. Saunders. 1992. Light emission and re-scattering in synchronously developing populations of early *Drosophila* embryos — evidence for coherence of the embryonic field and long range cooperativity. pp.387–406 in F.A. Popp, K.H. Li and Q. Gu (eds). *Advances in Biophotons Research.* Singapore: World Scientific.
51. Glauber, J. 1970. Quantum theory of coherence. pp.53–125 in S.M. Kay and A. Maitland (eds). *Quantum Optics.* London: Academic Press. See also Ho 1993b (Note 43).
52. Jones, A.K. 1990. Social symbiosis: a Gaian critique of contemporary social theory. *The Ecologist.* 20:108–13.
53. See Barzun 1958 (Note 6); also Ho, M.W. 1988c. On not holding nature still: evolution by process not by consequence. In M.W. Ho and S.W. Fox (eds). *Evolutionary Processes and Metaphors.* Wiley.
54. See Ho 1993a (Note 3); and 1993b (Note 43).
55. Mead, M. 1961. *Cooperation and Competition Among Primitive Peoples.* Boston: Beacon Press. I thank E. Goldsmith for directing me to this book.
56. Mead 1961 (Note 55), p.485.
57. Mead 1961 (Note 55), p.480.
58. See Alexanderson, O. 1976. *Living Water: Viktor Schauberger and the Secrets of Natural Energy.* Trans. K. and C. Zwigbergk. Bath: Gateway Books.
59. This visit was part of the International Honours Programme on *Global Ecology.* 1990–91.

I am grateful to Elias Khalil and Kenneth Boulding for their comments on this manuscript.

– 20 –
Ethical Implications of the Gaia Thesis

Kate Rawles

The papers offered in this collection so far have been largely scientific in their approach, so I will begin with a few remarks on what a philosophical approach to the Gaia thesis might entail. In fact, the 1994 Green College conference on Gaia was not the first such — primarily scientific — gathering to have had a philosopher or two in attendance. David Abram, Elisabet Sahtouris and Ron Brady brought philosophical perspectives to bear upon the two Camelford conferences on Gaia and the proceedings of the conference in San Diego in 1988 include a substantial section on the 'Philosophical Foundations of Gaia,' in which the papers by Kirchner and Abram are perhaps particularly well-known.[1]

In *The Gaia Hypotheses, Are They Useful or Testable?* Kirchner distinguishes five possible interpretations of the Gaia thesis and takes issue with all of them.[2] And he compares Shakespeare's claim that 'all the world's a stage' with the claim that 'all the world's a living organism' remarking that neither can be tested, and thereby adding a further dimension to Lovelock's uniqueness by making him one of the very few who have been compared with Shakespeare as a means of criticism. Kirchner's paper is at times famously exasperating. Yet two key philosophical questions are certainly embedded within it. First, what sorts of claims are advocates of the Gaia thesis making? Second, a question we were constantly pulled back to by one of the strongest philosophical undercurrents of the Green College conference; what, exactly, do we mean by 'Gaia'?

A great deal of debate surrounds attempts to answer to the second question, but I will not engage with it here. Instead, while acknowledging the existence of alternative definitions, I will use the phrase 'the Gaia thesis' to refer to the claim that the biotic and abiotic elements of the earth form a tightly coupled system which, by means of diverse feed-back mechanisms, help to regulate the earth's atmosphere and temperature within parameters conducive to the continuation of life.

In the context of debates about Gaia, or any other hypothesis, questioning the meaning of the thesis and subjecting it and its component concepts to thorough scrutiny, will be an important part of a philosophical approach. Such an approach helps to prevent incidence of the scourge referred to by Lynn Margulis as *The Fallacy of Misplaced Concreteness,* a phenomenon whereby a concept is used so frequently that, after a time, everyone assumes (a) that they mean the same thing when they use it; and (b) that it refers to something quite solid and uncontroversial. These apparently solid concepts can then be used as foundations for other ideas, in extreme cases resulting in what I once heard described at a gathering of economists, with devastating scorn, as Pagodas of Nonsense.

The role of the philosopher, of course, is to come in and re-examine the foundation stones. Hence the popular description of philosophers as building inspectors of thought. In the case of the Gaia thesis, while even Kirchner may not have exposed any wobbling pagodas, there certainly have been, and continue to be, interesting and helpful inspections both of the thesis itself, and of related concepts such as stability, resilience and diversity.

Philosophers as building inspectors, then, take a hard look at the strength and propriety of foundational concepts for the structures they are intended to support. But their attention may turn also to the building itself. What shadows does it throw upon others? Does it enhance its surroundings or block out somebody else's sunlight? And how does it affect our perception of structures and landscapes we already hold dear? Does it complement or clash with other features which we value?

An example is to be found in Abram's elegant and exciting paper, *The Mechanical and the Organic: On the Impact of Metaphor in Science.*[3] Here, Abram responds to Kirchner's claim that the Gaia hypothesis is merely metaphorical, and hence untestable, and hence not 'true science,' by revealing Kirchner's own allegiance to metaphor. Much contemporary science, Abram argues, is founded on the notion that the earth is best understood by treating it as if it were a machine. It is this metaphor that underpins 'true' science as Kirchner understands it, and which gives content, for example, to his notion of testability. If Abram is right, Kirchner's mistake is to try to understand and evaluate the Gaia thesis from within the framework of a science based on the earth-is-a-machine metaphor. For the Gaia thesis in fact offers us an alternative metaphor, that of the earth as a living organism, around which science itself might be reshaped.

Here, then, the building inspectors indicate the existence of two edifices that had better not stand side by side. And the example suggests a further role for the philosopher; that of revealing and making explicit the metaphors which structure our thought, and exploring their strengths, weaknesses and implications, as Abram proceeds to do.

Gaia and ethics

The Gaia thesis is particularly fecund in terms of its implications for other areas of thought. Those which arise for our view of science are but one example of this. My particular concern in this paper is to try to explore some of the implications which the Gaia thesis may have for ethics. I will use the term 'ethics' in a very broad sense, to refer not only to the obligations we consider ourselves to be under to others, but also to the range of values which we endorse as individuals and as societies and, even more broadly, to the way we view ourselves as humans. Does the Gaia thesis have any implications for this view of ourselves or for our understanding of the place we inhabit under the Sun? Does it change the way in which we understand the relations between humans and the rest of nature? And, does anything follow from the Gaia thesis about the way 'Gaia' ought to be treated?

Within Western philosophy, ethics, since Aristotle and even before, has been concerned with the ways in which humans treat other humans; but no other species. This is true almost without exception. Contemporary environmental problems indicate that some of our activities may, through their detrimental impact upon the environment, adversely affect human well-being. Thus it is possible to call for a modification of these activities without moving away from the exclusive concern with human well-being that our ethical tradition endorses.

Such approaches to environmentalism are sometimes referred to as shallow. The pejorative tone is unfortunate, for it tends to beg the crucial question of whether a human-centred approach to environmental issues can ultimately yield either an adequate response to these issues or an adequate account of the human/nature relationship. And, however this question is finally answered, it is clear that shallow environmentalism currently represents a powerful set of arguments which carry with them a strong motive for change.[4]

Nevertheless, some argue that the 'humans only' account of the range of ethics is far too restricted, and that we have moral relationships with, and perhaps even obligations towards, various members of the non-human natural world as well.[5] For example, concern over the living conditions of intensively farmed animals has raised the question of our ethical responsibilities towards sentient animals — those animals who are conscious, and capable of experiencing pleasure and pain.[6] Many would now agree that we have at least some responsibilities towards such creatures and that some of the ways in which they are treated are, therefore, unacceptable.[7] Here, then, while debate continues over the implications of acknowledging the moral status of animals (should we eat/ride/farm/hunt/experiment upon, animals? which animals and under what circumstances?) there is a growing consensus that sentient animals do count, morally. And the point is that they are held to count in their own right, and not, or not just, because their mistreatment harms humans. But what about non-sentient life? Do other individuals, or collections of individuals, such as species and ecosystems, also count in this way?

This is one of the central issues in environmental ethics, and it is far from resolved.[8] A question of particular interest, then, is whether the Gaia thesis has any tendency to contribute one way or another to the debate over the *range* of ethics.

A second question concerns the *content* of ethics. Figuring out the range of ethics, the range of beings or entities towards which we have moral obligations or responsibilities, is not yet to tell us what these obligations or responsibilities are, nor what general values and ideals we should, as individuals or as societies, seek to pursue. Can the Gaia thesis help us to establish the content of our ethical systems?

A third question is really a more specific form of the second. Does the Gaia thesis have any implications for *environmental* goals and values, specifically? Does it yield any implications for action and policy in the environmental arena?

Finally, it can be argued that our ideas about both the range and content of ethics will be crucially influenced by the underlying view that we have of ourselves and of the human/nature relationship. Many environmentalists maintain that the 'humans only' view of ethics rests on an arrogant and misguided view of humans as the 'Apex of Evolution'[9] and that it is this arrogantly anthropocentric world-view which is the root cause of our environmental problems. Hence, if the Gaia thesis has any tendency to alter this view, this will, if such environmentalists are correct, be of the first importance. So, are they, and does it? What implications, if any, does the Gaia thesis have for our view of ourselves and our place in nature? I will look briefly at each of these questions in turn. First, however, it is worth considering whether any ethical implications follow from the Gaia thesis when it is considered in conjunction with a conventional understanding of ethics. I will explore this question in the context of environmental ethics, that is, those ethical obligations, relationships and responsibilities that we have towards the non-human, natural world.

Gaia and shallow environmentalism

Human welfare is, typically, something we value and which we believe we should try to foster rather than frustrate. Actions deleterious to human welfare may, therefore, be legitimately criticized. Thus, if the Gaia thesis suggests ways in which human actions and lifestyles, in virtue of their impact on the environment, threaten human welfare, it will have ethical implications even from the relatively limited perspective of the 'humans only' account of the range of ethics. For example, if the thesis helps us to predict the impact of anthropogenic carbon dioxide emissions on the global system on which humans depend, it will also help us to assess the significance of these emissions from an ethical standpoint — and to establish what we should do about them. Do these emissions threaten sufficient damage that we should try to reduce them? By how much? Or do they lack significant implications for human well-being? In which case the shallow environmentalist will consider that they are ethically irrelevant and need not be regulated at all. Similar questions can be asked about deforestation, anthropogenic biodiversity reduction, and all other areas in which the impact of humans upon their environment may give cause for concern.

To what extent, then, do human activities threaten to damage humans themselves? In attempts to answer this question, the Gaia thesis has been evoked in support of two conflicting positions. The first assures us that there is no such threat, and hence no need for humans to change their ways. Carbon dioxide emissions, to stay with that example, are irrelevant in terms of their impact on Gaian regulatory mechanisms. They will neither harm the environment nor threaten environment-dependent humans. Hence their production does not raise any ethical issues, at least not on this count. This conclusion is reached by way of the observation that humans are such a tiny and insignificant part of the Gaian system, and the system itself so potent, that whatever temporary mess we puny creatures might make, Gaia will certainly sort it out. To worry that humans might damage or destabilize Gaia is rather like worrying about the impact that a child with a nail file might have on a forest, or with a plastic bucket and spade on the Atlantic coastline. So we can proceed as we are, business as usual, in the knowledge that the Gaian waves will soon erase our imprints from the sand. We might call this the *Gaia-will-fix-it* position.

The second position warns that we need to be very careful indeed. We do not fully understand the mechanisms we are dealing with and perhaps never will. Moreover, these mechanisms are not only very complex but also rather delicate. And, if they are tipped into turmoil, there is no guarantee whatsoever that they will eventually restabilize at a set of conditions conducive to human flourishing — or even survival. We might call this the *Gaia-is-fragile* position.

These positions are clearly incompatible. In order to adjudicate between them, we need answers to questions which are essentially empirical rather than philosophical. How close are we to the parameters within which Gaian regulation may occur? Is there, within the scientific community, a substantial sense of how robust these mechanisms are?

These questions lie outside my own area of expertise, although my impression is that the jury is still out on them both. On the other hand, the evidence from all quarters seems to confirm the suspicion that the systems under discussion are immensely complex: perhaps complex beyond our ability ever to understand them completely. It may therefore remain impossible to predict with any useful degree of accuracy the ramifications of intervention. But if this is correct, we may never know which of the two positions sketched above is closer to the truth, and hence whether we should change our ways or not.

Arguably, however, the complexity that keeps us from closure on this issue suggests its own conclusion. Caution. We are part of this astoundingly intricate and interconnected system, and our survival depends on its continuing to function. Wisdom would thus seem to suggest that we treat it with great care, rather than refuse to change our ways until we know for sure exactly what the results of not changing them will be. At present, we are rather like patients in a hospital bed, gaily throwing our grape-seeds and Lucozade bottle-tops into the life-support system.

One implication of the Gaia thesis may be, therefore, a caution which in fact prescribes substantial change. If the side-effects of our industrialized, consumerist lifestyle combine with sheer human numbers to threaten the Gaian system, then a host of implications for action and lifestyle immediately becomes apparent. Implications follow also for the ideals and values to which we, as societies and individuals, are at present committed. If the cost of our aspirations towards progress and the good life, as these terms are understood by the industrialized world, is the destabilization of the system which regulates our atmosphere and temperature within parameters conducive to our own survival, it may be that the time for a rethink of these ideals and values is well nigh. This does not necessarily mean that standards of living must be lowered, only that we ask ourselves what our priorities really are. Many argue that such a review would incline us towards rather different conceptions of both progress and the essential ingredients of the good life.

These comments suggest, then, that the Gaia thesis, in conjunction with the 'humans only' view of ethics, yields considerable implications for human action and values. But some argue that the 'humans only' view of ethics is not only mistaken but also at least partly responsible for the environmental problems with which we are increasingly beleaguered. A more adequate view of ethics recognizes that our treatment of many non-humans raises serious moral issues and recommends that, in so far as is possible, we should respect and make room for their lives and ways of living as well as our own. Moreover, this should be done whether or not the 'humans only' view is bringing down trouble upon our own heads.[10]

Needless to say, much debate then swarms around the question of what is possible or 'within reason.' Certainly in order to live well ourselves, we will often need to use or to kill living things. But it does not follow from this that all accounts of what it is to live well are equally acceptable, nor that the needs and wants and interests of humans should always and automatically take priority. The human interest in cosmetics, for example, might reasonably give way to the interests of rabbits who would rather not have these products tested on their eyes. And the human interest in having a cluster of cars per family might reasonably yield to the interest which other creatures have in being able to breathe unpolluted air. Neither of these are particularly contentious examples. But some would argue that these obvious cases are, to use a singularly useful cliche, just the tip of the anthropocentric iceberg. Humans regularly take themselves to be the only beings of real value on earth; and they regularly override the interest and needs of other living things in order to further their own. Now, if the range of ethics extends beyond humans, the Gaia thesis will presumably have whatever implications conceded above, only more so; for many beings other than the human one would be adversely affected by the destabilization of the earth's regulatory mechanisms. But does the thesis contribute one way or another to the debate over the range of ethics itself? Towards whom, or what, do we have ethical responsibilities and obligations?

I want to approach this via the question of 'world-views,' which I use, very loosely, to mean the way in which we see ourselves, our world and our place within it.

Gaia and world-view

'Goddess or thermostat?' asked Crispin Tickell of the Gaia thesis in a recent paper in *Biosystems*.[11] The thesis might equally well prompt us to ask how best to describe ourselves. 'Humans: Lords of Creation or spanner in the works?' for example. I have already hinted that the latter appellation may be the more apt. But Abram might well take issue with the concession to the machine metaphor which talk of humans as spanners involves. For what the Gaia thesis tells us, according to Abram, is that the earth to which we belong is like a huge organism and not at all like a huge machine.

Now, if the earth is like an organism rather than a machine, humans will not be appropriately compared with spanners. Nor with Lords of Creation, for organisms, or at least the Gaian one, tend not to have creators. Or, if they do, it was not, in this case, us. On this analogy, humans will be revealed as (pretty small) living parts of a greater living whole. What sort of part? Working within the organism metaphor, different descriptions of humans have placed them on a spectrum which ranges from the brain or consciousness of the earth to a form of planetary cancer. I will return to the question of which description might be the most fitting in a moment. First, I want to introduce a different question; that of whether the organism metaphor has implications for the way we relate to the non-human world. In particular, does it imply anything about (a) the moral status of the non-human world and (b) the ways in which we ought to treat it?

It is, in fact, often presented as axiomatic that the machine to organism shift in our perception of the world will lead us to acknowledge its hitherto denied moral status and hence to treat it better. Thus, if it is true that the Gaia thesis reveals the world to us as a living organism rather than a machine, it would seem to follow that the thesis has implications both for the range of ethics — which should be broadened to include much of the non-human world — and for their content: we should treat the world and its non-human inhabitants very much better than we do at present (whatever 'better' turns out to mean).

How are such claims supported? Two points are commonly made.

1) We are naturally more inclined to respect and value organisms, which have their own modes of life independent from our designs, than machines, which do not, and which depend on their makers for purpose, function and value. Note that this is not the same as saying

that we ought to value and respect organisms more than machines — it is the claim that, as a matter of fact, we do. The significance of the Gaia thesis is that, in revealing the earth to us in this way, it prompts an ethical response towards it. This sort of approach to ethics is said to have its roots in the philosophy of David Hume and has been extensively worked out in the environmental context by the North American philosopher, J.Baird Callicott.[12]

2) The machine metaphor typically suggests that we can study the machine from the outside, as it were; and that the machine is something radically different from ourselves. But the organism metaphor dispels the detached observer and substitutes humans who are very much part of the earth, even as they try to study it. Abram details some of the implications which this has for our conception of science and how we pursue it. In the ethical context, it is often said that, once we realize that we are part of the system, rather than detached observers of it, we will realize that damage to the system amounts to damage to ouselves, and we will constrain our behaviour accordingly.

Thus the Gaia thesis, by revealing the world to us as an organism within which we live out our own lives, has a double tendency to elicit respect and/or love, and careful and considerate treatment. Or so the story goes.

The first argument can be put like this:

> We are naturally more inclined to love and respect organisms than machines.
>
> The Gaia thesis shows us that the earth is like an organism rather than a machine.
>
> Therefore, the Gaia thesis inclines us to love and respect the earth.

But doubts can be cast on both premises and on at least one underlying assumption.

Premise 1

Are we 'naturally' more inclined to love and respect living things than machines? A cursory glance at contemporary Western society reveals no shortage of disrespect for living things — even highly intelligent, sociable and sentient ones. Moreover, much, presumably, will depend on the organism and the machine in question. Cars, I would bet, will be loved much more than caterpillars by many. Indeed, it does not seem implausible to suggest that greater love and respect for machines than for living things is quite typical. Certainly the socially enforced prohibitions against damaging the machines of others (consider dad's car) are often stronger than those against damaging, say, plants or insects, especially ownerless ones.

In reply, it might be suggested that this is simply the result of social conditioning. Our natural response to living things is much more benevolent. It is society which teaches us that computers are marvellous and corncrakes expendable. But it is not clear what a truly natural response to living things would mean for a creature which has lived in social groups, and mediated its response to the world through language, for most of its brief history. And if there is such a thing as a natural response to living things, one might in any case expect that this would range from sympathy and affection (small furry creatures with faces) through fear (large carnivores) and disgust (the slimy, scaly and many-legged) to indifference. Do we then need to know what kind of organism the earth is like? But this starts to sound silly.

Perhaps, then, the real point is that we *ought* to treat living things better than machines. This may be correct. But in order to support this claim, to provide a response to the 'why?' that inevitably follows it, we need to do more than reply: because the earth is like one. To support the claim that we ought to respect living things will require an independent argument that the Gaia thesis by itself will not yield.

Premise 2

The second premise states that the Gaia thesis reveals the earth to be like an organism rather than a machine. But does it? If the emphasis in exposition of the thesis is shifted from talk of the earth as a single organism to talk of the earth as exhibiting a complex network of regulatory feed-back mechanisms, then the thesis becomes a subject amenable to discussion in the language of systems theory. But not all systems are organisms. Systems theory is also applicable to physical processes, for example, the weather, and at least some machines.

This brings me to the underlying assumption in the argument that may be questionable. The assumption is that there is a clear and useful distinction to be drawn between machines and living things. Stephen Hawking has recently argued that computer viruses are the first living things to be created by humans, thus undercutting 'not created by humans' as a criterion which can be used to distinguish organisms from machines.[13]

Other characteristics often cited in this context are complexity, the capacity for self-regulation, and unpredictability. Whatever is made of Hawking's claim, it seems hard to deny that there are many machines which also exhibit these traits. Thus the machine/organism distinction may not be quite as clear as is sometimes supposed.

My own view is that, while machines and organisms perhaps occupy places on a continuous spectrum rather than opposing and unconnected polar regions, real and helpful distinctions can nevertheless be drawn between them. However, if it is true that these distinctions are at least made fuzzy by systems theory and other considerations, then any argument which presupposes sharp distinctions will be undermined. This, then, may be a further problem for the argument sketched above. As an aside, a more positive consequence of softening the sharp organism/machine distinction may be that the earth-as-machine and the earth-as-living-organism metaphors, which are so often pitched against each other, can in fact co-exist. In which case, it may be possible to have the best of both worlds, to retain what is best and most useful from the machine metaphor, while developing what is new and constructive in the other.

The second argument can be put like this:

> We are inclined to care about, and look after, ourselves.
>
> The Gaia thesis shows us that we are inseparably interconnected with the rest of the non-human world; that, in a sense, we and the world are one.
>
> Therefore, the Gaia thesis will incline us to care about, and look after, the non-human world.

But on second thoughts, this argument is not so robust either. For while we are indeed inclined to look after ourselves up to a point, we are also notorious for risking long-term damage to our own health for short term gains, or when the causal mechanisms of the damage are abstract or obscure. But both descriptions apply to the kind of damage we risk causing to the Gaian system. It is, we hope, long-term, and the mechanisms are hidden from us and difficult to comprehend. We are quite capable of risking such damage even though we know that it will adversely affect ourselves; even though we know that we and the earth 'are one.'

In any case, the sense in which the Gaia thesis really does show us that we and the earth are one is not altogether clear. My experience of the world around me is, in the main, of a world populated by entities which are separate and different from myself. They may be fascinating, fearful, awe-inspiring or droll; but they are not *the same as* me. And, even if the Gaia thesis (or, as is sometimes claimed, scientific ecology), shows me that this ordinary perception is mistaken, I still need an argument to show why I should rest my ethical response to the world on a scientific thesis about it rather than on the way I experience it for myself.

These, then, are some doubts which may be raised about the claim that the Gaia thesis, in so far as it changes our perception of the world from machine to organism, inclines us to extend moral status to the non-human world and to improve our treatment of it accordingly. Whether these doubts are crippling or merely irksome I leave open. My own view is that changing the way we see and describe the world is a necessary but not sufficient condition for changing our ethical attitudes towards it. Anthropocentrism is deep-rooted. If we are to move beyond it, prescription as well as description will be required. We need to be confronted with sound arguments which lead firmly to the conclusion that we ought to respect our planet and its non-human inhabitants more than we do. Although we will not deduce such prescriptions from the Gaia thesis, and although the thesis by itself will not infallibly elicit such respect, the more we understand about the extraordinary complexity of the system within which we live out our lives, the more likely we are to be receptive to these more earth than human-centred injunctions.

Gaia and the apex of evolution

So much for the influence which the Gaia thesis may have upon the way we perceive the world. What about its influence on our perception of ourselves? One question is where we humans might be located on the brain of the earth to planetary cancer spectrum. In the context of the Gaia thesis, this will presumably depend in large measure on whether or not we think we are in danger of destabilizing the Gaian systems. As before, I leave this question to those who might reasonably claim to answer it. But whichever way this question is resolved, the extraordinary complexity of the regulatory mechanisms remains in focus. The Gaia hypothesis thus depicts humans as minute parts of an astoundingly complex system that they may never manage to bring within their intellectual grasp. And this will be so whether or not the system is best understood as organic or mechanistic.

This picture, however, contrasts rather sharply with the 'Apex of Evolution' portrayal of humans that I have already alluded to. Of course, the view that humans are the pinnacle of achievement towards which evolution has inexorably progressed is one which, in industrialized countries at least, has a long pedigree — as does the belief that humans are the most, if not the only, important creatures on the planet. But some argue that the former is the root cause of our contemporary environmental problems, while increasing numbers take issue with the claim that, of all forms of life on the planet, humans are the only ones which really matter. The Gaia thesis, by redescribing our place on earth, may bring us to see what an extraordinary statement the latter is. More generally, if the thesis effects a change in the way we see ourselves, from the Apex of Evolution to not particularly privileged members of a complex ecological community, this may in turn help to open the way for a new dialogue about our relationships with the non-human world and about the goals and values which we, as individuals and societies, pursue. Such a dialogue will arguably be a key component of any successful attempt to resolve current environmental concerns.

One of the most significant ethical implications of the Gaia thesis may be, therefore, that it contributes, albeit indirectly, to a general debunking of arrogant human views about their place in the scheme of things, and to the value-shifts that such debunking might precipitate.[14] For this kind of change sets the scene not only for a rethink of our own self-image, but also for a critical review of the relationships we have with the non-human world, and of the values we endorse.

Gaia and environmental policy

An area in which the Gaia thesis may have rather more specific ethical implications is that of environmental policy. In Britain, conservation bodies have recently undergone fairly radical reorganization. One side-effect of this shake-up has been to bring to the surface some hard questions about what, exactly, particular conservation organizations are trying to achieve, and why. At the same time, the currently favoured and potentially very powerful concept of sustainable development has come to the fore. Sustainable development, writes Peter Holway, is now 'a declared aim of every politician in the world and probably the great majority of its inhabitants.'[15] It is likely also to become increasingly prominent in the declared aims of the conservation movement, and in the formulation of environmental policy in many other contexts.

But what does 'sustainable development' mean? The Brundtland Report defined it as development which 'meets the needs of the present without compromising the ability of future generations to meet their own needs.'[16] Bill Adams, in *Green Development* has described it as a 'convenient rhetorical flag under which ships of very different kinds can sail.'[17] Whether or not this is too harsh, the term could clearly have been purpose-built to excite the building inspectors, and a veritable shanty town of misplaced concreteness has sprung up all around it.

Perhaps this does not matter. Jonathon Porritt has suggested that a bit of misplaced concreteness may sometimes be a good thing. It is of primary importance, he suggests, that terms such as sustainable development become widely used and accepted.

This is a position with which, up to a point, I am sympathetic. For example, I think there is a real tension between philosophers as building inspectors, carrying out rather crucial work that will prevent wholescale collapse in the the future, and philosophers as vandals, pulling to pieces structures which are in fact functioning perfectly well. But the appropriate response here, surely, is not to prohibit entry to philosophers altogether, on some sort of slippery slope principle, but to keep an eye on their behaviour — and evict the unhelpful kind. As has been well said, when confronted with a slippery slope, the best response is to learn how to ski.

In the case of sustainable development, philosophers, I think, should most definitely be let in. If the concept is to be adopted as the basis of conservation policy, and as a central plank in governments' environmental agendas, some serious attention needs to be paid to its foundations, its structural details and its relation to its neighbours. Otherwise *(a)* the concept will obscure, not clarify, the aims of environmental organizations and *(b)* we will risk being lulled into a false sense of security, as governments and institutions everywhere proclaim sustainable development as one of their chief goals. We must know what this means if we are to establish whether we want it, and to what extent it is sufficient as an environmental objective.

This suggests a further role that the philosopher may play; that of bamboozle resistors, refusing to take on trust the story as told by anyone. Philosophers in this guise are the antidotes to simply accepting receiving wisdom (and this goes for the received wisdom of greens as much as any other kind). They are the antidotes to propaganda and brainwashing.

Can the Gaia thesis contribute, then, to a genuine solidification of the concept of sustainable development, and hence inform environmental policy that rests upon it? A start might be made with the suggestion that sustainable development must be development that, in addition to meeting the needs of the present without compromising the ability of future generations to meet their own needs, does not adversely affect Gaian mechanisms. What this would entail in practice, and how much solidity this would actually yield, is another question that must be handed over to others. But it would immediately introduce a less anthropocentric tone to the definition.[18] And it would act as a brake upon those who take sustainable development to be consistent with current notions of economic growth, and who take the we-have-no-reason-to-change-our-ways line about western-style industry, progress and success.

Conclusion and postcript — Gaia and education

I have suggested a number of ways in which the Gaia thesis, directly or indirectly, may bear upon the range and content of our ethical systems, and on the manner in which we perceive ourselves, the non-human world and the human/nature relationship. In the process, I have tried to indicate some of the means by which philosophy may be of use when a thesis, such as Gaia, is under discussion.

The suggestion I wish to make in closing is that the Gaia thesis might also yield important implications for education. An initial observation here concerns the accessibility of the papers presented at the Green College conference, even to a non-scientist. This, I think, is not, or rather not just, a tribute to those who gave them, for the Gaia thesis is one which simply cannot be tackled by specialists working alone. Thus the thesis itself fosters — and even forces — communication across disciplines which so often speak only to each other, and then in exclusive tribal languages.

The environmental problems which are pressing ever harder upon our recent and fragile human cultures will not be resolved by specialists working in isolation, either. Their resolution will require an interdisciplinary approach, and an extraordinary level of human co-operation. Yet our education system still tends towards specialization rather than interdisciplinary approaches and, on the whole, towards fostering a competitive rather than a co-operative attitude. Moreover, suprisingly few opportunities yet exist for students or school-children who would understand environmental problems, and possible responses to them. Such understanding will require us to bring together the perspectives of many different disciplines, and to reveal the interconnections between these perspectives as well as the light they throw upon the issues in question.

An understanding of the Gaia thesis will require a very similar approach. Gaia, then, may effectively encourage the development of interdisciplinary communication and education, and hence facilitate the endeavours of succeeding generations to resolve the environmental problems created by our own. This, in the end, may prove to be one of the most important implications of all.

Notes

1. See P. Bunyard and E. Goldsmith (eds), 1988, *Gaia, the Thesis, the Mechanisms and the Implications,* Wadebridge Ecological Centre; P. Bunyard and E. Goldsmith (eds), 1989, *Gaia and Evolution,* Wadebridge Ecological Centre; also S. Schneider and P. Boston (eds), 1992, *Scientists on Gaia,* MIT Press.
2. J. Kirchner. 1992. The Gaia Hypotheses: Are They Testable? Are They Useful? In *Scientists on Gaia* (Note 1).
3. D. Abram. 1993. The Mechanical and the Organic: On the Impact of Metaphor in Science. In *Scientists on Gaia* (Note 1).
4. J. Passmore. 1974. *Man's Responsibility to Nature.* Duckworth.
5. R. and V. Routley. 1979. Against the Inevitability of Human Chauvinism. In *Ethics and the Problems of the Twenty First Century.* Notre Dame Press.
6. The publication of Ruth Harrison's book, *Animal Machines* (1964, Vincent Stuart), is often said to have awakened widespread concern about intensively farmed animals.
7. A philosophical exposition is in Peter Singer, 1976, *Animal Liberation,* Thorsons.
8. For an introduction to environmental ethics see J.R. DesJardins, 1993, *Environmental Ethics,* Wadsworth.
9. As Calvin puts it to Hobbes in one of Bill Watterson's splendid cartoons.
10. See, for example, the work of 'Deep Ecologists' (a particular species of deep environmentalist) such as Bill Devall and George Sessions, 1985, *Deep Ecology: Living as if Nature Mattered,* Peregrine Smith Books; Bill Devall, 1988, *Simple in Means, Rich in Ends: Practicing Deep Ecology,* Gibbs Smith Publishing; Arne Naess, 1989, *Ecology, Community and Lifestyle,* translated and revised by David Rothenberg, Cambridge University Press.

    Other 'deep' environmentalists include Paul Taylor, 1986, *Respect for Nature,* Princetown University Press; Holmes Rolston, 1988, *Environmental Ethics,* Temple; J.B. Callicott, 1989, *In Defense of the Land Ethic,* SUNY; Lawrence Johnson, 1991, *A Morally Deep World,* Cambridge University Press.
11. Crispin Tickell. 1993. Gaia: Goddess or Thermostat. *Biosystems.* 31:93–98.
12. See, for example, J.B. Callicott, 1988, Animal Liberation and Environmental Ethics: Back Together Again, *Between the Species,* 4:163–69; and J.B. Callicott, Can a Theory of Moral Sentiments Support a Genuinely Normative Environmental Ethic? *Inquiry,* 35:183–98.
13. Hawking adds, 'I think it says something about human nature that the only form of life we have created so far is purely destructive.' *The Guardian,* August 5, 1994. Responding, John Gribbin brings a scepticism to the issue, in the course of which he defines living things as 'complex systems that can make copies of themselves.'
14. This debunking comes from many quarters. See, for example, Stephen Gould's account of the recent reinterpretation of the Burgess Shale fossil record. Stephen Jay Gould. 1991. *Wonderful Life.* Penguin.
15. Peter Holway. 1994. Popping the right eco-questions. *New Scientist.* (1935).
16. World Commission on Environment and Development. 1987. *Our Common Future.* Oxford University Press. p.43.
17. W.M. Adams. 1990. *Green Development.* Routledge. p.3.
18. How un-anthropocentric depends on whether the concern about Gaian mechanisms was deep or shallow.

– 21 –
The Gaia Controversy: a Case for the Earth as an Evolving Organism

Elisabet Sahtouris

The Gaia hypothesis — increasingly called Gaia theory after the March 1988 American Geophysics Union Chapman conference (AGU) in San Diego — has been stated in radically different ways since James Lovelock first introduced it (Lovelock 1972). J.W. Kirchner, a participant in the AGU conference, sorted out various versions of the hypothesis, excluding those he deemed pure metaphor or analogy, in order to discuss their testability (Kirchner 1988). His list of alternative Gaia hypotheses are in essence four different ways of seeing the relationship between the biota and the abiotic environment. They can be ranked from a *mild* hypothesis of mutual influence that few scientists contest, to a controversial *strong* hypothesis of purposive control on the part of the biota.

Kirchner made it clear that he excluded Lovelock's proposal that the biosphere be considered a single 'geophysical' organism on the grounds that it was in the nature of a metaphor or an analogy that was not scientifically verifiable *'without some stipulation of how it does or does not apply.'* He added that it might be possible to test how the biota could function as a global organism, but that to date no such tests had been proposed.

Lovelock's far-reaching proposal — that the Earth, or at least the biosphere, is a living organism — is thus waved aside as unworthy of serious consideration because it has not been presented in scientifically testable form. Nor does the post-AGU conference debate in general indicate that the proposal be taken seriously that the Earth be considered a living organism.

Lovelock intuited the concept of a live Earth by noting, while he was consulting on the design of NASA's Mars mission, the qualitative difference between the chemically unstable yet persistent atmosphere of Earth and the chemically stable *dead* atmospheres of its planetary neighbours, Venus and Mars. In the English tradition of the independent scientist, Lovelock invented his own measuring instruments, set sail as far as

Antarctica to take the measurements, created his own computer models, and assembled his case for Gaia.

Lovelock's Gaia is (a) a planetary superorganism, (b) the living systems of Earth creating their own environments and conditions favourable to their continued existence, and (c) it is a homeostatic cybernetic mechanism in which biota and abiotic environment are tightly-coupled parts. This has confused the scientific community, which sees these statements of the hypothesis as very different in conception and appeal. But Lovelock is an independent thinker and practical engineer whose prodigious talents have flourished, as he acknowledges, by eschewing academic affiliations and arguments. To him, it is academic nitpicking that he is constantly pressed to distinguish between his overall conception of Gaia as superorganism, his description of Gaia as life creating its own conditions, and his portrayal of Gaia as represented in his cybernetic models.

What the four hypotheses as listed by Kirchner have in common, is the division of their domain into two distinct parts — the biota and the abiotic environment. Recent media coverage of the Gaia hypothesis in periodicals such as *Science* (Kerr 1988) and *New Scientist* (Pearce 1988, Postgate 1988) suggest that these versions of the hypothesis reflect a growing adversary contest between advocates for the biota (domain of biologists) and advocates for the abiotic environment (domain of geologists) as to what factors help determine general planetary conditions such as climate, atmospheric, soil and ocean chemistry, surface temperature, and whether any such influence on the part of the biota constitutes purposive control.

But can we reasonably expect a debate about whether the biota or the abiotic environment have the most influence on planetary conditions to prove any more fruitful than the related debate in the field of psychology that was supposed to resolve whether nature or nurture (organism or environment) was most influential in determining intelligence? Can we even define clearly what are the biota and what the abiotic environment in a system that is continuous over time — one in which scientists agree that rock is the raw material of organisms that are in turn recycled back into rock and fossil fuels? Do we even question in what sense the distinction may be useful and in what sense it may obstruct our progress?

The domain of life

The 'biota' in Gaia hypotheses are always equated with 'life.' Thus, though sometimes apparently recognized as a process, life is primarily identified as one part of the domain: as one of two distinct physical components — life and non-life — of a biospheric system. This gives us a Gaian theoretical context in which questions such as 'Does life control environmental conditions?' and 'Does it do so on purpose?' be logically, if not practically, constructed as meaningful.

But suppose we took seriously Lovelock's proposal that Earth (or the biosphere) is a living being. To be a meaningful hypothesis this proposal must be stated in a way that makes Earth/Gaia comparable to other living beings. This requires abandoning Lovelock's own division of the Gaian domain into life and non-life, for by any definition of a living being, life is the organized process of the whole and not one physical part of it. In this context we get no clearer an answer to the question as to whether life controls its environment than to that concerning physiological regulation inside a body or a cell. We can no more say '... the dynamic forces of life so dominate our planet that life has a controlling influence on the oceans and the atmosphere' (Pearce 1988) than we can say '... the dynamic forces of life so dominate our bodies (or cells) that life has a controlling influence on the blood (or cytoplasm) and the skin (or cell walls).' Notice that the question of purpose is also meaningless in this context: indeed, physiologists are not known for proposing that our bodies (much less the life within them) regulate temperature or any aspect of the body's chemical balance on purpose. Such regulation is simply an observable aspect of the body as an evolved system.

Getting rid of these somehow inelegant, unsatisfying and perhaps fruitless questions obviously does not justify a live-Earth version of Gaia theory, but the exercise is a first step in highlighting the relationship between the kinds of questions we ask about the function and our fundamental conception of structure — i.e. whether or not we divide the Gaian domain into a biota and an abiota.

Our scientific concept of non-living (abiotic) Earth upon which living things (biota) appear by accident and evolve by adapting to it through natural selection is an advance over our older religious concept of a natural world into which God put living creatures. But the fundamental duel of life and non-life persists. Gaia theory as formulated by Lovelock violates neither this fundamental dualistic concept, nor the Darwinian 'mechanism' of evolution by natural selection — it just adds feedback loops between biota and abiotic environment such that natural selection works both ways, with the environment shaping organisms and organisms shaping the environment. In Lovelock's scheme, billions of years ago, bacteria, the first living organisms, reached critical numbers such that their metabolic products altered the environment sufficiently to change it on a global scale, thus setting in motion the mutual control cybernetics he calls 'Gaia' (Lovelock 1988).

This view of biota and abiotic environment as 'tightly coupled' into a cybernetic system is indeed more holistic than the one-way Darwinian mechanism of accidentally varied organisms passively selected by their environments. Calling this kind of system an organism, however, is a strange contradiction in terms, for it defines life as part of life or as part of a living entity. This produces the confusing concept of a living being in which life fosters the continuance of life. What does it mean to say that 'Earth is a huge organism intentionally creating an optimal environment for itself' (Kerr 1988) when that environment is part of itself?

Logically, it would seem we must make a choice either to conceive Gaia as a system with life and non-life as its basic parts, or to conceive Gaia as a live planet-being or organism, such that we cannot divide it into life and non-life (even though this distinction may be useful in abstract models of particular Gaian functions, or at other levels of organization). Thus, we may speak of organisms and their environments within a live Earth as we speak of cells and their environments within a live body.

Before we reject the organism alternative, let us note that other apparently fundamental divisions of nature have been successfully integrated, and have thereby advanced scientific theory considerably. Perhaps life and non-life might be considered, at the level of the planet, as two aspects of an underlying unity very much akin to those complementarities of physics that were also formerly conceived as fundamentally different: matter/energy, wave/particle, time/space, structure/function.

Life and non-life as a complementarity

A conception of the underlying unity of life and non-life is actually not new to science, although it has not been taken very seriously in the West outside physics. The biogeochemistry of our planet, which is to say the entire range of changes it undergoes, was conceived as a unity earlier this century by the Russian scientist V.I. Vernadsky, whose work was unknown to the authors of the Gaia hypothesis until well after they formulated it, though it had been supported in the U.S. by the Yale scientist

G.E. Hutchinson. Apparently, Vernadsky's conception and work, which has recently been popularized in the Soviet Union, was initially inspired by the suggestion of his elder cousin, the philosopher Y.M. Corrolenko, 'that the Earth is an organism,' (Lovelock 1988) though Vernadsky himself apparently never made this claim.

Vernadsky himself wrote that life 'is, as it were, disperse of rock, extremely active chemically, and found in motion' (Balandin 1982). He observed that geological matter, transformed into living matter, has tremendous free energy; transforms cosmic radiation into other forms of energy; speeds chemical reactions; protects minerals against dissolution; increases diversity of compounds by a factor of a thousand; fills all available space by its own active and passive motion, packaging and reproducing itself, cycling itself through a trophic pyramid of organisms that live off each other, ultimately transforming back into its less active state (Balandin 1982, Lapo 1982).

This view construes living and non-living matter as continuous, such that life is no more, no less than a geological process that becomes a biogeochemical process through its own transformations over time. The non-living state of original geological matter, with its slow linear chemistry, undergoes transformations to a cyclic chemistry as it complicates into the high-energy state of self-reproducing living matter, then reverts back to the slower state at the death of living matter. In other words, *life and non-life can be seen as two states or aspects over time of the same material.* The whole biogeochemical process is cyclical, though it involves ever more of the original geological matter over time and is evolutionary in character. In short, this view suggests that *organisms are transient parts of a relatively permanent cyclic process in which they both result from and produce a planetary metabolic system.*

The definition of life

This view of planetary geobiochemistry as a self-producing system is extremely close to the concept of a definition of life in biology, not least for those physicists who have become interested in questions of life. This is Maturana and Varela's concept of *autopoietic* (literally, self-producing) systems. While we still have no single definition of life widely accepted across fields, as Lovelock has repeatedly pointed out, Maturana and Varela's definition (Varela *et al.* 1974) may be the best current candidate, emphasizing as the fundamental feature of life what few would contest: that beings are self-producing and that there is no separation between producer and product in a living-being. Is this not what Vernadsky demonstrated, in pointing out that the Earth's living matter is both result and origin of its metabolic process?

More formally, Maturana and Varela define the autopoietic organization of a living-being as continually producing, by its own rules, the components, including its own boundary, that specify it and realize it as a concrete unit in space and time (Maturana and Varela 1987, 43–49; Varela, unpublished paper 1988). This definition has been twice restated by Fleischaker (1988) as:

> Autopoiesis is the production of a network of processes whose operation results in the transformation and replacement of system components ...
>
> The principle of autopoiesis identifies as living a unitary self-bounded system capturing and transducing energy and undergoing material transformation away from thermodynamic equilibrium' (p.64).

Further, Fleischaker points out that:

> Determining whether any given system is autopoietic or not depends on its behaviour at the present moment and how it came into being (p.101).

Fleischaker also points out, following Maturana and Varela, that this new definition of life deliberately excludes the old criteria of growth, reproduction and genetic inheritance, which are specifically referred to as descriptive, but not definitive of life (Fleischaker 1988, 66) because they are *consequences* of the basic autopoietic phenomenon defining life. Neither RNA, DNA nor proteins are necessary components of Fleischaker's proposed *minimal terran cell.*

All these authors have confined the concept of autopoiesis (at least that of 'first-order' autopoiesis) to the molecular level at which they seek the simplest organization of life. Nevertheless, Maturana and Varela have extended the concept to metacellular and even social systems as second and perhaps third order autopoiesis. They state:

> we shall leave open the question of whether or not metacellular systems are first-order autopoietic systems until we know more about them (Maturana and Varela 1987, 88f).

Their definition of autopoiesis avoids any specification of particular molecular components in order to keep the definition broad enough to accommodate life on other planets.

The life of our own planet as an autopoietic organism has not been taken seriously by any of these authors, and their focus on autopoiesis at the molecular level would seem to preclude their doing so. But their decree that autopoiesis is founded only at the molecular level is not part of their definition itself. In fact, there is nothing in any of the ways of stating the definition that restricts first-order autopoiesis to molecular levels. In metacellular systems it is clear that they derive from single autopoietic cells, although it can be argued (and Maturana and Varela seem open to this) that first-order autopoiesis may happen in its own right at these 'grosser' levels, that is, in systems composed of cellular autopoietic elements.

The argument made here is that the Earth is not only an autopoietic unity, but one of first order autopoiesis — not derived from the molecular/cellular level, but organizing those levels as part of its own first-order autopoiesis. Actually, this proposal was made by Erich Jantsch, in terms of the Gaia hypothesis at that time (Jantsch 1980) but was not taken seriously by Maturana and Varela, perhaps because of the lack of rigour and unfounded leaps by which Jantsch extended autopoiesis to sociocultural and religious systems and ideas poorly grounded in any definable reality. Nevertheless Jantsch made an important contribution in recognizing the simultaneous organization of nature at macroscopic and microscopic levels. In physics we recognize this in the widespread assumption that some elegant principle unites relatively with quantum mechanics, even if it remains beyond our reach as yet. Perhaps this situation with respect to understanding the Earth is closer to resolution through the notion of autopoiesis functioning simultaneously at the levels of the whole planet and its tiniest cells.

Interestingly, Lewis Thomas suggested that of all familiar organisms, the Earth most resembles a single cell (Thomas 1974). Following this analogy, let us compare the macroscopic formation of the Earth's atmospheric boundary with the formation of membranes as autopoietic cells evolved at the microscopic level.

Most origins of life researchers are agreed that all candidates for the earliest protocells, the most plausible of which are Sidney Fox's proteinoid microspheres, are spherical in form and surrounded by bilayer membranes. These enclosing-membrane boundaries, whether formed of lipids, as in a number of laboratories, or of Fox's lipoidal proteinoid, form solely by virtue of their molecular properties when surrounded by water. The suggestion for the origins of life envisages proteins enclosed within such spheres setting up metabolic cycles, through bringing energy in from outside the selectively permeable membrane. Eventually the membrane structure is continually replaced and elaborated into a complex dynamic system by the living (autopoietic) cell.

Similarly, the bilayer boundary consisting of Earth's early atmosphere and crust formed solely by virtue of their physical properties when surrounded by a cold atmosphere — by congealing rock and outgassing. The replacement and continuous production of atmospheric and crustal components were then taken over by myriads of tiny autopoietic systems developing within this boundary itself, at the interface between layers, which is where the water collected. External (solar) energy is transported through the selectively permeable boundary, which is increasingly replaced and elaborated into a complex dynamic system by the dynamic Earth.

Lovelock points out that:

> apart from the small concentration of rare gases like argon and helium, all other gases of the air have recently existed as part of the solids and liquids in living cells. A similar exchange takes place between life and the oceans and the rocks, but it is much slower in pace (Lovelock 1988, 54).

On the surface of the Earth one is hard pressed to find anything, even a patch of bare rock, that has not been transformed by the process of life into something other than what it was originally. Taken together with Vernadsky's observation that 99.9 per cent of different molecules on Earth have been created in the life process of Earth, is this not a reasonable example of an autopoietic process producing the components that specify and realize it as a unity in time and space — as a living biosphere?

What of the layers of Earth inside or below the biosphere? Are they merely a lifeless supporting framework for life? On the surface, the atmosphere and oceans are essential in transport and transformation of materials; just so below the surface soft and molten layers assist in transportation and transformation. Subduction zones at the edges of tectonic plates absorb materials that have been through to the surface life process, apparently carrying them to a second 'crust' 400 to 650 kilometers below the surface (Anderson 1988). Through pressures and the heat of deep nuclear processes, these materials are transformed and eventually conveyed back to the surface as the fresh basalt of volcanic activity. More generally, the whole Earth system of magnetic fields and tectonic plate movement are increasingly recognized as intrinsic to life processes.

As Richard Monastersky (1988) describes in *New Scientist:*

> It is now clear that the separate regions (crust, mantle and core) are engaged in a multichannelled conversation. Across major boundaries and thousands of kilometres, these sections exert profound effects on one another.

In the same article, seismologist Don Anderson is quoted as saying, 'you have to treat the Earth as a system; you can't just look at a part of it.' All this suggests we can no longer consider the biosphere alone as a meaningful entity, but must speak of the whole Earth, from innermost core to the magnetic fields surrounding it, as one systematic entity.

Autopoietic criteria for living organisms

Vernadsky's biogeochemically unified concept of Earth, taken together with research on the origins of life and recent geophysics, seems admirably to fit Maturana and Varela's definition of life. Varela himself, in personal correspondence, finds these arguments persuasive and well worth pursuing. The table below compares the criteria for autopoiesis in the order mentioned in this paper with Earth's features.

— self-producing (no separation between producer and product);
— operates by its own rules;
— produces components specifying it as a unity in space and time;
— creates its own boundary;
— network of processes whose operation results in the transformation and replacement of system components;
— self-bounded system capturing and transducing energy and undergoing material transformation away from thermodynamic equilibrium (i.e. in direction of negative entropy).

Autopoietic features of Earth

— Living matter is both origin and consequences of Earth's metabolic process;
— operates by a complex of geological, chemical, biological 'rules' internal to the Earth/atmosphere system;

— oceans, atmosphere, rocks and soil as they are today are products of living matter;
— atmosphere created by early outgassing; transformed, complicated and maintained by organisms;
— planetary metabolism converts raw geological material into organisms and their organic products, then back into rock; oceans, air, rock and soil constantly replaced;
— self-bounded by atmosphere via which sunlight is transduced into chemical, electrical, kinetic and other kinds of energy; total system increasingly organized in direction of negative entropy.

Recall that Maturana and Varela's definition of living beings carries no requirement for growth, reproduction or genetic inheritance; nor any requirements to account for life's origin.

Lovelock's intuition that the Earth's chemically unstable yet dynamically maintained atmosphere is indicative of a live planet, in contrast to the lifeless atmospheric stability of Venus and Mars, seems justified. Like the spores, seeds and eggs of Earth's creatures, planets may well be scattered lavishly throughout the universe, yet, in contrast to Earth, few of them in exactly the right composition and conditions for the development of life.

Theoretical implications

If the arguments of this paper were accepted, we would not have a fifth version of Gaia theory *per se.* Once we accepted the Earth as a living-being by definition, its 'liveness' would no longer be a hypothetical proposition or theory subject to test, but rather a reasoned conceptualization and context in which to generate cross-disciplinary *geophysiological* theories and models of its systematic organization and functions. Clearly Gaia, if a living being, is unlike any other we know and is likely to remain unique in our experience for some time. Even if we identify other living planets at the distance of other star systems, our hope of studying them in any detail in the near future is virtually nil. How, then, shall we formulate theories of Gaian process, or geophysiology?

The answer lies in the approach already taken by such as as Charlson, Lovelock, Andreae and Warren (1987) in their revealing of the dimethylsulphide/hydrological cycle and various other proposed oceanic/atmospheric/land cycles (Lovelock 1988). We can look for organizational features, systems and cycles such as we know in smaller familiar living beings, for instance, circulation systems for nutrients and wastes, metabolic cycles, homeostatic regulation in physiological systems, division of labour among parts, definition of health and response to disease. Much work has already been done, as Kirchner (1988) notes, in 'unraveling contemporary biogeological cycles and tracing geophysical, geochemical and biological evolution of paleoclimate.' Although such efforts (apart from Lovelock's own) have not been construed as the geophysiology of a live planet, the information generated could be easily translated into that context.

Perhaps the most important feature of physiology is the constant need to relate events at the molecular/cellular level to events at other levels, such as organs, organ systems and the whole body. In the same sense, geophysiology will be a matter of relating molecular/cellular autopoiesis, together with its biological consequences, to parallel and interwoven phenomena at other levels, such as organisms, ecosystems and the planet as a whole.

We now know that bacteria, descended from the original prokaryotes that invented the main metabolic cycles, as well as generating the basic chemistry of seas, soil and atmosphere, are very much involved with each other on a planetary scale. While they satisfy the autopoietic requirement of autonomy, all bacteria belong to an extremely sophisticated, resilient and elegantly packaged DNA-trading system functioning worldwide, playing out functions we have not begun to understand (Sonea and Panisset 1983). Even the nucleated cells of eukaryotes that evolved from bacteria have to work at maintaining their integrity. As Lewis Thomas remarks:

> Any cell — man, animal, fish, fowl or insect — given the chance and under the right conditions, brought into contact with any other cell, however foreign, will fuse with it. Cytoplasm will flow easily from one to the other, the nuclei will combine, and it will become, for a time anyway, a single cell with two complete alien genomes, ready to dance, ready to multiply. (Thomas 1974, 147f).

This observation is included here as a reminder that the separateness of living beings is not as rigid a matter as we are accustomed to believe and Vernadsky's conception of 'living matter' should have as much place in our thinking as the usual conception of 'living organisms.'

If we end the adversary contest over biological versus geological influences on planetary conditions, the information we already have can be used in unbiased ways to demonstrate geophysiology. We will then get away from those vested interests that, for example, set out to prove that planetary conditions can be explained without involvement on the part of life, as we see in the work of Walker, Hays and Kasting (cited in Kirchner 1981) or of Kasting, Toon and Pollack (1988). By using the autopoietic definition of life that seems as suitable at the level of the whole planet as at the molecular/cellular level, we can see the complementarity of the life/non-life debate. At the level of the planet, we can distinguish other planets in our solar system from ours as non-living, and we can see the same matter on our planet in cyclic living and non-living states. At the level of cells, organisms and biota we can speak of their relationships to an abiotic environment as a convenient abstraction, while recognizing the inextricable role of life in that environment.

The appropriate role of mechanical models

Within the context of a live-Earth Gaia concept, models such as Lovelock's Daisyworld (1988) take on new meanings. Making cybernetic models of abstracted aspects or subsystems of a system need not imply that the entire system (or live being) is in essence cybernetic. Daisyworlds, for example, are models of possible planetary temperature regulation by living species coupled to their environment by feedback loops; they are useful abstractions in the same sense as are other mechanical models of physiological function, such as temperature regulation modelled as a homeostatic (thermostatic) system of blood vessels, sweat glands, pumping hearts, all keyed in to a complex nervous system. We thus learn about the unfamiliar precisely by drawing analogies with the familiar.

All this is appropriate, but we must avoid the Cartesian trap of seeing things the other way around — of seeing nature itself in the image of our inventions. Mechanical models cannot tell us anything about the assembly of parts in natural systems or how they replace parts and/or create new ones — nothing, that is, about their essential autopoietic nature. The natural systems being modeled did not come into existence via purposeful assembly as do mechanisms (any dictionary defines mechanisms as purposive assemblies) and thus their essential self-organization cannot be modeled mechanically.

Mechanisms do not produce themselves (even if they can be programmed to replicate themselves), not do they ever change on their own except for the worse. In fact we must hope our machines will not change at all between uses, since on their own they can only change for the worse, while we must hope that any living beings we care about will change constantly while we are not attending to them, for otherwise they will have died. Living systems literally must change in order to stay the same. Sadly, even systems scientists tend to forget that Von Bertalanffy, the father of systems theory, told us that 'formulations of physics are, in principle, inapplicable to the living organism' (Von Bertalanffy 1969). Or, in failing to recognize that models are not what they model, make the error that the logician Alfred Korzybsky warned against, in that the map is confused with the territory. Ironically, the notion of Gaia as a live-being is often rejected by scientists as a mere metaphor (Kirchner 1988), when it is Gaia as a cybernetic system that is more truly metaphorical!

Cybernetic systems, being subject to law from outside, are not comparable to *autonomous* or self-ruled autopoietic systems because they belong to entirely different conceptual frameworks with incommensurable terms (Varela 1979, Rorty 1979, Fleischaker 1988). Nature, as mechanism, was a logical, if erroneous, conception in Descartes' worldview, as he posited an inventor God. Hence, only the reinstatement of the Cartesian Grand Engineer could logically permit us to see Gaia as a cybernetic device. It seems a better solution to pose the self-production of Earth-life by autopoiesis, which occurs neither on purpose nor by accident. Autopoiesis is likely the inevitable consequence of certain naturally occurring conditions and configurations of matter that can apparently include whole planets. As Lovelock himself has been heard to say, and as many physicists are coming to realize, 'Given the specifications of the universe, life seems inevitable.'

The essential differences between living beings and machines, then, do not invalidate the mathematical/mechanical modelling of living systems, but put it into perspective, revealing both its use and limits. New kinds of mathematics, such as non-linear networks dynamics, promise to be more appropriate than cybernetics in modelling the emergent properties of autopoietic entities. Meanwhile, let us remember that while any mathematical model may help us understand how Gaia functions, none tells us what Gaia *is*.

General Implications

The live-Earth Gaia concept is as revolutionary as was the helio-centric concept of Aristarchos/Copernicus and will take time to become accepted throughout the scientific community. When it is, will the name 'Gaia' become synonymous with 'Earth' and thus redundant? No. 'Gaia' will continue to distinguish life as Earth's geophysiological organization and process from the older concept of life as an accidental occurrence on the surface of a lifeless planet, forced by selection to adapt or die out.

The heliocentric revolution in scientific understanding displaced humans from their fancied central position in the eyes of God and the structure of the universe. The Gaian revolution will displace us from our fancied position as the superior species, uniquely in charge of our planet. Will our powerful egos resist the Gaian conception for this reason? Or are we sufficiently mature as a species to accept our position and responsibility as one part of a larger organism?

It is crucial to the question of whether or not we adopt this revolutionary concept to keep in mind that scientific concepts and the theories generated from them are no longer judged in terms of chimerical 'truth' but of usefulness. By usefulness, we mean conducive to human survival. In fact, our self-centered views and practices threaten our very survival as a species. In that respect, a concept of ourselves as part of the life of Earth, coupled with scientific knowledge of its geophysiology, might prove useful in bringing about a reorganizing of our social structures and conduct, so that we rediscover our balance within Gaia and thereby insure our survival.

References

Anderson, Ian. 1988. Seismic waves reveal Earth's other crust. *New Scientist.* November 26, 1988.

Balandin, R.K. 1982. *Vladimir Vernadsky.* Moscow: Mir. Quote is given from V.I. Vernadsky's *Works,* 4(1):92.

Charlson, R., J. Lovelock, M. Andreae and S. Warren. 1987. Oceanic phytoplankton, atmospheric sulfur, cloud albedo and climate. *Nature.* 326:655.

Fleischaker, G.R. 1988. *Autopoiesis: System Logic and Origins of Life.* Ph.D. dissertation, Boston University.

Fox, Sidney W. 1988. Evolution outward and forward. In M.W. Ho and S.W. Fox (eds). *Evolutionary Processes and Metaphors.* New York: Wiley.

Jantsch, E. 1980. *The Self-Organizing Universe.* New York/Oxford: Pergamon.

Kasting, J., O. Toon and J. Pollack. 1988 (February). How climate evolved on the terrestrial planets. *Scientific American.* 258:90.

Kerr, R.A. 1988. No Longer Wilful, Gaia Becomes Respectable. *Science.* 240:22.

Kirchner, J.W. 1988. Testing the Gaia Hypothesis. *Reviews of Geophysics.*

Lapo, A.V. 1982. *Traces of Bygone Biospheres.* Moscow: Mir.

Lovelock, J.E. 1972. Gaia as seen through the atmosphere. *Atmospheric Environment.* 6:579.

—— 1988. *The Ages of Gaia.* New York: Norton.

Margalef, R. 1975. Perspectives in Ecological Theory. *Co-Evol. Quart.* 6:49–66.

Margulis, L. 1982. *Early Life.* New York: Van Nostrand Reinhold.

Maturana, H.R. and F.J. Varela. 1987. *The Tree of Knowledge.* Boston: Shambala.
Monastersky, R. 1988. The Whole-Earth Syndrome. *Science News.* 133 (June 11).
Pearce, F. 1988. Gaia: a revolution comes of age. *New Scientist.* 17 (March):32f.
Postgate, J. 1988. Gaia gets too big for her boots. *New Scientist.* 7 (April):60.
Rorty, R. 1979. *Philosophy and the Mirror of Nature.* Princeton University Press.
Sonea, S. and M. Panisset. 1983. *A New Bacteriology.* Boston: Jones and Barlett.
Thomas, Lewis. 1974. *The Lives of a Cell: Notes of a Biology Watcher.* New York: Bantam.
Varela, F.J. 1979. *Principles of Biological Autonomy.* North-Holland.
Varela, F.J., H.R. Maturana and R. Uribe. 1974. Autopoiesis: The organization of living systems, its characterization and a model. *Biosystems.* 5:187–96.

Professional literature on Gaia compiled by Lynn Margulis

1965. Lovelock J.E. A physical basis for life detection experiments. *Nature.* 207:568f.

1967. Hitchcock, D.R., and J.E. Lovelock. Life detection by atmospheric analysis. *Icarus.* 7:149–59.

1967. Lovelock, J.E., and D.R. Hitchcock. Detecting planetary life from Earth. *Science Journal.* April.

1968. Lovelock, J.E., and C.E. Griffen. Planetary atmospheres: Compositional and other changes associated with the presence of life. In Tiffany, D.L., *et al.* (eds). *Advanced space experiments.* 25. Amer. Astron. Soc.

1972. Holland, H.D. The geologic history of sea-water — An attempt to solve the problem. *Geochimica et Cosmochimica Acta.* 36:637–51.

1972. Lovelock, J.E., and J.P. Lodge. Oxygen — the contemporary atmosphere. *Atmos. Envir.* 6.

1972. Lovelock, J.E. Gaia as seen through the atmosphere. *Atmos. Envir.* 6:579f.

1974. Lovelock, J.E. and L. Margulis. Atmospheric homeostasis by and for the biosphere: The Gaia hypothesis. *Tellus.* 26:2–10.

1974. Margulis, L. and J.E. Lovelock. Biological modulation of the Earth's atmosphere. *Icarus.* 21.

1974. Lovelock, J.E. and L. Margulis. Homeostatic tendencies of the Earth's atmosphere. *Origins of Life.*

1975. Margulis, L. and J.E. Lovelock. The atmosphere as circulatory system of the biosphere — The Gaia hypothesis. *CoEvolution Quarterly.* 6:30–41.

1975. Lovelock, J.E. Thermodynamics and the recognition of alien biospheres. *Royal Society of London Proceedings.* Ser. B. 189:167–81.

1976. Margulis, L., J.C.G. Walker and M. Rambler. Reassessment of roles of oxygen and ultraviolet light in PreCambrian evolution. *Nature.* 264:620–24.

1977. Margulis, L. and J.E. Lovelock. The view from Mars and Venus. *The Sciences.* March–Apr. 10–13.

1978. Margulis, L. and J.E. Lovelock. The biota as ancient and modern modulator of the Earth's atmosphere. *Pageoph.* 116:239–243.

1978. Dutsch, H.U. (ed). Influence of the biosphere on the atmosphere. Basel: Birkhauser. (reprinted from *Pure and Applied Geophysics.* 116:213–582).

1978. Watson, A., J.E. Lovelock and L. Margulis. Methanogenesis, fires and the regulation of atmospheric oxygen. *Biosystems.* 10:293–298.

1980. Watson, A.J., J.E. Lovelock and L. Margulis. What controls atmospheric oxygen? *BioSystems.* 12.

1981. Dastoor, M., K.H. Nealson and L. Margulis (ed). Interaction of the biota with the atmosphere and sediments. Washington: *NASA Workshop Report for Meeting of Oct. 18–19, 1979.*

1981. Doolittle, W.I. Is nature really motherly? *CoEvolution Quarterly.* 29:58–63.

1981. Margulis, L., K.H. Nealson and I. Taylor (ed). Planetary biology and microbial ecology: Biochemistry of carbon and early life. *NASA Technical Memorandum 86043* (Summer program research report. 1980).

1981. Margulis, L. and J.E. Lovelock. Atmospheres and evolution. In J. Billingham (ed). *Life in the Universe.* Cambridge. Mass: MIT Press. pp.79–100.

1982. Brock, T.D., P.J. Cook, H.P. Eugster, A.M. Goodwin, H.L. James, L. Margulis, K.H. Nealson, J.O. Nriagu, A.F. Trendall, and M.R. Walter. Sedimentary iron deposits, evaporites and phosphorites. In H.D. Holland and M. Schidlowski. (eds). *Mineral deposits and the evolution of the biosphere.* Berlin: Springer. pp.259–73.

1982. Lovelock, J.E. and A.J. Watson. The regulation of carbon dioxide and climate: Gaia or geochemistry. *Journal of Planetary Science.* 30.

1982. Lovelock, J.E. and M. Whitfield. The life span of the biosphere. *Nature.* 296:561–63.

1982. Margulis, L. The biological point of view: The effect of life on the planet. In A. Brahic. (ed). *Formation of planetary systems.* Toulouse: Centre d'Etudes Spatiales, Capaude-Editions. pp.891–93.

1983. Lovelock, J.E. Gaia as seen through the atmosphere. In P. Westbroek and E. de Jong (eds). *Biomineralization and biological metal accumulation.* Dordrecht: Reidel. pp.15–25.

1983. Margulis, L. and J. Stolz. Microbial systematics and a Gaian view of the sediments. In P. Westbroek and E. de Jong (eds). *Biomineralization and biological metal accumulation.* Dordrecht: Reidel. pp.27–53.

1983. Watson, A. and J.E. Lovelock. Biological homeostasis of the global environment: the parable of Daisyworld. *Tellus.* 35:284–89.

1985. Sagan, D. (ed). Planetary biology and microbial ecology: The global sulfur cycle. *NASA Technical Memorandum* (Summer program research report. June–August 1984).

1986. Lovelock, J.E. Geophysiology: A new look at Earth science. *Amer. Meteorological Soc. Bull.* 67.

1987. Charlson. R.J., J.E. Lovelock, M.O. Andreae and S.G. Warren. Oceanic phytoplankton, atmospheric sulphur, cloud albedo and climate. *Nature.* 326:655–61.

1987. Lovelock. J.E. Ecopoiesis of Daisyworld. In J.M. Robson (ed). *Origin and evolution of the Universe — Evidence for design?* Royal Society of Canada. pp.153–66.

1987. Lovelock. J.E. *Gaia: A new look at Life on Earth* (2 ed). Oxford/New York: Oxford University Press.

1987. Margulis. L. Early life: The microbes have priority. In W.I. Thompson (ed). *Gaia: A way of knowing: political implications of the new biology.* Hudson, NY: Lindisfarne. pp.98–109.

1988. Lovelock, J.E. *The Ages of Gaia.* New York: Norton.

1989. Lovelock, J.E. Geophysiology. *Royal Society of Edinburgh, Earth Sciences.* 80:169–75.

1989. Lovelock, J.E. Geophysiology, the science of Gaia. *Reviews of Geophysics.* 27:215–22.

1989. Lovelock, J.E. The First Leslie Cooper Memorial Lecture: Gaia. *Journal of Marine Biology* 69.

1989. Margulis, L. and J.E. Lovelock. Gaia and geognosy. In M.B. Rambler, L. Margulis and R. Fester (eds). *Global ecology: Towards a science of the biosphere.* Boston: Academic Press. pp.1–30.

1990. Hinkle, G., and L. Margulis. Global ecology and the Gaia hypothesis: physiology and ecology Japan. Special issue: *Ecology for Tomorrow.* 27:53–62.

1991. Lovelock, J.E. Geophysiology of the oceans. pp.419–31 in R.F.C. Mantoura, J.M. Martin and R. Wollast (eds). *Ocean margin processes in global change.* Wiley.

1991. Margulis, L., and G. Hinkle. The biota and Gaia: 150 years of support for environmental sciences. pp.11–18 in S.H. Schneider and P.J. Boston (ed). 1992. *Scientists on Gaia.* Cambridge, Mass: MIT Press.

1992. Margulis, L. and L. Olendzenski (eds). *Environmental evolution: The effect of the origin and evolution of life on planet Earth.* Cambridge, Mass: MIT Press.

1992. Lovelock, J.E. A numerical model for biodiversity. *Roy. Soc. of Lond. Phil. Trans.* Ser. B. 338.

1992. Lovelock, J.E. Geophysical aspects of biodiversity. pp.57–70 in O.T. Solbrig, H.M. van Emden, and P.G.W.J. van Oordt (eds). *IUBS Monograph 8.* Paris: International Union of Biological Sciences.

1992. Schneider, S.H., and P. Boston (eds). *Scientists on Gaia.* Cambridge, Mass: MIT Press.

1993. Lovelock, J.E. *Las Edades de Gaia: una biografía de nuestro planeta vivo* (presentación de Ricardo Guerrero). Fundacío la Caixa. Museo do la Ciéncia.

Popular literature on Gaia

1979. Lovelock, J.E. *Gaia: A new look at life on Earth.* Oxford University Press.

1980. Margulis, L. After Viking: Life on Earth. *The Sciences.* Nov. pp.24–26.

1980. Margulis, L. and J.E. Lovelock. L'atmosphère est-elle le système circulatoire de la biosphère? L'hypothèse Gaia. *CoEvolution.* 1:20–31.

1982. Dawkins, R. *The Extended Phenotype.* New York: Freeman.

1982. Lovelock, J.E. From gas chromatography to Gaia. *Chromatographia.* 16:26–31.

1983. Margulis, L. and J.E. Lovelock. Le petit monde des pâquerettes: Un modèle quantitatif de Gaia. *CoEvolution.* 11:48–52.

1983. Sagan, D. and L. Margulis. The Gaian perspective of ecology. *Ecologist.* 13:160–67.

1984. Sagan, D. and L. Margulis. Gaia and philosophy. pp.60–75 in L.S. Rouner (ed). *On nature.* Notre Dame, Ind: University of Notre Dame Press.

1985. Lovelock, J.E. and M. Allaby. *The Greening of Mars.* London: Allen & Unwin.

1986. Lovelock, J.E. Gaia: The world as a living organism. *New Scientist.* December 18. pp.25–28

1986. Margulis, L. and D. Sagan. *Microcosmos: Four billion years of evolution from our microbial ancestors.* Summit Books.

1986. Margulis, L., L. Lopez Baluja, S.M. Awramik and D. Sagan. Community living long before man. In D. Botkin and A.A. Orio (eds). *Man's effect on the global environment.*

1987. McKay, C.P. Terraforming: Making an Earth of Mars. *Planetary Report.* 7(6):26f.

1988. Lovelock, J.E. *The ages of Gaia: A biography of our living Earth.* New York: Norton.

1988. Margulis, L. Jim Lovelock's Gaia. pp.50–65 in P. Bunyard and E. Goldsmith (eds). *Gaia, the thesis, the mechanisms and the implications.* Wadebridge Ecological Centre. Reprinted as Chapter 3 in this volume.

1988. Sagan, D. What Narcissus saw: The Oceanic 'I'/eye. In *The Reality Club 1.* New York: Prentice Hall.

1988. Sagan, D. and L. Margulis. Gaia and biospheres. pp.237–42 in P. Bunyard and E. Goldsmith (eds). *Gaia, the thesis, the mechanisms and the implications.* Wadebridge Ecological Centre.

1990. Haynes, R.H. Ecce ecopoiesis: Playing God on Mars. pp.161–183 in D. MacNiven (ed). *Moral expertise: studies in practical and professional ethics.* London: Routledge.

1990. Joseph, L.E. *Gaia, the growth of an idea.* New York: St Martin's. (Paperback: 1991. Arkana).

1990. Lovelock, J.E. Hands up for the Gaia hypothesis. *Nature.* 344:100–102.

1990. Rothschild, L. Earth analogs for Martian life: Microbes in evaporites. A new model system for life on Mars. *Icarus.* 88:246–60.

1991. Barlow, C. (ed). *From Gaia to selfish genes; selected writings in the life sciences.* MIT Press.

1991. Levine, L. *Gaia: Goddess and idea.* Levine (6870 Whysall Rd,. Bloomfield Hills, MI 48301).

1991. Lovelock, J.E. *Healing Gaia: Practical medicine for the planet.* London: Gaia Books/New York: Harmony.

1991. Margulis, L. and R. Guerrero. Two plus three equal one: individuals emerge from bacterial communities. In W.I. Thompson (ed). *Gaia 2. Emergence: The new Science of becoming.* Hudson, NY: Lindisfarne Press.

1991. Margulis, L. Gaia. a new look at the Earth's systems. pp.299–305 in W.J. Makofske, H. Horowitz, E.F. Karlin and P. McConnell (eds). *Technology, development and the global environment.* Mahwah, NJ: Institute for Environmental Studies, School of Theoretical and Applied Science, Ramapo College.

1991. Margulis, L. and D. Sagan. *Microcosmos. Four billion years of microbial evolution.* Bantam Books.

1991. McKay, C.P., O.B. Toon and J.F. Kasting. Making Mars habitable. *Nature.* 352:489–96.

1991. Sagan, D. *Biospheres: Metamorphosis of planet Earth.* New York: McGraw-Hill. (Paperback: Bantam).

1991. Westbroek, P. *Life as a geological force.* New York: Norton.

1992. Filipelli, G.M., and M.L. Delaney. Similar phosphorus fluxes in ancient phosphorite deposits and a modern phosphogenic environment. *Geology.* 20:707–12

1992. Haynes. R.H. 1992. How might Mars become a home to humans? *Gaia Science.* 2(3):7–9.

1992. Kluger, J. Mars, in Earth's image. *Discover.* 13(9):70–75.

1992. Lovelock, J.E. The Gaia hypothesis. In *Environmental evolution: Effects of the origin and evolution of life on planet Earth.* MIT Press.

1992. Sagan, D. *Metazoa: biology and multiplicity: incorporations, zone.* MIT Press.

1992. Williams. G.C. Gaia. nature worship and biocentric fallacies. *Quarterly Review of Biology.* 67.

1993. National Research Council. *Solid-earth sciences and society — summary of global overview.* National Academy.

1993. Margulis, L. and O. West. Gaia and the Colonisation of Mars. *GSA Today.* 3(11).

1995. Margulis, L. and D. Sagan. *What is Life?* New York: Simon & Schuster.

List of Contributors

James E. Lovelock, FRS, Coombe Mill, St Giles-on-the-Heath, Launceston, Cornwall.
Jacques Grinevald, Department of Political Science, University of Geneva.
Lynn Margulis, Professor of Biology, University of Massachusetts, Amherst, Mass. USA.
Andrew J. Watson, Marine Biological Association of UK, Plymouth, Devon.
Peter Saunders, Professor of Applied Mathematics, King's College, University of London.
Michael Whitfield, Director, Marine Biological Association of UK, Plymouth, Devon.
Gregory J. Hinkle, Department of Biology, University of Massachusetts, Amherst, Mass., USA.
Peter Westbroek, Director, Geobiochemical Research Group, Leiden, Holland.
Gerrit-Jan de Bruyn, Geobiochemical research Group, Leiden, Holland.
W.E. Krumbein, Professor of Geomicrobiology (ICBM), Carl von Ossietzky University, Oldenburg, Germany.
A.V. Lapo, All-Union Geological Research Institute, St Petersburg, Russia.
Brian C. Goodwin, Development Dynamics Research Group, Department of Biology, The Open University, Milton Keynes, UK.
Jan Sapp, Chair, Department of Science Studies, Atkinson College, York University, Ontario, Canada.
Ricardo Guerrero, Professor of Microbiology, University of Barcelona, Spain.
Peter Bunyard, Wadebridge Ecological Centre, Withiel, Cornwall, UK.
A.J. and E.C. Southward, Leverhulme Unit, Marine Biological Association of UK, Plymouth, Devon.
Patrick Lavelle, Ecole Normale Supérieure Laboratoire d'Ecologie, Paris, France.
Mae-Wan Ho, Bioelectrodynamics Laboratory, Open University, Milton Keynes, UK.
Fritz-Albert Popp, International Institute of Biophysics, Kaiserslauten, Germany.
David Abram, State University of New York, Stony Brook, New York State, USA.
Martin von Hildebrand, Director COAMA and Gaia Foundation, Santa Fé de Bogotá, Colombia.
Alwyn K. Jones, Principal Lecturer, Department of Environmental Studies, University of Glamorgan.
Kate Rawles, Department of Philosophy, University of Lancaster, UK.
Elisabet Sahtouris, American/Greek philosopher of evolution, Metochi, Agistri, Greece.

Index